LIFE SUPPORT

Surviving Guillain-Barre Syndrome – A Mother's Story of Hope and Recovery

Holly Frances

LIFE SUPPORT: SURVIVING GUILLAIN-BARRE SYNDROME – A MOTHER'S STORY OF HOPE AND RECOVERY

First edition. January 15, 2023

ISBN: 978-1-738757015 (paperback)

ISBN: 978-1738757008 (electronic)

Written by Holly Frances

Published by Blue Turtle Publishing, 2023

With support from the Alberta Foundation for the Arts

Praise for Life Support

"This highly sensitive and personal account of a life altering disorder is critical reading for health care professionals, particularly those who care for persons with GBS. Beyond the impact of GBS on Holly's own health, her unique and striking perspective is of battling this disorder as a new mother. The book is also important reading for those working on and funding neuroscience research, to highlight the incredible burden placed on those dealing with tough disorders of peripheral nerves. Yes, nerves can slowly recover and regenerate in some instances, but Holly reminds us to think about what it is actually like to experience this over many months, before recovery occurs. In a very readable account, she shares many personal details of the journey of a new mother through GBS and how she acquired the resilience and determination not only to survive but to thrive thereafter. Its an inspiring piece for all."—Dr. Zochodne, MD, FRCPC

"Rarely do we see a patient put into words and lay bare every detail and emotion experienced on a long and difficult GBS journey. This educational gift to the world conveys a message of hope. All of us at the GBS/CIDP Foundation of Canada are very proud of you." —Donna Hartlen, Executive Director, GBS/CIDP Foundation of Canada

"As a GBS survivor, I appreciate Holly for shining a light on this rare and debilitating disorder. The information she has amassed will provide needed support to anyone affected by GBS."—Christopher Cross, Singer/Songwriter, 5-time Grammy Award Winner, and GBS Survivor

"Life Support is the true story of what it took and how it was done for Holly Frances to survive GBS. A riveting account of courage and determination to succeed."—Gord Hira, Writer, 2008 GBS Survivor

This book was written for Casey, my heart, my strength, my guardian angel. I hope you forever know just how much I love you.

The first version of this book, a sort-of early road map, titled Happily Ever After was made possible because of my mother Marilyn, who documented my progress every day in a journal, and because of James, who helped fill in the blanks along the way.

This new book was written because of Jordan, who pushed me to go after my dreams and turn them into reality. Without his compassion, support, and guidance, this book would not exist.

This is based on my long journey through Guillain-Barre Syndrome, and I wrote it using hospital videos, interviews, notes, and recollections by me and others. I tried to be as accurate as I could and true to my story. Some names have been changed, specifically those that wish to remain anonymous, and those I could not reach.

Any mention of specific products or companies does not imply endorsement. I am not a health care provider, and this book is my story, not intended to provide health care advice. Dr. Douglas Zochodne reviewed my manuscript and indicated he is delighted to report that it's a valuable lived experience to relay, and that the health care information discussed is appropriately conveyed.

This book contains potentially triggering medical trauma content. Readers, more specifically survivors, should proceed with caution and take breaks as needed.

Contents

Note to Readers

I've been a planner for as long as I can remember. When I turned ten, I organized every detail of my birthday party myself; a fun-filled sleepover with eight of my closest girlfriends. I carefully chose an outfit to wear during the day, probably some tacky, neon 90s outfit that I loved, and the pajamas to wear that night. My mom made hot dogs and a chocolate cake, and I taped colorful balloons and streamers to the basement walls. I even wrote out a blueprint for where everyone's sleeping bag would go in the family room—so we knew who slept next to who.

My life plan was just as detailed. I had it all organized in my head and knew exactly what I wanted when I grew up. Drafted like a well-thought-out "To-Do list" that I could check off, I would grow up, get a job that I loved, and find and marry the man of my dreams. After that, we'd have our babies, raise them together and live happily ever after.

By the time I was twenty-six, I was almost there. I had a great career, a loving husband, and a brand-new baby girl. Living my dream, I was accomplished, proud, and excited about where things were going. I had my whole life ahead of me.

Then I learned that life rarely goes according to plan. I learned this first when I was diagnosed with a rare illness when my daughter was a month old. I learned it again when my decade-long marriage crumbled a few years later. You can plan out your life all you want, but sometimes you're meant for another path. Although at first, it made me sad my past went the way it did; that I lost out on the first few months of my daughter's life, and that I didn't end up with the man I loved since I was eighteen. Now, I believe everything that happens in our lives brings us exactly where we are meant to be. What I went through made me the person I am today. I've more than made up for lost time with my daughter, and I've found love again with my amazing partner Jordan.

In 2012, one year after I recovered from GBS, I wrote my first book, *Happily Ever After*. A chronological journal of my time in the hospital and subsequent recovery at home, its purpose was for me to process and ease the emotional trauma I'd been through and a way to explain my journey to family and friends. But that book reached farther than I imagined. People all over the world use *Happily Ever After* as a guide for fighting Guillain-Barre. That book led me on a new path in life, connecting me with other survivors to show them they are not alone.

With the addition of new chapters and years passed, this book is not just a revision of *Happily Ever After,* but a new journey that incorporates what I overcame with Guillain-Barre Syndrome, plus what happened after the wheelchairs, canes, and physical therapy were gone. My continuing journey to be the strongest person I can be and help and inspire others to find their strength.

No, life doesn't always go as we planned. Sometimes, in the most dire and challenging ways, it turns out even better.

Prologue

"When are you back, Mommy?" my daughter asked, tugging at the bottom of my grey cardigan as I stood at the front door of our home. Casey, a typical five-year-old, didn't like to be away from me for long. She held her favorite blankie in one hand—a pink and brown zebra print blanket the size of a hand towel she affectionately named Cici.

"I won't be long, Hunny." I crouched down, and Casey wrapped her little arms around my neck, making sure not to drop her blanket. Brushing my daughter's soft brown hair out of her eyes, I kissed her goodbye. "I love you, and I'll see you soon."

My mom was already waiting in the hospital lobby when I arrived.

"Are you ready?" she asked, taking my hand in hers with a nervous smile.

I took in a deep breath and nodded.

I'd been back to the hospital to visit my old nurses plenty of times since I was first there in 2011, but this was my first time going back into a patient room. I pressed the square button on the wall outside the intensive care unit, and the doors slowly swung open. The air smelled of strong antiseptic. Exactly as I remembered.

No flowers on the ward, a sign in the hallway read.

I remembered the sign and how everyone had brought me cards instead since flowers are dangerous in the ICU. They can carry bacteria, and patients are more susceptible to infections.

Mom and I greeted the nurses that sat at small desks outside each room. In the intensive care unit, it's always one nurse assigned to each patient. I glanced up at the numbers above the door and breathed a sigh of relief that the patient we were visiting wasn't in the same room I'd been in, the room which I was so certain I'd die in.

Lying in the ICU bed was an older man with a tube in his mouth. A petite woman, most likely his wife, stood beside him, clutching his hand.

"You must be Holly." The woman stood from her seat. "I'm Esther, and this is my mother, Sunny. Thank you so much for coming." She hugged me tight as if we'd known each other our whole lives.

Her mother muttered "Hello" with tears in her eyes; she couldn't speak much English. I approached the bed, and she wrapped her arms around me, squeezing me just as tight as her daughter had.

Sunny's husband Kyu was paralyzed, the paralysis so severe his eyes wouldn't close. His eyelids were partially sewn shut on the corners to protect his eyes from injury and to keep them moist. Though he was asleep, he had a pained look on his face. He began to gasp for air; the ventilator beside him beeped. The sound was chilling to my ears as I remembered the days, weeks, and months of being on a ventilator myself. On the monitor, his blood pressure and heart rate were dangerously high.

"We've never even heard of this disease," Esther said. "Until he was diagnosed."

Kyu had been completely healthy, playing golf one day, on life support, fighting for his life the next. The two didn't come out and say it, but I knew they weren't sure if he'd survive.

But that's why I was there, to show them there was hope. I, too, had been on my death bed in the very same ICU. I went from being a healthy new mom with my newborn baby at home to paralyzed on a ventilator in just a few days. I had completely recovered.

I had the same illness. And I survived.

*

Five years earlier, I woke up on life support with a plastic tube down my throat. I was coherent enough to know where I was but sedated enough that I thought I was in a dream. Then horrible pain in my neck resurfaced, and the flashbacks of the last few days brought me back to my reality.

I gasped for air once, then twice, unable to take in a full breath. A machine beside me beeped in a sing-song tone. A slight pressure of air in my chest forced its way through my lungs. The breath gave me a sense of relief, but why was it a hundred degrees in my room? My skin burned in an intense tingling, half asleep, pins and needles sort of way. I gasped for air again. More beeps followed.

The room was dim, the lights above me were off, but the morning sunshine peeked through the blinds of the frost-covered window to my right. Beside my bed sat my crying husband—our newborn baby in his arms. Mom and Dad were in the corner, whispering. I tried to call out to them, but the tube in my mouth made it impossible. No one realized I was awake. Barely able to catch my breath, I gasped again, wondering if it were the last breath I'd take.

I can't breathe.

My heart raced. I struggled for air.

I'm dying.

No one noticed me. I wanted to scream.

Another gasp. More beeping from the machine.

James stood from his seat; Mom rushed to the head of my bed. The machine beeped again, and more air was forced through my chest.

"M . . . o . . . m . . ." I tried to say.

She leaned in close to my face.

I didn't make a sound, but I could move my lips, even with the tube in my mouth.

"Holly, you're going to be okay," she whispered, her eyes wide with worry. My gaze moved to my husband; his cheeks were soaked with tears, his green eyes bloodshot. Our baby girl stared at me, innocently unaware of the situation. My dad stayed silent. His eyes were puffy and red.

How . . . can this be . . . happening? I'm a good person. I don't deserve this.

I shook my head in disbelief that I was dying so soon after the birth of my child. Tears trickled down my face.

"M . . . om . . ." I mouthed again. She leaned in closer.

"Just . . . let . . . me . . . go," I tried to say.

My mother's eyes widened.

"No! You're going to get better!" she insisted.

James took my hand in his. "The doctor's said you're gonna get through this, Holly." His voice cracked through tears.

I shook my head. I was in the ICU on life support. Unable to speak, barely able to move my own body. They were lying to me.

I'm not getting out of this.

They need to let me go.

We need to say goodbye.

I was terrified but ready.

"Mom," I calmly mouthed again, closing my eyes. "Just . . . let me go. I'm ready to go."

In this moment of surrender, I believed it was the end. In reality, my nightmare was just beginning. I had no idea how much worse things would get. But I would soon find out that I was a fighter, and on this journey, I would find my strength.

*

Mom and I stayed with Kyu and his family in the ICU for over an hour, to share what we had been through in the hospital ourselves.

"High blood pressure and rapid heart rate are common in GBS," I said. We shared every tidbit of information we could, walking them through the illness's typical progression and offering suggestions on how to combat common challenges. At one point, Kyu woke up, looking at me through tiny openings in his eyes. I leaned in towards him and held his lifeless hand.

"You're going to get better," I whispered, holding back my tears. I turned to Esther and her mother, who were both crying. "He's going to survive this," I repeated.

"Thank you again for coming," Esther said. "It means so much."

Mom and I gave them both long comforting hugs as if that would help ease their pain. I left the room with a heavy heart, knowing the long road they had ahead of them.

"It's so great you came to visit," an ICU nurse said as we left the room. "How old is your little girl now?" This nurse didn't know me personally, but she knew my story like most of the staff.

"Casey's five now," I smiled, my eyes starting to tear up. I couldn't believe it had been five years since I'd been paralyzed head to toe, unable to hold my baby in my arms. Thinking about how much had changed since—my recovery and my divorce—made it feel like a lifetime ago. In other ways, it still felt like yesterday.

"That was tough," my mom quietly said once we were in the hospital lobby. I knew being back in the ICU was just as hard for her as it was for me.

"Tough, but rewarding," I said.

She nodded and smiled. I hugged her goodbye and quickly made my way to my car in the parking lot. I didn't like to be away from my daughter any more than she did, especially now, when I could hold her as much as I wanted. With tears rolling down my cheeks, I sped out of the parking lot and headed home to my little girl.

My first ICU patient visit was much harder than I thought it would be.

1

In the Blink of An Eye

I hadn't showered in days. My long dark brown hair was in a messy bun, and I wore the same pink sweatpants I'd worn the day before. Our house was a disaster, and dishes piled up in the sink. I was drained from being up all night but loved sitting on my couch watching my husband hold our month-old baby on his knee. His hand rested under our daughter's chin, and she started to wobble her head back and forth. In a pink cotton sleeper, our baby Casey was trying to hold her head up on her own.

"Grab the camera!" my husband shouted.

Like most new parents, we videotaped everything our baby did. She was our first child. This tiny human we created was growing before our eyes, melting our hearts with each move she made. We treasured every first moment and didn't want to miss anything.

James lowered his fingers from Casey's chin for a second while I filmed; our daughter's bald head wiggled from side to side. I looked on as a proud new mom and smiled at my husband. He was such a good dad already. These milestones made the late nights worth it.

Suddenly, with the camera in my hand, a slight tingle stung my finger as if something had burned me. I put down the camera and examined my hand—no burns or cuts, but the tingle was there. When I rubbed my fingers together, the tip of my index finger was numb. I thought back to my day but couldn't think of anything that could have caused the numbness.

Weird, I thought.

James passed Casey back to me, and I quickly forgot about the odd feeling. I put my face up to my baby's and kissed her again and again.

As much as I loved having my husband at home with us, I was excited for alone time with my baby girl. After four weeks of paternity leave, James was headed back to work in the morning. As a Canadian, I had twelve months of maternity leave ahead, and I couldn't wait to bond with my daughter.

I worked as a Benefits and Compensation Specialist in the Human Resources department for a large casino in Edmonton, Alberta. Having worked at least one and often two jobs since I was fifteen, I was enjoying the change from career-orientated woman to new wife and mother. I dreamed of me and Casey's first year together; walks to the park with her in her stroller, having play dates with my girlfriends, and going to Mommy & Me classes together. Motherhood meant everything to me. My life was going exactly how I planned it. I was the happiest I'd ever been.

Later that evening, my legs felt abnormally tired, as if I had run a marathon. I blamed it on the first thing I could think of: being an exhausted new mom. Breastfeeding was a breeze but waking up multiple times a night was not something I was used to.

Or maybe it was the start of the flu?

When I walked up the stairs to my room, I was weak and shaky, as if my legs were made of rubber. Sudden, sharp pain in my neck quickly changed my mind about it being the flu.

"My neck hurts really bad," I said to James, clutching the back of my neck. Intense pain radiated from inside. I'd had neck pain before, usually from sleeping on it funny, but told James this was different. Unbearable, all of a sudden. And I hadn't done anything that would explain it.

"Why don't you Google it," he suggested.

Great idea. Within a minute, I had a Web MD diagnosis—a pinched nerve.

James nodded. "That makes sense. The pain; feeling weak. Remember when I had a pinched nerve?" He pulled at the back of his shoulder.

It did make sense and even explained the tingle I'd forgotten about in my finger. "Yeah, well, I think I need to see a doctor."

It was February, and we were in the middle of an extreme cold snap of about −30°. We hadn't left the house in days. The throbbing was immediate and so severe I left Casey with James, braved the cold, and drove myself to the nearest medical clinic.

Thankfully, there were less than a handful of people in the waiting room. Most people weren't leaving their house at eight o'clock at night in this weather. I skimmed over the pages of different magazines, but the throb in my neck made it too difficult to focus. I just wanted to see a doctor, get some meds, and get back to my baby. Looking back, I now know how wrong I was to think it would be this easy.

A half-hour later, the nurse called my name.

"Definitely a pinched nerve," the doctor agreed once I told him what was wrong, and he took a look at my neck. "Here's a referral for a physiotherapist and a prescription for Tylenol 3's." He barely lifted his eyes from the prescription pad, then rushed out of the room, though the medi-center was practically empty.

While walking down the clinic hallway with my prescription in hand, my toe suddenly caught the ground. I threw my arms out, barely stopping myself from falling on my face. The flooring was a linoleum tile; nothing for me to trip on. Why was I stumbling over my feet? Every step forward, I consciously lifted each leg to avoid catching the ground again. A part of me wanted to believe medication would help, but an uneasy feeling inside disagreed. I couldn't even walk properly.

By the time I arrived home, the searing pain in my neck had reduced me to tears. I wouldn't get the T3's till the morning, so I popped back two Advil instead. I pushed through the pain, kissed Casey in her white and green lace bassinet beside our bed and crawled in with James.

"The Advil will eventually kick in," my husband said reassuringly, turning to his side of the bed.

"I hope so," I sighed, looking up towards the ceiling. "I probably just need a good night's sleep." Trying to ignore the pain, I closed my eyes, but sleep was impossible. I tossed and turned, my neck feeling stiffer by the hour. With tears rolling down my cheeks, I pressed my fingers deep into the tissue on the back of my neck. Not wanting to disturb James, with tomorrow being his first day back at work or my daughter sleeping peacefully beside us, I quietly slid out of bed to sit on the floor. I tried every neck stretch possible, but the fiery pain only grew stronger.

With my phone in my hand, I researched other possible causes of neck pain. Maybe I broke my neck somehow? Or were pinched nerves really this painful? I found it hard to believe.

A small cry from the bassinet interrupted my thoughts. The time had flown by, it was now three in the morning, and Casey needed to eat. I stood from my cross-legged position on the floor to go to my baby, but suddenly my legs buckled and gave out on me. Like a slow-motion scene from a movie, I crumbled to the floor, putting my arms out in front of me to brace my fall.

Hungry, Casey continued to cry. I tried to stand again. This time I carefully locked my knees in place, straightened my legs, and stood. I cautiously walked over to James' side of the bed.

This couldn't be just a pinched nerve. I thought of the time a doctor misdiagnosed my husband's shingles as some other skin condition. Maybe this doctor was wrong too.

"Take me to the hospital," I whispered to James, gently resting my hand on his back. "I just fell, and my neck is getting worse."

James opened his eyes with a look of concern. He had to be at work in less than five hours.

"Just drop me off. I'll be fine," I reassured him. James was a machinist who worked on dangerous equipment and needed more sleep than this. "You can feed Casey with a bottle from the fridge," I said. I'd pumped a few bottles of breast milk for the first time earlier in the week.

Sensing my urgency, James loaded our daughter in his silver SUV and drove to the Grey Nuns Hospital ten minutes away.

"I probably just need some pain meds," I said as James pulled up in front of the emergency room entrance. Growing up, I dealt with severe migraines and stomach aches that sometimes required medical attention so I'd been to the ER a few times in my past.

"Let me know how it goes," my husband said, his hand on the steering wheel.

"I'll call you as soon as I'm done," I said and got out of the truck. Casey was bundled up in her car seat in the back. I opened the door and kissed her cool cheeks goodbye, then dragged my wobbly legs through the glass sliding doors of the hospital.

I had no idea this would be the last time I'd step outside for months.

Weeks earlier, I waddled into this same hospital with James. In the joyful throes of labor, I had a big round belly and a smile on my face. I was in pain and nervous about the delivery, but I couldn't wait to meet our daughter. I'd been anxiously waiting for her for weeks, dreaming about her for years. Having a baby was a moment I'd waited for my entire life, and I was thrilled it was finally time.

Tonight, I staggered up to the same nurse's station alone, without a smile on my face. I wore an anguished expression from the agonizing ache in my neck. I explained my symptoms to the nurse, who walked me over to another waiting room—a triage room—and I took a seat. The woman took my vitals; another drew blood from my arm.

The room was full of people, and doctors and nurses rushed in and out every couple of minutes. As much as I wished James was with me, this was no place for a newborn. A man violently threw up in a plastic bucket across from me; another bled heavily from his hand wrapped in gauze. I briefly caught a glimpse of myself in the glass window beside me; other than the bags under my eyes from being tired, I didn't look all that bad. I was exhausted and in excruciating pain, but outwardly I appeared fine. I almost felt guilty for coming to the ER for what might still be a pinched nerve.

I waited in my seat for over an hour before a man in green scrubs approached me. He had thick, white hair and was likely in his early sixties.

"Hi, Holly," he said in a cheerful voice. "I'm the on-call doctor. I understand you're in pain, and your legs are weak. Let's have a look." His demeanor was caring, and I relaxed in his presence. We walked to an empty bed alongside the wall a few steps away. My legs felt even wobblier than before, though I was sure he wouldn't notice.

I sat on the bed, and he closed the curtain around us. I told him the medi-center doctor said I had a pinched nerve and that I had taken Advil for the pain, but it did nothing. It was my fall I was worried about. I was hesitant to ask if this could be something else. I didn't want him to think I didn't believe what I'd been told.

"Give me your hands and squeeze mine as hard as you can."

I grabbed his hands and tightened my grip.

He had me push and pull against his resistance, walk a straight line, and follow a light with my eyes. "Any medical conditions?"

"No, nothing. But I had a baby less than a month ago. I had a c-section." I told him I'd also had mild flu-like symptoms the week prior, but otherwise, I was a healthy twenty-six-year-old.

"I think we're dealing with more than a pinched nerve. I'll get you something for the pain, and let's wait and see what your blood work says. We'll go from there, okay?"

The smile on his face comforted me. A few minutes later, a nurse came over and injected me with morphine, and I dragged my feet back to my seat. It took the edge off enough for me to drift to sleep, a reprieve from the growing anxiety about what the blood work would find.

When I opened my eyes again, the same doctor stood before me. I glanced at the clock on the wall to see it was now seven in the morning. I'd been in the ER for more than three hours. At least the pain in my neck was completely gone—the morphine worked.

"Your blood work came back. It's completely normal," the doctor said.

Well, that's good, I thought, relieved. I can go home.

"But there are some red flags from your neurological exam," he added. "Something's wrong, and if I'm being completely honest here, I don't know what. I called a neurologist to come down and examine you. Okay?"

I nodded again, at a loss of what to say. I thought doctors knew everything. This doctor had likely worked in the ER for decades; how could he not know what was wrong with me? I thought that's why you go to the ER.

My cell phone had died shortly after I'd arrived, so I walked over to the hallway and called James from the lounge phone. I explained he'd have to stay home with Casey till I got back. What terrible timing; his boss would not be happy if he missed another day.

"I already fed Casey the bottles in the fridge. You need to come home and feed her." James said, panicked.

"I can't," I said and paused for a moment. "Just give her formula." I sighed. The hospital gave us one small container when she was born, though I wanted her to stick with breast milk and had tucked it away in the back of our pantry with no intention of ever using it. "I'll call you back when I know more." I staggered back to my chair, noticing my legs were still weak. I had time to feel the heartbreak of Casey taking formula when we'd wanted her to stay on breast milk before morphine-induced sleep overtook me.

Maybe it was the drugs, but when the neurologist, who quietly introduced himself as Dr. Clark, woke me up, I had to laugh. He looked exactly like the actor Ed Helms from The Office and The Hangover, with similar square glasses and light brown hair. He wasn't as funny, though. He barely spoke a word as he had me squeeze his hands then tested my reflexes.

Everything felt normal to me. But it wasn't.

"You're very weak," he said. "You have no reflexes in your arms or your legs. I think I know what's wrong with you."

"What is it?" I was oddly intrigued.

"You need to have some tests done before we can confirm anything. We're going to have to admit you to the ER."

My breath quickened.

I'd never been admitted to the hospital before other than having a baby. What did he think was wrong? And why wouldn't he just tell me?

Did I have cancer or something? That was the first thing that came to my mind.

I steadied my breath to calm my panic.

You're healthy, Holly, I told myself. Other than the odd stomach-ache and migraine, I was always healthy, at least up until now. Growing up, it was a joke in our family. We called my brother Jay, who broke multiple bones, "the bone breaker." My brother Brett, who had more stitches than we could count, was "the stitch maker." And I was called: "healthy." I told myself this couldn't be anything serious.

After the neurologist left, I staggered back down the hall to call James again. This time my instincts kicked in and told me to grab the railings, or I might fall. I shuffled to the wall, and with one sluggish step at a time, I made my way to the lounge.

"Should I come there?" James asked quietly from the other end of the line when I told him I was being admitted and my legs were getting worse.

"No, I'm sure it's nothing. Stay home with Casey. I'll call you back once I know more."

A nurse brought me to a private room. I changed out of my pink sweatpants and hoody and into an oversized white floral gown that tied up in the back. The nurse returned, fastened a plastic hospital bracelet around my wrist, and whisked me away in a wheelchair for x-rays.

Outside the x-ray lab, an older man who looked as if he could be dying lay in a bed. I forced my gaze from him, not wanting to make eye contact. No longer in pain anymore, I looked fine. Back in the room where I was admitted, I wondered if I truly needed to be here.

Until a couple of hours later, when I woke up and tried to get out of bed to go pee. I could hardly stand. I used the call button to ring the nurses, and it took two of them to get me into a wheelchair then onto the toilet. When the nurse bent down to pull down my underwear, terror washed over me.

I can't even use the bathroom by myself.

My body was failing me. Yes, I belonged in the hospital.

What the hell was wrong with me?

Shortly after, the Ed Helms look-alike returned with another man in scrubs. Another doctor, I presumed.

"Your x-rays came back normal," Dr. Clark said.

What the fuck? Still no answer, even though I'm getting worse.

Dr. Clark introduced the man in scrubs to me. He was an anesthesiologist.

"We need to test the fluid in your spine," the man spoke. I'd forgotten his name already.

To confirm the neurologist's theory of what was wrong with me, I needed a spinal tap, also called a lumbar puncture. The anesthesiologist explained this is done by inserting a giant needle in my back. I had an epidural with Casey, so I knew what to expect. After the anesthesiologist finished, I sat alongside the bed, my jelly legs dangling over the edge.

Dr. Clark pulled over a stool and sat down in front of me.

He said, "I think you have Guillain-Barre Syndrome."

My mind raced, trying to grasp what that meant. *Syndrome? Is that a disease*? I'd never heard those words before.

He explained that Guillain-Barre (pronounced Gee-yon Barr-ay) is a rare autoimmune disorder that triggers the immune system to produce antibodies that attack the nerves, leaving them unable to transmit signals. He went on to say that my body—the same body which only four weeks ago gave birth to my daughter, could be attacking itself. "But we won't know for sure until the spinal tap results come back in a day or two." He handed me a piece of paper, an internet print-out with the words Guillain-Barre Syndrome on top. "You need to stay here until we know more. Call your husband and your parents and tell them to come."

"My mom is in Toronto," I said. "And my baby probably shouldn't come to the ER." There was no reason for them to come.

"Holly. Call your family. This is a medical emergency." He handed me a phone. All optimism I had left was stripped away, and a knot grew in my stomach. I dialed James then my mom on her cell. Each time I said, "You need to come to the hospital," I choked back tears.

"Come as soon as you can," I said to my mother, who was across the country in Toronto. "The doctors think I have a rare illness." Saying it out loud suddenly made this more real. I explained what I knew so far, but I couldn't even pronounce the stupid name of the syndrome. Tears turned to sobs, and I wiped my tears with my hands. My mom later said the twelve hours it took to drive to the airport in Toronto rush hour traffic, catch a plane and fly home to be by my side were the longest, most grueling hours of her life.

Immediately after I spoke to my mom, nurses moved me to the stroke and Neurology ward on the fifth floor. I have no recollection of this or when James and Casey arrived shortly after. Exhaustion, fear, and anxiety took over my body. I was nearly delusional the rest of the day and night. I have very few memories; flashbacks of being half-asleep in bed, Casey breastfeeding in my arms. Crying hysterically from the torturing pain which had resurfaced in my neck. I vaguely remember nurses prying Casey from my arms, placing her in a bassinet they brought up from the labor and delivery ward, and injecting me with more pain medication. I don't remember my mom and stepdad Dennis arriving at midnight or James leaving to take Casey back home for the night.

The next morning, I opened my eyes to find a heart rate monitor clipped onto my index finger. I couldn't believe I had spent the night in the hospital. The throbbing ache in my neck was back with a vengeance and now ran down my entire back. A horrific new symptom, a tingling, burning sensation, penetrated my skin.

"Morning, Babe, how do you feel?" James asked. He was right beside my bed with our daughter in his arms, anxiously waiting for me to wake up. My mom, Dennis, and my dad, Chester, who lived an hour and a half away, were there too. Mom must have called my father.

"I'm in so much pain," I cried. The pain was a hundred times worse than the day before. James, with bags under his eyes, held Casey over my bed. I reached to touch her, and a nurse walked into the room.

"Good morning," she said. "I'm going to check your temperature and blood pressure. The doctor will be in to see you shortly."

She grabbed my arm, and a sharp pain shot like a flash of lightning through every part of my body. I thought she stabbed me with a knife. "Stop! Please stop!!" I screamed and pulled my arm away. The pain was so severe it made me light-headed, and I thought I might pass out.

"What's your pain level right now, from one to ten?" the nurse asked.

"TEN!" I shouted. Tears gushed from my eyes. This pain was on a level I'd never experienced before. Labor seemed like a walk in the park compared to this. I jolted up in bed.

"Stay still, Holly," the nurse demanded.

"I need to pee," I snapped back.

"You have to use a bedpan. You're not strong enough to get out of bed," she said, then walked out of the room.

What was she talking about? What's a bedpan? Why can't I get out of bed?

She returned with a metal bowl shaped like a toilet seat under her arm.

"Lay back down, and I'll put this under your butt." I looked around the room. Did she expect me to pee in that? In front of everyone?

"We'll come back in a few minutes," my dad said, steering Dennis out of the room and closing the door behind them.

The nurse grabbed my leg and placed the cold, metal bowl underneath me. Another sharp pain shot through the front of my legs.

"Stop!" I screamed. The pain ripped through every nerve in my thigh. My mom watched on with a look of horror in her eyes.

"I can give you something stronger for the pain," The nurse placed her hand on mine. "But you'll have to stop breastfeeding."

My heart sank. I was no longer concerned about the bedpan and pulled my hand away. "I don't want to give her more formula. I'm breastfeeding." I'd made the decision long before our daughter was born. I knew the nurse was only doing her job, but I despised her in that moment for her suggestion. I looked to my husband to back me up.

"Holly, I'm sorry," the nurse interrupted. "If I keep giving you opioids, you can't breastfeed anymore. It can harm your baby."

The unfathomable pain radiated down my legs while I contemplated what to do. If I stopped breastfeeding, I might not produce milk again.

"It's for the best," James said, looking at my mom for reassurance. She nodded. Apparently, they discussed this while I slept.

"Okay," I tearfully conceded. I didn't know which hurt worse; the searing pain in every cell of my body or giving up breastfeeding my weeks-old daughter. I looked at Casey, my tiny newborn, who shouldn't even be here.

We should be at home. I should be breastfeeding her. We should be going to our first Mommy & Me class together, scheduled for the next day. *I shouldn't be in a fucking hospital right now!*

"I can't be here! I need to go home!" I cried uncontrollably. I jerked my body in a desperate attempt to get out of bed. I hardly moved an inch. I tried to move again. Nothing. My legs weren't just weak anymore. They were now completely paralyzed.

2

Girlhood, Womanhood, Motherhood

My parents separated a few months shy of my fourth birthday. With our belongings crammed into the back of mom's blue Ford Mustang, she pulled out of the back alley, and I waved goodbye to my dad from the passenger side window. This was the late eighties, before car seats. My two older brothers stayed behind. That's how our parents handled custody: me with Mom, the boys with Dad—at least the first few years.

My father, with tears in his eyes behind his thick glasses, and a phony smile across his face, got smaller and smaller as we drove away. When he faded into the distance, I turned around. "Well, I don't have a dad anymore," I said candidly to my mother. I'm not sure what made me think that.

Mom choked back tears. "You'll always have a dad, Hunny," she muttered. She took one hand off the steering wheel and reached out to hold mine. "You just won't see him as often anymore."

We moved to Edmonton, an hour and a half away from small-town Drayton Valley, where my mom and dad grew up. They married young; mom was eighteen, dad was twenty-five, after knowing each other for just three months. Three kids and twelve years later, it ended, and they divorced.

I remember two things about how I felt the day we left—devastated to leave my dad but thrilled to get out of Drayton Valley and move to the big city. Every time I'd visited Edmonton, the bright lights and towering skyscrapers took my breath away. Staring out the car window, I was in awe of the number of people who lived there. It wasn't New York or anything; less than a million people lived in Edmonton, but something about it drew me in, even at a young age. A part of me was excited about this new beginning: just me and my mom.

Even though we lived in different towns, our parents were determined to keep us all close. Every weekend our parents met at a gas station on the side of the highway, halfway between Drayton Valley and Edmonton. I went to Dad's to be with him and my brothers; on the alternating weekends, Jay and Brett came to our place in the city. I'm not sure it helped us bond, though. I think my brothers were pleased I'd moved away.

"You know you were adopted, Holly. Why do you think there are no baby pictures of you?" my eldest brother Jay, three and a half years older than me, always teased.

"Mommy lost my baby album when we moved!" I shouted back every time. With dark hair like my mom's and light blue eyes exactly like my dad's, I knew being adopted wasn't a possibility. I was clearly my Metis (Indigenous and French) mother and European father's daughter. My brothers loved to get under my skin.

"You're a girl. We don't like you," Brett, two years older than me, said and slammed the door in my face. I cried and cried, usually ratting out my brothers whenever they left me out.

Brett and Jay's tormenting ranged from humorous jokes, like when they woke me up at two in the morning and got me ready for school, to more cruel ones, like the time one of them peed in a cup and told me it was apple juice. Despite all that, I followed them everywhere and begged them to play with me. The only time they ever would was when the other was away, at least that's how it felt.

In all fairness, they were typical older brothers. Closer in age and both boys, they had a stronger bond, something I understood early on. For a long time, I wanted their attention and their approval. At one point, I wished I'd been born a boy. I once asked my mom to give me a pixie cut, short, just like theirs. Maybe then they would like me.

But deep down, I loved being a little girl. I liked Barbies and the color pink. I hated bugs, even ladybugs, and despised sports. Around the age of five, I understood I had little in common with my brothers. While they played video games and soccer, I painted pictures and played mommy to my stuffed teddy bears. I'm sure my brothers were ecstatic when I went back to Mom's for the week.

I was a daddy's girl, though, and leaving his place was always tough. My dad was fun, he took us swimming and camping, and he made me laugh with his ridiculous dad jokes.

"How was your trip?" I remember him asking whenever I took a tumble.

"Dad!!" I shook my head at him. I'd have skinned up knees from hitting the pavement, but his humor always seemed to take away the pain.

Being away from him was the hardest part of my parents' divorce. I was never vocal about it, but I wanted them to get back together again. I remember being in kindergarten, and I was the only child with divorced parents.

"I miss my daddy!" I cried to my mom at bedtime after I returned home from another weekend away. My heart was aching.

"I know you do," Mom said as she pulled back the covers and crawled into my white day bed. She pulled my hand into hers, and in a circular motion, she massaged the tip of my thumb, then gently rubbed each finger, slowly moving down one joint at a time. My eyelids grew heavy, my heartbeat relaxed. She did this whenever I was upset and always stayed until I fell asleep or was no longer in tears.

Mom was a highly compassionate woman. She worked full-time as a social worker helping vulnerable children. It couldn't have been an easy job, nor was raising three kids in two separate homes while working full time in a city away from her family. I often heard my mom crying alone in her room, though I'm uncertain why. I cried a lot in my room, too, because I wanted my family together again.

That's not to say that I wasn't a happy child and didn't have a great childhood—I was, and I did. My brothers weren't *always* cruel to me; we had a lot of fun memories, too, like playing with stuffed animals that drove around in a white Barbie limo. We went swimming and watched movies, and my brothers taught me how to play Supaplex on our first computer.

I was a bubbly, happy-go-lucky, and affectionate little girl, full of energy. Life was exciting to me, and I always rubbed my hands together whenever something fun was going on. I lived for the moment but looked forward to the future. I couldn't wait to grow up.

As the years went on, Brett and Jay took turns living with Mom and me. Dad started dating and later moved a woman and her kids into his place. I wouldn't say we all got along, but, like my brothers and I, we tolerated and even played nicely with one another for the several years they were together. As time passed, I came to the realization my parents were not getting back together.

"We get along much better now that we're apart," Mom always said, which was true. My parents were, dare I say it, friends, now, and if they did argue, it was behind closed doors.

Mom had a couple of boyfriends over the years—nothing too serious from my view anyways. But I hoped she'd find happiness with someone again. I wanted her to meet a nice man, get married, then have another baby. Another girl this time.

"Dear God. Please give me a little sister to play with," I often prayed at bedtime. I believed if I prayed enough, it would come true.

As I got older, those regular bedtime prayers dwindled down to annual birthday cake wishes. By the time I was a pre-teen and with Mom still single, I gave up on my desire for a sister and dreamed about having my own little girl instead—a little girl who could one day be my best friend. I couldn't wait to grow up, get married, and have my own family. I wanted to accomplish what I believed my family had failed at. And thanks to my love for Disney movies, I wanted a fairy-tale story, the prince, our babies, and a happily ever after. Cliché, I know, but I knew I was destined to be a wife and mother. I felt it deep in my soul.

*

Our family moved back to Drayton Valley when I was fifteen. My auntie Donna, Mom's younger sister, was diagnosed with lung cancer, and Mom not only wanted to spend more time with her, but she also wanted us to be closer to my dad. I was still a bubbly girl with a zest for life, but now with a side of teenage attitude that I don't think Mom appreciated. The move ended up being the best decision for her, as she found her happily ever after with Dennis, a charming man originally from Newfoundland. They married in the summer of 2002 when I was seventeen, shortly after I graduated high school. Along with Dennis' daughter from a previous relationship, my brothers and I stood in their bridal party. We were delighted that they had found love again.

A year later, after I moved back to Edmonton, I found my own happiness with James—a tall, handsome, and incredibly funny young man with dark hair and green eyes. We were immediately smitten and spent every possible minute together, cruising around the city in my silver Chevrolet Cavalier. I'd had a few boyfriends before James, typical "teenage loves" that never lasted, but this was different. I fell fast, the way I did in most of my past relationships; the difference this time was that he fell just as hard for me.

"I've never felt anything like this before," James said to me one night as we cuddled up on the couch watching movies in the home I shared with a friend. He had never had a serious girlfriend before me, and these feelings were all new to him. "I love you," he said. Then he passionately kissed me. I didn't say anything back at the time; we'd only known each other a few weeks, and to me, it was too soon. Probably because I'd had my heart broken a few times by boys who said they loved me. But I believed James meant it. And as we spent more and more time together, I knew I loved him too. We moved in together after just a few months of dating.

We spent the next several years building our lives for the future. James got a job at a shop working as a machinist. I worked several years serving shooters at a posh nightclub before going back to school and settling in a career in Human Resources. We both worked hard, gradually accumulating more and more things for the various houses we lived in. We got two dogs—a light brown Pug-a-Poo named Hugo and a white American Eskimo called Bentley. James and I were inseparable and genuinely happy. We had a close group of friends and made a life together full of memories.

But we weren't without problems. We were two kids growing up together with nasty tempers we both got from our fathers. We had ups and downs, and sometimes we fought a lot, which usually ended with us breaking up then quickly getting back together. Despite our differences, we were madly in love, and all that mattered was that we were together. We were married after seven years together in a beautiful church ceremony followed by a reception with our close family and friends.

We started trying for kids eight months later. Now in our mid-twenties, we were ready to start a family. It was part of our plan. I bought a pregnancy test when my period was three days late and hid the box of Clear Blue in my purse so James wouldn't see. When I got home from work that day, he was lying in bed watching one of our favorite shows, American Idol.

"How was your day?" he asked, his eyes fixated on the monitor.

"It was good," I said casually and took off my sweater. Inside, my heart was pounding. Now off birth control, my period was irregular, and three days late probably meant nothing; hence my desire to hide the test until I knew for sure.

"Come lay down. Lee Dewyze is singing next," James said. We'd been watching since the beginning of the series. Lee was our favorite contestant on the show this year.

"I'll be right back—I just need to pee." I said, then practically ran to the bathroom beside our room. I dug the test from my purse.

Even if I am pregnant, it's probably too early to tell.

After I finished, I placed the stick on the counter, stood in front of the mirror, and studied my body.

Do my breasts look bigger? I turned to the side.

Do I have a baby bump?

Don't get your hopes up, I thought to myself. Most people don't get pregnant on their first try. While I waited for the stick to change colors, Lee Dewyze belted out Leonard Cohen's *Hallelujah*, one of my all-time favorite songs.

A thin blue cross gradually appeared.

Oh my God...am I? I fidgeted with the instructions to confirm what I'd already read.

Blue line. Not Pregnant.

Blue cross...

Holy shit! I'm pregnant! My heart raced, and I fell to the floor. The beautiful chords of *Hallelujah* from the other room made it feel as if I was in a movie.

"James! Come here!" I screamed. This was a moment I'd imagined since I was a child. "We're having a baby!" I cried through tears of joy.

James was just as excited as I was.

Three months later, we had our first ultrasound.

"Let's see if we can find out the sex," the technician said, holding a gadget in his hand. I laid back on the bed and shot James an eager grin. Secretly, I was praying for a girl. I'd grown into a woman who adored dresses, high heels, sparkles, and everything pink. A little girl would make all my dreams come true. My husband was undoubtedly rooting for a boy to play video games and watch Sunday football with. In the end, all that mattered was that the baby was healthy.

The technician pushed the probe into my lower abdomen. The pressure on my bladder was painful. But then a blurry image appeared on the TV beside the bed, making it all worth it.

"This is the head," he pointed to the screen. I could also make out tiny fingers. I couldn't believe I was looking at my own child. It was hard to fathom I was growing a baby inside my body.

"I can't tell you for sure..." the technician paused, "but it looks like you're having a girl."

A daughter!! I rubbed my hands together as I had done since I was a kid. Instant visions of my little girl and I playing dress-up, painting our nails, and getting into makeup together flooded my mind. Having a daughter meant everything to me. I looked over at James as he smiled from ear to ear. I knew he was as thrilled as I was.

But he was also nervous. We were one of the first couples in our group of friends to have kids. "We haven't been around a lot of babies," James reminded me once we were back at home. "How do we know if we're doing things right?"

I sat down on the couch and stretched my legs out in front of me, resting my hands on my growing belly. "We'll be fine," I reassured. "We'll get the hang of things fast. Don't worry. You're going to be an amazing father.

"You'll be an amazing mother, too," he said.

James and I were a young couple without a lot of money; we bought a second-hand cherry wood crib and changing table for our daughter's room. Our parents gifted us a matching rocking chair with cream cushions. I visualized breastfeeding my daughter night after night in that rocking chair. I painted thick white stripes on the beige walls; James stenciled the words *Such a big miracle in such a little girl* above her crib. By the time her due date rolled around, all the teeny tiny diapers, onesies, and sleepers were folded neatly in the top drawer of the changing table. All her cute clothes hung in the closet. We were as ready as we could have ever been.

I went into labor three days after she was due. The first grandbaby on both sides of the family, everyone anxiously awaited her arrival. We had three names picked out for her; we were still going back and forth between the three the day she was born.

I imagined labor from what I'd seen on TV, a screaming woman, legs in the air, doctors and nurses frantically running everywhere. But for me, it was the opposite. The epidural worked like a charm. I spent the next twelve hours without pain, watching movies in bed on my laptop and talking with James and my parents. My nurse, who started her shift right when I arrived, was the only nurse I saw all day. She kept the lights in my room dim. It was a much quieter and more relaxing experience than I imagined. However, when it came time to deliver, my baby would not come out, even after two hours of pushing.

"You're gonna have to have a C-section, Holly," explained a doctor who'd I met just a few hours before. My obstetrician wasn't on call that day.

'No! I can do this." I was determined to deliver my baby. I still had lots of energy, no pain, and wanted to keep going.

"I'm not asking," the doctor asserted. "The baby is at an angle. All the pushing is putting pressure on her head. You're having a C-section." His voice was stern.

Tears instantly rolled down my cheeks. I didn't even read the C-section part of the childbirth book because I was so sure I wouldn't have one. Surgery was not part of our plan. The nurse explained that this doctor was one of the best at Caesarean deliveries and assured me everything would be fine.

The decision was final. My body trembled as a nurse rolled my bed to the operating room.

"You're going to be okay, Babe," James comforted me as I lay on the operating table in the massive room.

Bright, white lights shone down on me. I squeezed my husband's hand as tight as I could while doctors pulled and prodded my organs. Thanks to the copious amounts of drugs they gave me, the operation was also painless, though I threw up a couple times.

Before I knew it, my baby was here.

"It's a girl!" the doctor shouted.

Our daughter was born at 8:30 pm on January 26th, 2011. Nurses took our baby to the side of the room while they stitched me back up. James went with them. After what felt like a few minutes later, he came back with our camera in his hand.

"Look at how cute she is!" he said, clicking through photo after photo after photo. How had he taken so many pictures of her already? I hadn't even seen her yet.

"Just give me my baby!" I cried, lying helplessly on the table. A nurse handed her to me seconds later.

In an instant, like every new parent says, my life changed forever. She was wailing, but she was beautiful. A C-section was worth it, I was fine, and our baby was healthy. That's all that mattered.

Our daughter was big: eight pounds, eleven ounces, and long. Mostly bald with big dark blue eyes and heart-shaped lips. Her eyebrows were furrowed like she was upset—mad that she was pulled so abruptly from my belly. She had the biggest cheeks I'd ever seen on a baby. Neither James nor I could tell who she resembled most. She didn't have our dark brown hair.

"I want you to name her," James said once we were settled in our room for the night. He felt terrible her birth hadn't gone the way we thought it would and that I now had to recover from surgery.

I smiled and stared down at my baby girl in my arms. I thought of the first name we came up with back when I'd found out I was pregnant.

We named her Casey Marie.

3

Losing My Breath

Less than a month after having Casey, I was back in the same hospital, this time on the stroke and neurology ward. Trapped in a hospital bed in unimaginable pain, unable to walk or even move my legs anymore, I wept. I felt like I was in the medical drama House, where doctors were trying to find a diagnosis for their mystery patient. Dr. Clark, the Ed Helms look-alike, couldn't yet confirm if I had this rare disease or not.

"We're going to test you for other conditions while we wait for the results of your spinal tap, he told us the morning of Day 2. "We need to rule out other possibilities."

It was surreal to hear all of this. How was I being tested for syndromes and conditions—at twenty-six? It was a stark reminder that young people get ill, too.

"Let's stay positive," Mom said as she sat beside my bed. My mother, big into personal development, was always optimistic.

James paced the room with Casey in his arms. Our daughter was her usual quiet self. Dad and Dennis stood off to the side. In these moments of stress, I was grateful everyone got along so well. My parents, though divorced, had remained cordial for twenty years now, and although I wouldn't label my dad and Dennis as friends, they were kind to one another. Dad never remarried, but it felt like we were one big happy family. Our holiday dinners included everyone.

"We're going to do an MRI," Dr. Clark said after he tested my hand strength again and noted they too had worsened.

My body tensed up. Horror struck me with the doctor's words. "I can't do that." I looked at James and began to cry.

"She's extremely claustrophobic," James told the doctor.

Ever since I was little, elevators, small rooms, even waterslides sent me into a suffocating state of panic for no reason that I can think of. I might have been able to talk myself through the MRI on a good day, but, at that moment, I was in no state of mind to handle being in what I imagined was a small, dark tunnel. With everything I was going through, it all felt like too much.

"We need to figure out what's wrong with you," the doctor said.

Mom got up from her chair. "I'll go with her," she said.

I understood I didn't have a choice.

With the side rails up on my bed, my nurse rolled me out of my room to the basement of the hospital. I cried the whole way to the Diagnostic Imaging department, then even harder when I saw the massive white machine with the tiny opening for my body to squeeze into.

Using the bottom of the sheet, four people transferred me onto the flatbed of the MRI machine. The technician placed a pair of headphones over my ears. "Just listen to the music," he encouraged. "And press this button if you need to come out."

I clutched the tiny remote he gave me in my hand. As I slowly moved into the tunnel, my body tensed with fear. I tried to focus on whatever Top 40 song played in my ears, but I panicked when everything went dark.

I can't breathe. I need out! I squeezed the button. Slowly my body moved out of the machine. The technician's face came into view.

"You need to stay in longer. Close your eyes. You can do this." He gave me a thumbs up.

Back in the machine, I went. I squeezed my eyes shut and took in a deep breath. Tears poured down my face. The walls of the machine closed in, and the air became thinner. I pressed the button again when I couldn't handle it any longer. Back out of the machine, I went.

"Holly. Every time you come out means, the more times you have to go back in."

I swear the guy rolled his eyes. Back in the machine once more.

I shut my eyes, breathed deeply, counted, and prayed.

Please let me get through this. I can do this. I said it over and over in my head, choking back tears. My body pain was magnified and increased the feeling of being trapped. By the time it finished, I was hysterical.

"Please don't ever make me do that again!" I cried to my mom when the technician rolled my bed back out of the lab.

It wasn't just the MRI I was crying about. My body hurt as if I'd fallen off a building. And I needed to know what the hell was wrong with me.

Later that evening, after having slept most of the day, thanks to the cocktail of medications I was on, a tall, thin man in a designer grey suit and brown pointed leather shoes walked into my room. He couldn't have been older than forty. He introduced himself as Dr. Yousef. He was a neurologist—an independent consultant.

He pulled a chair up beside my bed. Exhausted and heavily medicated, I could hardly open my eyes.

"The test results from your lumbar puncture show that the protein levels in your spinal fluid are elevated. You have Guillain-Barre Syndrome. GBS," he said with sheer confidence and a lack of emotion in his voice.

He explained that in GBS, most patients will have elevated CSF protein with an average cell count.

I stared back at the fancy doctor with disbelief. I had something I never imagined I would deal with in my life—a rare disease.

James walked over to my bed and intertwined my fingers in his. I glanced at our daughter napping beside me in the bassinet.

“What happens now?” Mom asked.

I was thinking the same thing. Exhausted, dazed, and in too much pain to talk, Mom was already speaking for me most of the time.

Dr. Yousef explained that while there is no cure for GBS, it's an acute illness. Meaning once patients hit their absolute worst and their condition plateaus, they start to improve. “People with GBS recover and return to their lives. They just have to get through the initial stage.” He added that there are varying degrees of GBS. Patients with mild cases could be better and home in a week. Those with severe cases could become completely paralyzed, needing to learn to walk again. “Recovery in severe cases takes anywhere from six months to years.”

We all looked at one another, but no one said a thing.

The neurologist turned to my family.

"We’re hopeful that she'll plateau soon and start to improve. The paralysis might not get any worse than this.”

Oh, thank God, I thought.

“But you need to be prepared, Holly.” Dr. Yousef turned back to me. “The paralysis may continue to spread. It could happen very quickly,” he warned. "If you end up with a serious case, you won't be able to move, and you’ll be here at the hospital for a while. You may feel hopeless, depressed, even suicidal because of how quickly your life will change."

I looked to James for some sort of reassurance, but his eyes were wide with fear.

That’s not going to happen, I said to myself. *Mine will be a mild case. Only my legs are paralyzed, and that’s as far as it will go. I will not need to learn to walk again. I'm gonna be okay.*

These are the lies we tell ourselves to make it through times like this. The excruciating pain already had me questioning how I could handle this for much longer, never mind up to a year.

"We're gonna start you on treatment to help speed up recovery," he said enthusiastically. We later found out that Dr. Yousef was brought in specifically to consult on my case. The doctors here at the hospital knew very little about the condition compared to him.

The treatment for GBS was something called IVIG or Intravenous Immunoglobulin, a process that adds proteins from the blood of donors to reduce the autoimmune attack in my nerves. It would supply me with healthy antibodies found in donor plasma, neutralizing the harmful antibodies in mine. I would have five treatments of IVIG through an IV in my arm and stay in the hospital for the next week or so. Being in the hospital for that long felt foreign to me. I had a baby I needed to take care of.

Within minutes, a nurse hooked up the IV sticking out of my hand to a bottle of clear fluid beside my bed. I later learned these glass containers, about the size of a Coca-Cola bottle, cost upward of ten thousand dollars and could have the antibodies from over one thousand donors inside.

"How will I know if it's working?" I finally spoke.

"You'll regain the strength you've lost," Dr. Yousef said. "The neurologists here will monitor you, and I'll be back to see you in a few days."

I sighed a breath of relief that this treatment would help.

I pictured the new antibodies surging through the IV in my hand, into my body, my limbs quickly starting to move again. The paralysis in my legs would fade before my eyes. I'd be all better and I'd get to go home before the doctor came back to visit. That's how I imagined it would happen. I went to sleep that night believing I'd wake up to my usual self, even with the unbearable aches and pains in every part of my body that kept me up screaming all night.

The next morning, shortly after my second IVIG treatment, I went into respiratory failure.

It's strange the things that stand out in my mind about moving to Intensive care. All my memories to this point are foggy, some non-existent. Suddenly, everything was crystal clear. When my bed rolled into the ICU, the first person I remember was a young nurse about my age with medium-length brown hair and glasses. I was short of breath, moaning in pain, and looked to her for help. She gently rubbed my forehead and wiped the tears off my cheeks as we rolled into one of the ICU rooms. Doctors and nurses rushed around me.

It had taken less than seventy-two hours from my first symptom with GBS, that tingle in my fingertip, for the paralysis to reach my diaphragm. My case was progressing fast.

A man in scrubs crouched beside my bed. “Holly, we’re going to do another treatment for GBS, something called plasmapheresis. We’re going to take out your blood through an IV catheter in your thigh and pump it into a machine to remove the harmful antibodies. Then we will infuse your blood back into your body.”

I didn't understand why they weren’t doing IVIG anymore, but I didn’t care. I just needed the treatment to work. My heart raced, and I scanned the large room for a familiar face.

“Your family is in the waiting room,” this new doctor said. “Once you’re prepped for treatment and intubated, they’ll be allowed to come in.”

The young man reached down to my legs. They may have been paralyzed, but I could feel everything. Burning tingles shot through my nerves when his hand touched my skin. Something was wrong with my sense of touch. When the doctor moved my leg to the side, it felt as if he had a vice around my leg. I couldn’t understand what was happening and continued to cry.

“We’re gonna insert the catheter now,” the doctor said and slowly moved his hands back between my thighs.

Pressure and pain. Then stinging lacerations as if the doctor had sliced my leg in half. I screamed, loud. “Please get me something! It hurts so bad!”

The nurse grabbed my hand. "We'll get you something," she assured.

The doctor tugged at the same right leg; piercing pain intensified by the second. It felt like the doctor's fist was in my thigh. Blood rushed to my head.

I'm going to pass out.

The nurse abruptly let go of my hand, then switched places with the doctor, who rushed out of the room while she kept her hand on my thigh. He appeared moments later with another doctor behind him. They pushed the nurse aside.

"It hurts! It hurts so bad!" I screamed as loud as I could. I watched as this second doctor leaned between my legs, and it again felt as if he had his whole hand inside my thigh. If the pain the day before was a ten, this was a twenty.

"You're going to be okay." The nurse stared into my tear-covered eyes with my hand in hers. Her tone of voice was calm, but her eyes filled with fear. After what felt like ten minutes, but I'm sure it was not even one, someone injected me with another drug. The pain subsided to a six or seven.

The next thing I remember, they wheeled me down a hallway into a different room. Doctors and nurses hovered over me. I looked up at the bright lights shining down, then at the white walls surrounding me.

I'd been here before.

This room. My c-section.

I was in an operating room.

Then everything went dark.

"Is everyone here that needs to be?" A doctor who introduced himself as Dr. Yang asked James, who sat with Casey and my parents in the waiting room outside Intensive care.

Mom quickly looked around. My brother Brett had arrived; Jay, who worked in the oil patch out of town, was still days away.

"Yeah, everyone's here that can be . . ." she said, confused.

"We . . . we screwed up," the doctor muttered. Then he gazed down at the floor.

Mom and James shot each other a look of concern.

"While we were inserting the catheter into Holly's vein to administer the plasmapheresis, we punctured her femoral artery. She needs emergency surgery and a blood transfusion." He paused for a moment. "We don't know if she will survive."

Silence.

My mom later told me you could have heard a pin drop.

She looked at my husband, then at my father, wondering who would speak first.

Neither one said a thing.

Someone had to say something; Mom decided it would be her.

"Can we see her before she goes in?" Mom's voice stuttered.

"No, I'm sorry, she's already in surgery," Dr. Yang explained. "She'll be in there for a few hours."

Mom, feeling nauseous, rushed out of the room. Dennis chased after her. She told me later that while in the bathroom, she looked in the mirror and prayed.

"Please, God, don't take her from me." My mom, a spiritual person, needed God now more than ever. After repeating this to herself, she worked up the strength to return to the waiting room. James was in tears, already on the phone with his parents.

*

Six hours later, I opened my eyes. The room echoed with loud beeps and breathing sounds. The breaths came from me. Tubes and cords were everywhere. In my mouth and down my throat was a plastic breathing tube, kept in place by two thick, brown stickers on both my cheeks. Speaking was no longer an option. My arms were flimsy and weak, and I couldn't move my torso anymore. The paralysis had spread even more in just six hours.

Remarkably, I didn't *feel* as bad as I looked. The intolerable pain I'd been suffering through the last couple of days was gone entirely, and a sense of peace warmed my heart.

Surrounding my bed stood my parents, Brett, James, and Casey, in his arms. Off to the side was my best friend, Deanne. She flew home from a job interview in another province the second she got the call from James. The first thing that came to my mind to say was, "How did your interview go?"

Deanne smiled. It was practically impossible to understand me because of the tube coming out of my mouth, but she understood what I was trying to ask.

"I got the job," Deanne grinned. She had the type of smile that lit up a room.

Even in my dire state, I was happy and proud of her, and I tried to smile back.

My mother pulled my hand into hers and stood beside me. She explained what had transpired; the ruptured artery, the emergency surgery, how I had almost died. It must have been all the drugs I was on, but none of what she told me seemed like a big deal. I had no more pain and felt confident I'd be all better soon.

It's all going to be okay, I wanted to say.

Shortly after, the door to my room opened, a young doctor approached my bed and sat down in the chair beside me. He rested his elbows on my bed and leaned in as close to me as he could get. His face looked familiar.

"Hi, Holly. I'm Matt." He spoke slowly. "I'm the resident doctor in ICU." His eyes filled with tears. "I don't even know what to say. I'm so sorry." He folded his arms across my bed.

I realized he was the doctor who had his hand in my thigh. He must have been the one who accidentally ruptured my artery. No one knew I had such tiny veins.

"I'm so sorry," he repeated, barely able to keep his head from collapsing on my bed.

I reached out my arm with what little strength I had left and held his hand.

It's okay. I'm okay.

I shook my head and tried to smile through the thick, plastic tube protruding from my mouth.

Though I was barely alive, my heart ached for him. This young man, who probably hadn't been a doctor for long, had made a mistake. It turns out that doctors are human too.

I was breathing on a ventilator in ICU, but I was alive. My family was grateful, and of course, I was too. The doctors assured us I would get better; it would just take time. They were hopeful things would turn around soon.

"Once her breathing improves again, she'll get off the ventilator, and we'll move her back to the stroke and neurology ward," Dr. Matt explained.

"You hear that, Holly?" James smiled. "You're going to get better. The plasmapheresis will help."

I attempted to smile back and tilted my head to look at my beautiful baby girl in his arms, her big blue eyes staring back at me.

The treatment will work. I am going to get through this. I'm going to get back to you, Casey.

I had to.

4

The Monster in the Mirror

I woke up to throbbing aches and tingling burns the morning after the emergency surgery. I had now been in the hospital three days. The anesthesia that numbed me the night before had worn off, and the suffocating pain now consumed my body from head to toe. I would have screamed if I could have, but the tube in my mouth made it impossible.

My room was scorching hot, like a sauna. I was lightheaded and faint. It was hard to breathe. I felt something in my nostril, which I later learned was a plastic nasogastric (NG) tube which went down my esophagus into my stomach and is how I was fed. A catheter protruded out the side of my jugular to administer the plasmapheresis—they couldn't go through the vein in my thigh anymore because of the ruptured artery. Taped to the inside of my elbow was an IV tube (called a PICC line), which is where they gave me my meds. I could feel the air as it pushed its way from the ventilator to my lungs. Loud beeps came from beside my bed every two to three seconds.

More aware that I was on life support, fighting for my life, I no longer felt optimistic. Each breath was a struggle. I was in more pain than I ever thought possible. I was sure I was dying. My family had all come and surrounded me in the ICU. All I could hear were lies about my condition and getting better.

"Just . . . let me go...." I mouthed to my mom and James beside my bed. "I'm ready to go." There was no time to think about my situation, only enough time to say goodbye.

"No, Hunny. You're going to get better. The treatment will help," both Mom and James insisted.

I wanted to believe them, but it felt as if I was underwater, about to run out of air—only there was no surface for me to swim up to. Every breath felt like it could be my last.

What if I stop breathing?

What if no one is around?

What if the pain is too much, and no one is here to help me?

"Please . . ." I tried to say, then reached my hand out to James ". . . don't leave me."

The thought of being alone for even a moment made my heart beat faster than it already was.

Mom leaned in close to my bed and titled her head to the side. "I can't understand what she's saying," she said, turning to James.

My husband saw the fear in my eyes and squeezed my hand tight. "We won't leave you, Holly," he promised.

Mom shook her head in agreement. "Don't worry, Hunny. Someone will always be here with you."

That's the type of family I had. James had no intention of going back to work; he spent every day with me at the hospital and took Casey back home each night. My mom never left; she slept beside my bed on a blue fold-out sofa chair.

Word traveled fast about my condition, and soon my room in ICU was a revolving door, with someone new coming in every few hours. James and I had a large, tight-knit group of friends who rushed to the hospital when they found out what was happening. Only a couple of months before, we'd all been together for a huge co-ed baby shower my girlfriends had thrown us. I wanted my husband and all of our friends there. Now they were visiting me on my death bed.

Though I assumed an ICU only allowed one or two visitors at a time, my room was always jam-packed with at least six people—first with my closest friends; then with people I hadn't seen in years. When my cousin Spencer, my late auntie Donna's son, stood by my bed, it validated how serious my situation was. Spencer flew down from Dease Lake, a small village up north by the Yukon border twenty hours away. He was stationed there as a new police officer with the RCMP. He'd flown in to surprise me a week after Casey was born to meet his new niece. I wasn't supposed to see him again for at least a year.

Day after day, friends, aunts, uncles, cousins, and other relatives stood by my bed with looks of horror on their faces, tears rolling down their cheeks. I couldn't blame them. I didn't even look like the same person. On top of all the tubes I had coming out of me, my normal hundred and forty-pound frame had ballooned out, making me look well over two hundred and fifty pounds. I was swollen and looked like I'd been in a car crash. My pupils were dilated from all the drugs, and I had a hard time keeping my eyes from rolling all over the place. Because of the breathing tube, I couldn't say a thing. I simply lay there with tears in my eyes.

But I could hear the surrounding conversations.

"I've never seen a case of GBS before," I overheard one of my nurses say to another. One nurse was always assigned to me, but there were often two or three in my room at a time.

"Neither have I," the other nurse replied. "I think about one in a million people get it," she said.

Months later, I would learn that two out of every one hundred thousand people get GBS, but at the time, it felt like I was one of the very few people fighting Guillain-Barre in the world.

I was desperate to know what was happening to me.

"Why am I in so much pain?" I tried to say out loud, but no sound came out of my mouth. Not being able to communicate and ask the simplest of questions was beyond frustrating.

My nurses had the physiotherapy team bring in a communication board—an eight by ten piece of paper with the letters of the alphabet written across it.

"Point to the letters, Holly," my nurse said, then placed the paper under my hand.

My eyes barely open, I slowly pointed out P-A-I-N.

No matter how many drugs the doctors gave me, the torturing pain was always there.

"We're going to get her an air bed," another new doctor explained. The ICU doctors were different every week—this doctor was young like Dr. Matt, and with bright blue eyes and light golden-brown curls, he was strikingly good-looking. He explained that an air bed, or an alternating pressure mattress, would redistribute my weight not only to control pain but to prevent bed sores. "The nerves in her body are inflamed," Dr. Handsome continued. "Some GBS patients are hypersensitive to touch. An air bed will help."

Hypersensitive? That was the word he chose?

It felt like a semi had run me over, then I'd been stabbed a thousand times. Every time someone touched me was like another sharp knife to my skin.

"How do you think Holly got GBS?" my mom asked him. "She's so young."

"GBS affects people of all ages. It's an autoimmune disorder. Anything can trigger an immune response. And I've heard of GBS coming on after pregnancy, birth, and even surgery. The fact that she had all three . . ." he paused, "well, we will never know for sure."

The exact cause of Guillain-Barre Syndrome is unknown. However, about two-thirds of cases are presumed to be triggered by an infection—such as a respiratory illness and food poisoning from the Campylobacter bacteria sometimes found in undercooked chicken. Some vaccines can also trigger GBS. It is *not* contagious.

Out of nowhere, the room felt a hundred degrees. I thrashed my body to get my mom's attention.

She shot up to a standing position. “What do you need?”

I wiggled my fingers, my attempt to show I wanted the communication board.

She placed it in front of me.

I spelled ‘H-O-T.’

Mom pulled the blanket down to the bottom of my feet. “Better?” she asked.

I tugged at my hospital gown, pulling it up as high as possible. I shook my head. HOT, I mouthed. SO HOT.

The doctor put a cool cloth on my forehead. Mom put cold cloths across my thighs.

It felt as if the room were on fire.

MORE, I mouthed again.

I can’t breathe. I’m going to faint.

Mom turned the thermostat on the wall and cranked the air conditioning as high as it would go. The instant cool air from the fan above my bed helped a little.

“How’s she doing today?” Deanne asked as she came into the room, leaving her jacket on when she felt the chill in the air.

“Holly can’t regulate her body temperature,” the doctor explained. “Her autonomic nervous system is affected, the part of her body that unconsciously regulates body functions. Her blood pressure, her heart rate, and her body temperature are all over the place.”

It was odd having people talk about you as if you weren’t there, as if I was a child again.

“That’s why we’re monitoring her so closely,” the doctor added. “She’s stable now, but she has a severe case of GBS. And the surgery didn’t help the situation. She’s not out of the woods yet.”

I clung to his words. I wanted to know every detail of what was happening.

After the doctor left the room, Deanne placed her cold hands across my cheeks. I used to tease her for her lack of circulation and how freezing her hands constantly were, but here, they were a godsend.

I wiggled my fingers; Deanne moved the paper close to my hand. I pointed to the letters H-O-T, then slowly spelled the word DOCTOR.

"You're still hot? You want us to get the doctor back in here?" she asked.

I slowly shook my head, mouthed the words, and tried to smile.

It took her a few minutes to figure out that I was trying to say, HOT DOCTOR.

Surely, she noticed his good looks, too.

Deanne laughed, cutting the tension in the room. It was my first attempt at humor in days.

I was just grateful we had some way to communicate. Deanne was one of my best friends and a bridesmaid in my wedding party. She and James were best friends from high school, and although we didn't like each other at first, our forced interactions blossomed into a beautiful friendship over the years. Deanne was a Sponsorship Manager in Edmonton but was quitting her job to pursue her dream of working on a cruise ship in the Caribbean. With her getting the job days before, I worried she'd be flying out soon.

"I'm not leaving for a while," she assured me as she sat down in the chair beside my bed.

My memories from this time in the hospital are few and far between. Half the time, I was so high I could hardly keep my eyes open. But I remember clearly on the fifth or sixth-day James asking if I wanted to see the incisions from the surgery. I could feel how swollen and tender my stomach was and nodded my head.

Mom seemed nervous about him showing me, but James knew I'd want to see. He gently pulled my hospital gown up just under my chest and snapped several photos of my body on his flip phone.

I don't know what I expected, but when I stared at the picture, I couldn't believe I was looking at my own body. My stomach was swollen like I was eight months pregnant. A seven-inch gash, with at least thirty steel staples sealing it shut, ran from the bottom of my rib cage all the way to the top of my pubic bone. The cut itself was a thick blackish-purple color. I had been sliced in half. Most of my torso, and what I could see of my legs, were stained orangey-red from the iodine from surgery.

"There's more." James skipped to the next photo. A feeling of anxiety rushed to my head. Another cut, on the inner side of my right thigh, went up towards my pelvis in a slight c-shape. It was thick and jagged, covered in stitches that seemed to cross over everywhere. This was where they tried to insert the catheter and ruptured my artery. The gash on my stomach was where they opened me up to stop the internal bleeding.

I looked away from the phone. As a new mom, I didn't consider my body perfect by any means, but I was content with it, knowing all it had done to grow my baby girl. Now it was destroyed.

"Don't worry about the scars," James said. Together for almost eight years, we had a level of closeness and comfort you only experience after years of being with someone. I knew he loved me, no matter what my body looked like.

I thought back to the days after my c-section when I'd first got home. I couldn't believe that was only a few weeks ago. I'd stood in front of the full-length mirror in my room and pulled down the front of my yoga pants to see the barely noticeable scar I'd been left with. I was so impressed with how precise and tiny the incision was. Resting just under my panty line, no one would even know it was there.

I looked back at the photo of my now mutilated body on James' phone. If I survived this, I'd have these horrifying scars for the rest of my life. They may not have bothered James, but they bothered me. Overcome with sadness, I sobbed myself to sleep.

To me, my body was disgusting.

That first week, I drifted in and out of consciousness. Doctors kept me sedated as much as possible, and the majority of the time, I looked like I was in a coma. When I was awake, I cried in pain. I had five treatments of plasmapheresis, which seemed to do nothing for my condition. Mom said each one took hours and made my pain even worse. Then again, everything did. The nurse's gentle moving of my limbs felt like sledgehammers to my body. The thin white cotton sheet on my bed was like sandpaper to my skin. My feet were the most sensitive, so James made sure nothing ever touched them. Otherwise, I screamed in agony.

As the pain surpassed what I thought possible to endure, so did my anxiety. Every minute felt like chaos, and no one could understand what I needed. Thankfully, my family came up with gestures I could do, our own form of sign language, like how I wiggled my fingers for the communication board. When I was in pain and needed meds, I shook my head back and forth. When I was hot and wanted a cold cloth on my forehead, I looked up and down. James kept the room temperature under 60°F—even with the temperature outside hovering around -30°F—which kept my hot flashes under control. Being so cold in the room, it was uncomfortable for my visitors, so Mom brought in blankets for them to bundle up in.

One night I woke up to find my brother Jay sitting in the blue sofa chair beside my bed. It was almost pitch black in my room and must have been late. He wore a women's black fur jacket and thick winter gloves.

Was I hallucinating?

I didn't know what was real and what wasn't. Every time I had a visitor, I'd ask James if they really came or if I dreamed it. Other times, he would talk about people who'd visited, but I had no recollection of them being there.

My gaze darted around the room, trying to figure out if I was dreaming.

"It's Jay. I'm here." My brother held my hand.

My breathing calmed.

I recognized the fur jacket as an old one of my mom's and giggled to myself at how cold it must have been in my room. And I relaxed knowing my brother was here.

Jay was now one of my dearest friends. As adults, we had a lot more in common than as kids; we were both hard-working, introverted social butterflies, and we bonded over our love of music, dancing, and going out for drinks with friends. The first time I went to a bar was with my brother despite being underage. He convinced the bouncer to let me in.

"Before you know it, Holly, we'll be back in the club, dancing up a storm," Jay said. "Once you're better, we'll go back to Vegas, and you can drink this time."

Nine months earlier, Deanne and I had met up with Jay and my cousin Spencer in Vegas. I found out I was pregnant a few days before we left, which ultimately changed the direction of how my trip went—I stayed sober. They went on the rides on top of the Stratosphere, drank way too much tequila, and stumbled down the Las Vegas Strip with yard glasses in their hands. And while I still had a blast (because I was so delighted about my pregnancy), I wanted that drunken Las Vegas experience one day too.

Would I get the chance to go back to Vegas someday? It was difficult to think about my life outside of the ICU. I wondered if I'd ever experience the little things again, like being able to use my legs to walk, run and dance. Since I was a young teen, I loved dancing. In Drayton Valley, there was a youth club at the junior high every Friday and behind the curtain on the gymnasium stage was a dancefloor with a DJ, lasers, and fog machines. My girlfriends and I danced to songs like *Wannabe* by the Spice Girls' and laughed while doing the Macarena—and the stresses of adolescent life seemingly disappeared. Whether it was sneaking into Drayton's local bar before I was legal or when I was an adult and visited the big city clubs, the reason I always went was to dance. My form of therapeutic release, the thought of never dancing again, terrified me.

"You're going to get better soon," Jay said, taking the time to wipe my forehead with a cold cloth.

I wiggled my fingers and looked toward the communication board beside my bed.

He handed me the board.

'L-E-G,' I spelled.

"What's wrong?" He looked down towards my legs. Both were tucked under the pink checkered blanket. But one was moving.

'MOVING,' I spelled out to him. "My leg is moving!" I tried to say.

He looked down again.

My legs were completely still.

"Your legs are paralyzed, Holly."

"No!" I shouted in my mind, then slowly spelled out on the board.

My leg! It fell off the bed! Jay wrote the letters on a piece of paper with a black sharpie, then looked back down at the foot of my bed.

"Your leg did not fall off the bed. It's not moving, I promise."

I didn't understand. I could have sworn my leg had fallen off the bed and was now on the floor—away from the rest of my body but somehow still attached.

ICU psychosis, also called ICU delirium, is common in patients in intensive care. I've never done acid, nor would I ever, but I'm sure it's comparable. Some days felt as if my entire body was floating above my bed—above everyone else in the room.

Why are they just letting my body float around like a balloon? I would wonder.

I was paranoid and saw things that weren't there. One time I was convinced human skulls were scattered around the room, and I didn't understand why no one seemed to care. I panicked over a group of strangers standing in the corner that turned out to be just a bunch of balloons someone brought me. One night I frantically screamed and cried, and when my mom finally calmed me down, I told her that cats were eating me. The lucid hallucinations caused my anxiety to spiral out of control.

"We're putting her on Ativan," Dr. Handsome said. An anti-anxiety medication. "It will also help her sleep." And it did.

But things felt backward. When I slept, I dreamed about living my normal life. I was at home. When I was awake, I was paralyzed, living a nightmare.

I kept track of time by the number of days I'd been in the hospital. On Day 9, when the plasmapheresis treatments finished, doctors lowered my sedatives.

I remember looking around the room I'd spent the last week in; pictures of my friends and me, of Casey when she was born, and James and I on our wedding day plastered the walls in front of me. 'Get Well Soon' cards and pink feather boas bordered the room. I had no recollection of seeing anyone put these up.

Out of the corner of my eye, I noticed Casey was beside me in my bed.

Oh my God. My baby!

She was lying on the pink nursing pillow Deanne gave me as a baby gift at my shower.

Had she been here the entire time?

I thought back over the last several days and remembered, yes, she was. James brought her in every morning to be with me. She was often nestled right up to me on my bed.

I'd barely noticed.

Casey was awake, her eyes fixated on all the tubes coming out of me. She stared at my chest as it rose, and each breath from the ventilator made its way through my lungs.

Tears welled up in the corner of my eyes.

I couldn't believe this was happening to me. This kind of thing only happens in movies or to people on the news. I never expected to get sick like this, especially now, so soon after meeting my daughter. Before this, my life was perfect; everything was going according to plan. This wasn't supposed to happen.

The next thing I noticed was that I was wearing a diaper. I learned that my autonomic nervous system also caused bladder and bowel dysfunction. A catheter was draining my bladder, and I was being given strong laxatives to combat constipation. So far, the meds hadn't worked.

"We change your catheter out every few days," one of my nurses said as she unwrapped a plastic tube in her hand.

James scooped Casey in his arms and moved to the side of the room.

The nurse pulled back the sheet on my bed, then yanked my white gown up to my waist. Another nurse helped lean my body to the side, and they tore the diaper out from underneath me.

I squirmed in pain and embarrassment. The nurses never used the term diaper, it was always a "brief", but that didn't make the experience any less humiliating.

The nurse shoved my legs apart, crushing pain pulsated through my hips. The other used a cold cloth to wipe my privates.

I screamed; the cloth felt like a cheese grater on my crotch. Of course, I couldn't make a sound because of the tube in my mouth. Had I not been paralyzed, I would have slammed my legs shut. Unable to move, I had no choice but to lay naked from the waist down, spread-eagle in front of these two women I didn't know while they changed me, then my catheter. There were no holding back tears this time.

Later that day, the doctor came into my room with a tall man in scrubs with light brown hair. His name was Mike, the doctor said, one of my respiratory therapists—also called RTs. RTs are the team of professionals who manage the ventilator. I vaguely remembered seeing him fiddling with the machine beside my bed the last little while.

"We need to talk about Holly's breathing," Mike said to my mom. "She's not improving as we hoped. We suggest doing a tracheostomy."

A tracheostomy (also referred to as a 'trach' and pronounced 'tray-ke') is where an opening is surgically created in the trachea (windpipe), where a tube is inserted to create a path for air to reach the lungs.

"It will be more comfortable for you, Holly," he said, standing beside my bed. I'd no longer have the breathing tube in my mouth, making it easier to mouth words. The trach would also allow me to speak on a special valve for short periods.

My family was all for it. "They just need your permission," my mom said.

Wanting that tube out of my mouth, I nodded my head in agreement. It seemed that Mike knew a lot about GBS and genuinely cared about my condition.

I don't remember the procedure, but the tube was gone an hour later. The thick plastic trach in my neck stretched down and across my chest to the ventilator beside my bed—a small old-school-style computer monitor on wheels. I still couldn't talk; the tracheostomy blocked air from passing through my vocal cords. And it was even more challenging to breathe than before.

"Because your cough isn't strong enough, you're unable to clear mucus from your airways," Mike explained. "You need to be suctioned by the RTs."

Another respiratory therapist stood alongside my bed with a six-inch tube in her hand. She wore a clear, plastic face shield. My eyes grew wide as she fiddled with the strap on my neck, then proceeded to feed the plastic catheter through the trach.

As soon as I felt it in my throat, I gagged and coughed again and again, with no relief. But because my vocal cords were bypassed, no sound came out. I simply looked like I was violently choking.

James and my parents stood back, utterly helpless, while the therapist continued to wiggle the tube in my throat.

"It's okay, Holly. Keep coughing. You're doing good." The therapist put her hand on my shoulder then pulled out the tube. "As soon as you finish coughing, you'll catch your breath." The machine beside me beeped, and air forced its way through my lungs.

I took a deep breath in. With the mucus now cleared, breathing was easier. Unfortunately, suctioning had to be done several times a day. Each time I thought I might choke to death and all the pain and horror I'd suffered would be for nothing.

*

As the hours passed by, I'd look down at Casey curled up beside me on my bed, and I overanalyzed why this was happening to me now. While there is no perfect time to be in an ICU with a rare disease, weeks after the birth of my daughter seemed especially cruel and unfair. I hadn't even put my baby in her stroller yet. By now, we missed two of our Mommy and Me classes. Would I get to do these things with her? I wasn't sure. But I didn't understand what I did to deserve all this. I was hardworking, kind, and loyal. I was a great friend and daughter, a loving wife, and finally a mother.

Why am I being punished?

Just weeks ago, which now felt like months, I was a healthy new mom at home enjoying my time with my daughter, documenting everything in our baby's First Year calendar, like her first day home, her first visit from her uncle Jay, and when she slept four hours straight. Casey was an angel our first weeks at home. She didn't often cry, only to eat, and she slept pretty well through the night. We were blessed to have such a chill baby. I spent a sizable amount of my time in the cream-colored rocking chair in Casey's room, breastfeeding her in my arms. I often sang her love songs while rocking her back and forth, her mouth on my breast. I wasn't a great singer, but she stared up at me with her big blue eyes as if she worshipped my voice.

Four weeks together was not enough time.

Now, I was incapacitated, barely able to reach out and touch my child. I depended on the machine beside me to breathe. It seemed that in the blink of an eye, I'd lost everything. Everything I worked so hard for. Everything I wanted since I was a little girl. Everything I imagined doing as a mother had been taken from me.

I couldn't tell my baby I loved her. I couldn't hold her in my arms. I couldn't breastfeed her, hold her bottle, or change her diaper. I had no idea if I'd ever take care of her again and felt utterly worthless.

I was only twenty-six years old. I'd barely lived my life. James and I were new parents; we'd been living in the house we bought for less than a year. I had so many plans for my future with my husband and baby. We were supposed to take Casey to a family reunion in the summer. We were already thinking about what to dress her up as for Halloween. We were supposed to be starting our life together.

Now, I had nothing.

And I knew I was not getting out of this hospital any time soon.

I cried for hours at the injustice of all of this when I did not deserve any of it.

Everyone could see the pain in my eyes.

"We're going to put her on Cymbalta," the doctor said to my family. Medication not only used to treat depression but also nerve pain.

On top of my despair, my neck still ached as if it were broken. Some days it seemed like I shook my head back and forth, pleading for pain meds all day long. Doctors eventually doubled my dose of Dilaudid (hydromorphone) and then allowed me a top-up every hour if needed. Tops-ups were given through the IV in my arm. As soon as the nurse injected the drugs, a cool sensation spread through my forearm and into my body. Then the ache in my neck disappeared. A wave of euphoria washed over me; my eyes rolled back in my head. For a moment, I felt better—happy even—as all tension left my body. Then within a few minutes, the euphoria faded, and the throbbing gradually returned.

I looked up at the clock on the wall that looked just like those in school. Fifty-five minutes until I could ask for another injection. As someone who barely took prescription pills and only dabbled in drugs, I'd never been addicted to anything in my life; I wasn't that type of person. I couldn't believe how dependent I'd become. Nor did I care.

Though the anxiety and sharp pain were usually unbearable, some moments seemed not so bad. One morning when James and Casey came into the room, I enthusiastically wiggled my fingers to communicate.

Mom grabbed the board, the sharpie, and the pad of paper from the counter beside me.

'S-H-O-E-S,' she wrote out as I pointed.

Casey wore tiny pink Converse runners on her feet. James positioned the nursing pillow on my bed, then placed her on it, as he did every morning when they arrived.

"I know!" My mom said. "Aren't her shoes adorable?"

I continued to point furiously; Mom kept writing. For nearly ten minutes, I spelled out that someone gave the Converse shoes to us as a gift at our baby shower.

James and my parents laughed. "I can't believe you spent all that time just to tell us that," my dad said.

I don't know why, but it gave me a tiny sense of joy to see my baby wearing the things I had yet to put her in. And it made my family happy to see me trying to communicate no matter how long it took me. Hour after hour, I pointed to the letters on the board, and my family anxiously wrote down the things I wanted to say.

'Pain.'

'Hot.'

'See Casey.'

'Reposition me.

'See Mom.'

'See James.'

"I'm in so much pain."

'What meds am I on?'

'Adjust bed.'

'You guys are awesome.'

I'd spend what felt like forever forming sentences for things that weren't even important, like the time I told James, 'We need to get our kid some rubber boots.' I'm pretty sure our newborn baby did *not* need rubber boots in the middle of winter.

Usually, the pain made it too difficult to think straight. But sometimes, I surprised myself.

One time I spelled out asking where my pink Victoria's Secret sweatpants were—the ones I wore to the hospital.

James laughed. "They're at home. Don't worry."

My family was constantly taking off the lid to the sharpie and losing it somewhere in the room, so I spelled 'Click-Lid' on the board.

You guys need to buy a marker with a click top. So you don't have to look for the lid constantly, I said in my mind.

My family laughed that I was even worried about losing the sharpie lid.

One afternoon, Mike asked, "Do you want to try the speaking valve?"

My ears perked up; I hadn't heard my voice in over a week. The speaking valve was a one-way valve attached to the tracheostomy tube. When I breathed in, the valve would open, bringing air into the trach. When I breathed out, the valve would close, and air would travel through my vocal cords, allowing sounds to be made.

I took a deep breath and nodded my head. Another RT, a young woman in a face shield, jiggled the trach on my neck. I coughed, as I usually did when the tube in my throat was touched. I couldn't see what she was doing and held my breath as if my life depended on it as she removed the tube and then replaced it with another.

"Say something," James said enthusiastically once the valve was in place.

It was a challenge to speak while simultaneously breathing out. The sound that came from my throat sounded like a growl. "I sound scary," I whispered. My voice was hoarse and scratchy but so quiet my family could hardly hear me.

James leaned into my face. "This is scary?" he asked.

I shook my head. "I sound scary," I said again.

James smiled. "That's all right."

Mom stood in front of me with a video camera in her hand.

I took another deep breath in, then slowly breathed out.

"I'm in so much pain," I whispered to my husband.

"You're so drained?"

I shook my head and mouthed the words again.

"This is all a dream?" James asked.

"I'm. In. So. Much. Pain," I carefully articulated. No one understood how horrible the radiating body pain was, like aches from the flu, times a thousand.

"Awww, Babe, I'm sorry," James said, understanding this time. He knew I could only have pain meds so often. "Anything else you want to say?"

"I don't know what to say," I whispered. I'd been using an alphabet board to communicate for days, but now given a chance to talk, I was at a loss for words.

"Say something to Casey," James encouraged. He scooped her out of the bassinet beside my bed then held her out in front of me.

Short of breath, I shook my head. "I don't know what to say," I repeated, then turned my head away from my child. I thought breathing through the trach was difficult—speaking at the same time was almost impossible. My breathing shallowed. I mustered up the strength to say, "Just take me off."

The RT quickly removed the valve from my throat. When I finished coughing and looked around at my family, everyone was smiling.

"You did it!" My mom squealed. Even if it was just a few short sentences that didn't sound anything like me, my family was thrilled to hear me speak again.

"Talking for the first time again is a huge milestone," Mike said.

Barely saying a few words didn't seem like an accomplishment to me. I was on my death bed.

"You need to celebrate every victory she makes," Mike told my parents. "Improvements are progress, no matter how small."

I guess he was right.

"We could make stars for the milestones I reach and put them above my bed," I tried to say, then spelled on the board. A few days before, I'd noticed neon pink cardstock on the counter; I think my mom was going to decorate my room some more.

"What a great idea!" she said with a smile on her face.

This would give her something to do, as she practically lived in the ICU now.

Mom proceeded to cut out a pink star and wrote: 'First time on the speaking valve.' Then she stood on a stool and taped it to the ceiling.

That night, as I lay in my bed staring up at the neon pink star taped to the ceiling, I could only hope there would be more milestones to come.

*

No one could tell us how long they expected me to be in the hospital or what would happen next. With my prognosis unclear, James took a leave of absence from work and applied for paternity leave to take care of Casey. Our friends collected donations for our family, with neither of us working, and with the added cost of formula, our bills were piling up. People sent diapers, baby clothes, and money. Their love and generosity made a world of difference, and James and I were so appreciative.

"Thank you," I mouthed to my best friend. I wish I could have said more. Not just to her, to everyone. Mom and James rarely left my side in the ICU. They wiped my tears and held my hand while I writhed in pain. Mom slathered my body with lotion, and James picked the dry pieces of skin off my lips. Dad drove in from Drayton every couple of days, and to keep costs down, Dennis kept the room stocked with food and drinks. Gifts came in from strangers—one lady sent a handmade pink and green checked pillowcase to replace the drab white one on my bed—to show support and cheer me up. When my girlfriends visited, they painted my nails, plucked my eyebrows, and brushed the knots out of my matted hair. Anything they could do to help make me feel human again.

My family and friends were my strength when I had none.

Mom put Casey on my chest, as soon as James came in every morning. Our only way to connect, I had them place her as close to my face as possible. I pressed my cheek against her soft baby skin and closed my eyes. Casey smelled like Aveeno, the lotion I'd bought her before she was even born. We frequently fell asleep cheek to cheek;

my mom captured these special moments together on camera. I like to think despite the tubes and lack of maternal attention, Casey knew who I was.

When I was awake, I found strength from the star on the ceiling and the pictures on the walls. One evening, a particular photo caught my eye, a picture from my wedding day—me and my bridesmaids at our reception. My wedding dress was a white tulle ball gown with a sweetheart neckline, and I looked like a princess. My bridesmaids wore short, form-fitting black dresses. The photo was a candid shot of us on the dance floor; we had already switched out of our heels into the matching pink Old Navy flip-flops I'd bought us to dance in. My veil was off, and my dark brown curls were already relaxed. With one arm up in the air and drinks in our hands, we had big drunken smiles on our faces. The bartender came over right after someone snapped the photo to tell us we weren't allowed drinks on the dance floor.

"Girls just wanna have fun!" We screamed at the top of our lungs, then kept dancing to the classic Cindy Lauper song. I spent the whole night on the dancefloor at our wedding, which wasn't even a year and a half ago. I was so carefree back then. I worried I'd never be that person again.

"You have a great life to get back to, Holly," a nurse said from the doorway, eyeing up the pictures on the wall. Most of my nurses were around my age, and many newlyweds or new moms themselves. I presumed a young mom, like them, was tough to see in the ICU.

With the tube gone from my mouth, I smiled back at the nurse, then took in a deep breath.

She was absolutely right. I had an incredible life to get back to. I knew I had to fight through the horrific pain for that.

Not just for my baby or my family and friends.

For me.

5

Live in the Light

An average of two out of every one hundred thousand people get diagnosed with Guillain-Barre Syndrome each year, not one in a million like I initially thought. It doesn't discriminate—it affects people of all ages, sexes, and any ethnic backgrounds, though it is slightly more common in adults and older males. GBS is considered a rare disorder, but we learned there was not only an entire community of survivors out there but there was also an organization that supported patients like me, the GBS/CIDP Foundation of Canada, based out of Ontario.

In the fall of 2011, three months after I got out of the hospital and was finally back home with Casey and James, the Foundation organized a medical conference in Edmonton, and Mom and I registered to attend. We were fortunate, as these regional conferences were only held every couple of years, and there just happened to be one in our city the year I was diagnosed. Mom and I were eager to hear the medical professionals speak about the devastating illness that wreaked so much havoc in our lives just a few months before. Casey stayed home with James.

I was still recovering from GBS. My movements were wobbly and slow, but I walked into the conference hall without assistance. Scattered around the room were people of all ages, some walking independently, others using walkers or canes. Several sat in wheelchairs. I noticed a few people had small circular scars on their throats, as I did—remnants of a life lived in the ICU.

"Hi, I'm Alice," a woman who looked to be in her thirties said to Mom and I. "Did one of you have Guillain-Barre?" Her eyes turned to Mom.

I extended my hand to her. "I'm Holly—I had GBS. I was diagnosed in February, a few weeks after giving birth to my daughter."

Alice's mouth dropped open, and an older gentleman using a walker quickly turned to join our conversation.

"After giving birth. That's awful," the man said. "How long were you in the hospital?"

I shared my timeline of events with the pair; my first symptoms, the paralysis, time spent in ICU, then rehab.

Their eyes widened when my mom said, "She got out of the hospital at the end of June."

Alice looked me up and down. "June, as in three months ago? That's incredible! You had a severe case but a fast recovery. I had GBS three years ago," she continued. "It took me a long time to get to where I am now." Alice didn't have a scar on her throat, and standing tall, she appeared to have recovered completely. "The only thing I can't do anymore is run." She peeked down at the ballet flats she wore. "Or wear high heels."

I glanced down at my white slip-on running shoes, thinking of my closet full of stilettos at home. I prayed I'd get back into heels one day.

"I was diagnosed five years ago," the man with the walker said. He shared his experience, his first symptoms, how long he spent in the hospital. "I obviously can't run either," he snickered.

Four or five others joined our circle to share their stories, and we took turns asking each other questions. It was fascinating to hear the differences in each of our cases. Like me, some of their symptoms had progressed quickly; in others, it had taken days, sometimes weeks, before being hospitalized. Only two of us were on ventilators in the ICU; the others were on a neurology ward. A couple of people had only paralysis from the waist down. Some of them, now using walkers and canes, still needed assistance to walk. Even with the worst of GBS behind us, we all dealt with residual struggles, including weakness, pain, and fatigue.

It comforted me to be with others who'd been in my shoes. Despite the variances in our stories, we shared plenty of similarities. We all understood the heartbreak of losing our independence so suddenly, the triumph of getting our lives back, and the roller coaster of emotions in between. We were a select group of people who understood how quickly life could change. We all had a new lease on life. When you go through such a traumatic, life-changing medical event and then meet others who've been through it, too, you can't help but feel connected to them. It was like spending time with family I never knew I had.

"Look at you, Holly," a familiar voice called out.

I turned to see Dr. Yousef, the neurologist who'd delivered the news of my diagnosis, approaching from the snack table with a plate of fruit in his hand. He also looked me up and down, then smiled.

"Wow," he said.

He once told me I would not walk again for at least two years.

I smirked. "Yeah, I walked on my own after five months," I said with defiant confidence in my voice. I was more than proud to show I proved this doctor wrong.

"You had a severe case at first. You recovered much faster than we expected."

From my conversations with the rest of the group, I understood. Out of the hospital for only a few months, I was blessed to be where I was. Sure, I had a severe case of GBS in the beginning, and though my recovery wasn't complete, it was quicker than most. Some of these survivors were still recovering years later.

Mom and I learned more about GBS and its variants (and similar disorders such as CIDP, the chronic counterpart) throughout the conference from the multiple specialists who spoke. Most people would find this kind of medical information dull and monotonous but learning how my immune system attacked my nervous system and caused damage to the myelin sheath (the coating around the nerves) was captivating. I enjoyed learning about what happened to my body and how it miraculously healed and repaired itself over time.

At the end of the conference, James and Casey came to pick us up, and I got to show off my delightful smiling eight-month-old little girl to the rest of the group. Casey was a curious baby fascinated by people, and with her in my arms, she reached out her chubby hand to Alice.

"She is so beautiful, just like her mama," Alice said, reaching out her hand to touch Casey's. "I'm so happy you're back home with her again."

I smiled and pulled Casey close to kiss her on the cheek. I was incredibly grateful to be a mom again. My time in the hospital gave me that blessing.

After we said our goodbyes, an older gentleman approached me just as we were about to leave the hall. "My name is Jim," the man said, offering his hand to shake mine, my mom's, then James'. "I'm one of the board members of the GBS/CIDP Foundation. I had GBS in 1997." Jim was probably in his mid-sixties, and with no walker or cane, he looked like he also recovered well. "I hear you recently got out of the hospital," he said.

"Yeah, at the end of June," I replied.

"That's great! You're doing amazing. The best advice I can give you is to stick with the mobility exercises."

I glanced at my mom, a little confused. I had already finished all my outpatient therapy. "How long do I need to do the exercises for?" I asked. I thought I'd done all that was required, and my walking would improve on its own over time.

Jim laughed. "You need to exercise for the rest of your life!"

I gave him a look of concern.

"I'm serious," he said. "Moving your body through exercise is the best thing you can do for your recovery. Stay active. It will help you in the long run."

"All right, thanks, I will," I replied, unsure if I actually would. Exercise wasn't exactly part of my lifestyle before GBS.

I had no idea this conversation with Jim would later play such a massive role in the rest of my recovery.

*

Returning to the Grey Nuns for the first time after being discharged was like visiting a place from my childhood. I had plenty of memories, but the details were hazy, like a dream. The ICU isn't exactly a place you think of visiting with a baby, but I wanted my nurses to see how much Casey had grown in the few months since I'd left. They practically helped raise her during the time we were there. Mom came along for the visit.

A tight knot built up in my stomach as soon as we got to the Intensive care Unit. I couldn't help but peek at the patients lying in their beds as we walked down the hall. The pungent smell of antiseptic and loud beeps from the ventilators overwhelmed me. Every patient was in critical condition, most of them being kept alive by a machine. It made me want to cry thinking about being back in their shoes, struggling for breaths of air, but as much as being here was difficult, it was important to me. I wanted to see the nurses who cared for me, to thank them for all they had done, To show them how great I was doing now. I had been determined not to come back to the ICU till I could walk in by myself, and now here I was.

I recognized almost everyone as we approached the nurse's station; a few I knew from connecting on Facebook, others I was sure I'd met at some point in my time here. That's what happens when you spend over two months in a hospital ward.

"Can we help you?" one of the nurses I remembered as Yvonne said to me. She looked down at Casey sitting in her stroller and smiled at her. "Are you guys here to see a patient?" She looked back up at me.

I grinned. With my dark hair in loose curls and a face full of makeup, I looked quite different from when I was here fighting for my life in a hospital gown several months ago. And Casey, now a bouncy, smiling baby, had grown and changed a lot.

"We came to visit you!" my mom said, knowing Yvonne would remember her.

At the sound of mom's voice, Yvonne turned her head. "Oh, my goodness, Marilyn! And Holly—and Casey!" she shouted. "I didn't recognize you two!" She wrapped her arms around me. "You look amazing, Holly! And look at you walking!" She turned to the other nurses behind the counter. "You guys! It's Holly!"

Before long, about nine or ten medical staff came over to see the commotion. I immediately noticed Mike, the respiratory therapist I'd never forget. He spent a lot of time in my room and helped me through many dark times.

I stayed to chat with everyone for about fifteen minutes. I knew they were busy—ICU always was. We reminisced about my time there, and I shared the things I'd accomplished since getting out of the hospital, most importantly, walking again. When we were ready to leave, Mike walked us back to the elevators.

"Do you remember the first time you met me?" he asked as we waited.

"No, not really," I replied. I only remembered bits and pieces from those first couple of weeks in the ICU.

"Good," he replied. "That means we did our job."

I looked at my mom out of the corner of my eye. It hadn't occurred to me they'd purposely drugged me so I wouldn't remember. On one hand, I wished they sedated me the entire time to avoid all that pain. On the other hand, I was thankful I remembered some of the traumatic events I experienced, so I knew what I'd overcome.

"You could practically write a book about all the things you went through," Mike said. He wasn't kidding. "What you experienced with GBS was awful, but your story is inspiring."

As the elevator door opened, a metaphorical lightbulb flickered on in my brain.

"I should write a book," I said to myself as I hugged Mike goodbye. Ever since my return to real life, people bombarded me with questions impossible to answer in one conversation. How do you explain what life in an ICU is like in five minutes? The procedures, the pain, the anxiety, the many doctors, nurses, and other medical staff I'd dealt with—I had lots to explain. I knew that if I wrote it all out, I could illustrate through words to my family and friends what it was like to go through Guillain-Barre.

As an introvert, writing has always been my favorite way to communicate and express what I feel in my heart. Ask any ex-boyfriend, and they'll tell you about the letters I wrote. I didn't have the best grades in high school, but I excelled in English. I enjoyed reading and writing and thought it would be an amazing accomplishment to write a book one day. Only I had nothing worth writing about—until now.

In ICU, Mom documented everything that happened each day on a large calendar on the wall. She took hundreds of pictures and videos of me, which helped bring me back there. Piecing my time together in the hospital ended up being quite simple. The hardest part of writing the book was looking at myself in that state and rehashing the memories from my most challenging days. Yet, I was compelled to write about them anyway and pushed through the sadness and pain. I spent ten months writing *Happily Ever After*, and when I finished, it had been over a year and a half since I was diagnosed.

In November of 2012, I threw myself a book launch party in the lounge of a venue where Deanne previously worked. She was home from working in the Caribbean. Deanne had fallen in love with an English man she met on the ship, so here she was back in Canada, pregnant for the party. The event was as much a celebration of my survival as it was for writing and publishing the book. I stood at the podium in three-inch stilettos and looked towards the crowd of the two hundred people who came to celebrate.

"Thank you, everyone, for being here tonight," I said. "You all played a part in my recovery, and I wouldn't be where I am today without your support." I turned to look at James, all dressed up in a collared shirt and blazer, with our almost-two-year-old in his arms. Casey looked adorable. My husband had put her tiny strands of hair into pigtails, and she wore a light grey dress with white polka dots I picked out for her.

It was still hard to believe our little family made it through what we did.

At the end of my speech, I played a video on the projector screen of my time in the hospital for the crowd. I'd spliced together some of the photos and videos from the ICU and rehab to help show what I'd overcome. I knew the book would answer questions people had, but the contrasting footage of me on life support in Intensive care, then walking on my own again, was powerful. When the video finished and I looked towards the audience, almost everyone in the room, myself included, was in tears.

Through the video, and my book, my friends and family would finally understand Guillain-Barre Syndrome and how it affected me.

I spent the rest of the night sitting at the bar, connecting with friends, and drinking way too much. Even my mom, who rarely drank alcohol, got tipsy that night, as we had much to celebrate. At twenty-seven years old, I'd experienced more suffering than most people experience in their lives, but I was on the other side. And I felt this release within me, like the past was in the past, and it was time to move forward.

The following day, I shared my recovery video online. A few of my nurses who attended the event commented the video could help inspire others going through GBS, and I agreed. I set up a YouTube account and uploaded the video titled "Holly's Journey – From Guillain-Barre Syndrome to Happily Ever After."

And with the click of a button, my path in life drastically changed.

It started with a short email I received from a man named Frank in Michigan, USA. His twenty-five-year-old brother Davey was diagnosed with GBS the week prior, and he came across my story while researching GBS online. Like ours, his family knew nothing about the disorder when Davey was diagnosed, and they were uncertain about his future. But after seeing my video, they hoped that he, too, would make it through this. Frank requested an autographed copy of my book for his family to read.

I was in awe that a stranger from another country wanted to read my book. I wasn't just educating my family and friends anymore. I was helping the family of someone else going through GBS. My heart was full as I signed a copy of my book and shipped it out.

A few days after the email from Michigan came a lengthy Facebook message from a family in South Africa. Melisa, a wife, sister, and mother of three, was paralyzed from the neck down, breathing on a ventilator, also recently diagnosed with Guillain-Barre.

"How is she going to get through this?" the message read. *"What is going through her head all day as she just lies there? Will she ever be her old self again? So many questions, so many worries. I came across your amazing video on YouTube. We showed it to my sister and her daughter, and we were all very emotional but so inspired afterward. Your story changed my outlook on life, and I know your determination and strong spirit will help my sister get through this!"*

I was thrilled to see how far my video traveled in such a short time. But it was hard to read the woman's words. I knew how scared she was, not only from the tone in her writing but also from knowing my family faced the same questions and fears. Thinking back to my time in the ICU, I gave her suggestions—things that helped me when I was there. I emphasized that her sister would get through this, just as I did. The most important thing was that they all maintained hope, even on the darkest days, that she would eventually get out of ICU.

After typing up my words of encouragement for the second time in less than a week, I came to the life-changing realization that although I wasn't a doctor or a neurologist, people were coming to me with questions about GBS, and I had a unique perspective to share. Specialists may study the disease, but nothing can compare to living through it.

I was certainly not the only person who had GBS in the world as I sometimes felt back in ICU, nor would I be the last. From what I learned at the conference the year before, people survived this disease all the time. Those fighting GBS needed to be aware of that. Through my experience and the power of social media, I knew I could provide valuable support to newly diagnosed patients wherever they were in the world.

I made a Facebook page, which I later named *Holly After GBS*. I joined online support groups, where I connected with other survivors around the world. I talked about the disease that devastated my life, never shying away from the heartbreaking details. I wanted my story to help others. It wasn't long before my video made its rounds on the internet, and hundreds of people were reaching out to me. People of all ages, from all parts of the world. Some were even diagnosed after giving birth, like me.

What sort of things helped you get through GBS?

What medications were you on?

Can you give me suggestions on how to improve my strength after getting out of the hospital?

Many messages were from family members pleading for advice. I replied to every message I received, happy to offer guidance to those who desperately needed it.

And that was when I became certain I was diagnosed with GBS for a reason.

This treacherous journey had been assigned to *me*—the girl who fought through hell— so I could show others how to get through it.

6

The Bottom

I'd been fighting for my life in the hospital for less than two weeks. It felt like forever. As the doctors continued to lower my sedatives, I became increasingly aware of my personal crisis. Confined to a bed in a room with one window, I was a prisoner suffering through the worst pain of my life. My window faced the opposite side of the five-story brick building; all I saw were rows upon rows of hospital windows—the roof of the building blanketed in snow—a bleak, never-changing view, like my condition.

"You're going to get better soon," repeated the nurses, taking turns to pat my forehead with cold, yellow cloths and injecting me with more pain medication in my arm. They said it with smiles on their faces, but I was not convinced. It's hard to believe you'll get better when you're suffering through excruciating pain, you can't speak, and you're struggling to breathe through the tube in your throat.

One morning I woke up to my stomach churning and instantly felt like throwing up. I tried to reach out to my mom beside me, but my arm didn't budge. The paralysis had spread, which told me I wasn't getting better; I was getting worse.

In a desperate attempt to get my mom's attention, I stuck my tongue to the roof of my mouth and clucked—loudly.

Mom turned and leaned towards my face, attempting to read my lips.

"I feel sick . . ." I mouthed. The room spun around me.

"Use the board, Hunny," Mom said, not understanding what I was trying to say.

I looked down at my hand and tried to move my fingers.

"I can't . . . "I mouthed again.

Mom pulled her hand to her mouth, her eyes widened.

"She can't move her arms! Get her doctor!" she shouted.

My nurse hurried out of the room.

"I'm sorry, everyone," the doctor said a few minutes later. "Sometimes things get worse before they get better. She hasn't plateaued yet."

Later we learned that IVIG and plasmapheresis don't always stop GBS in its tracks (though sometimes it does), but patients that receive these treatments have better outcomes than those that don't.

"We just have to give it more time," the doctor said.

My chest tightened as I realized I could no longer point to the letters on the communication board. How would anyone know what I needed?

Another wave of nausea, this one flooded over me. I let my head fall to the side and threw up on my shoulder. My mom rushed to grab a wet cloth while my nurse placed a kidney-shaped metal bowl under my chin. I gagged, then vomited again, this time in the bowl. Then again. And again. Mom wiped my chin, the nurses changed me into a fresh gown, then put the bowl back under my head, and I continued to vomit.

After several hours of throwing up, then dry heaving, the doctor decided I was sick from being constipated. I hadn't had a bowel movement since I'd been in the hospital, more than ten days now. My stomach distended like a beach ball as if I were still nine months pregnant.

"The buildup of stool in her intestines might be making her nauseous. We're going to have to do an enema," the doctor explained—a procedure where water or medication is injected into a patient's rectum to empty the bowels.

I shuddered at the idea, feeling even sicker to my stomach. I already knew what an enema was; I thought it was only for old people. I wanted to shout, "No, you can't do this to me," but there was no sense in debating. Everyone else, it seemed, made every decision for me. I convinced myself that it would be worth it if it helped my nausea.

A few hours later, after the procedure did what it was meant to do, a twenty-some-year-old nurse spread my legs apart, pulled the brief out from underneath me, and cleaned me up like a newborn baby. Crushing pain radiated through my thighs with every push and pull of my legs. The putrid smell filled the air. Tears rolled down my cheeks.

"I'm sorry. I'm so sorry . . ." I mouthed through sobs.

Everyone knows what a nurse is; few have any idea of the shit they deal with.

"It's okay, Sweetie." The nurse wiped the most private parts of my body clean with a scratchy, warm cloth, then the inside of my thighs as if it were no big deal. "This is our job."

I continued to cry, turning my head away in shame. It was the most degrading experience of my life.

After that, I had daily suppositories to fight the constipation. Every time the nurse turned my body and inserted the medication up my bum, I cried—from the complete loss of my dignity and the literal pain in my ass. With my face in the pillow, out of the corner of my eye, I'd look up at the pink feather boas that bordered my room, praying for the enema to be over quickly. When I finally did have a bowel movement, which wasn't often, I'd communicate on the board, 'privacy please," to signal to my family to get the hell out of my room. Then my nurses would clean me up, and I didn't have to be any more mortified than I already was.

Sadly, these invasive procedures did nothing to curb my queasiness. Nurses injected me with several medications to fight my nausea, including Gravol, Zofran, and Motilium. Sometimes one of them would work for an hour or so, and I'd get a short reprieve from feeling sick. Then my nausea returned, and we'd try another medication—once a certain amount of time had passed. The meds did nothing most of the time, and I'd feel like vomiting all day long.

As if the horrific pain wasn't enough, now I had this to deal with.

Unable to use my hands anymore, my family pointed to the communication board, and I slowly nodded when they picked the letters I wanted to use. Clucking my tongue against the roof of my mouth became a way to get others' attention, especially at night when it was just mom and me alone in the dark. During the day, I worked on articulating my words so others could better read my lips.

"I . . . need . . . you," I carefully mouthed to James one afternoon, ". . . to bring . . . me weed." Marijuana was my go-to for nausea in the past, whether from a hangover or the flu; I knew I'd feel better if I could just smoke some pot.

James placed a cold, wet cloth across my forehead and grinned. "I can't bring you weed, Babe," he said, holding back a chuckle.

"James—" I mouthed again with tears in my eyes. "Pleeease."

The room was spinning, and I felt an urge to vomit.

"I'm so sick. Pleeease," I begged.

His smile dissipated. Out of everyone, my husband could read my lips the best. "I can't just bring you weed into the hospital, Holly. A doctor is not going to let you smoke a joint in your bed, with a breathing tube down your throat."

Tears poured down my cheeks.

I knew it sounded ridiculous, marijuana wasn't even legal at the time, but I was desperate to feel any sense of normalcy again.

With feeling nauseated so often, Casey rarely lay on my bed anymore. She'd spend a few minutes here and there; then, I'd feel the burning bile rise in the back of my throat again.

"Take her off," I'd mouth. I couldn't stand her near me when I felt so ill. I hated that anyone, even her, saw me like this. Vomiting. Gagging. Wailing in pain. Depressed. Except for a couple of close friends, I stopped letting visitors in my room. But utterly afraid to be by myself, I made sure either my mom or James were always there.

It was hard to believe I'd get better even with constant reassurance. No matter how hard I tried, my body never moved. My limp body parts were inanimate objects attached to me. Everything ached from the stillness of my limbs. I was terrified that if James or my mom left for even a moment and I couldn't breathe, I'd have no way to call a nurse, and I'd die alone in that room. The saddest part was that as profoundly afraid as I was of dying, sometimes I thought it would be easier if it just happened already.

Instead, I lay frozen in bed, gagging into a silver bowl that rarely left my side.

"Holly's losing hope," I overheard my mom tell the nurse beside my bed. "I can see it in her eyes." Between retching sessions, I stared out the window, unfocused on anything in particular.

"I think we should phone Kit," the nurse suggested.

Mom nodded.

Kit, I learned, was a patient who had Guillain-Barre two years prior. His case was severe like mine, and he'd recovered. Some of my nurses had cared for him while he fought for his life in the ICU. In the early days of my diagnosis, a nurse had shown my family a video Kit's wife created of his battle with GBS. Jay had played me Kit's journey, but I had no recollection of watching it.

Mom said that was why they were filming me—they wanted to track my progress the way Kit's family did.

On Day 14, after getting my permission, Kit came to visit. A tall Asian man in his late twenties with his wife and three young daughters walked into my room. Kit looked normal, healthy, and happy.

"Hi, Holly. I'm Kit, and this is my wife, Tanya," he said as he approached my bed. "I had Guillain-Barre Syndrome when my second youngest was six months old. I know it doesn't feel like it, but you're going to get through this."

His words brought immediate tears to my eyes.

"How long were you in the hospital?" James asked. I noticed a small circular scar on Kit's neck.

"About four months," he replied.

Four months?

It was like a punch to the stomach. I'd been here for two weeks.

I couldn't do this for four months. I had to get better so I could go home to take care of my baby.

"Just keep fighting. I know it's hard." He proceeded to tell me everything about his case; how before getting GBS, he was young and healthy. Like me, his body declined quickly, and he was intubated after just a few days. He and his family had never heard of GBS before his diagnosis. He was a young husband and father, his two oldest girls, under three at the time. Kit had also been completely paralyzed from the neck down, not only in the same ICU but the exact room I was in. Our cases were eerily similar so far.

Tanya answered questions for James, the kinds of questions he'd only get from someone who had lived through the nightmare we were living. Her insight into the situation was invaluable. While they shared experiences, I watched Kit holding his youngest daughter in his arms, not much older than Casey. My daughter lay on the nursing pillow beside my paralyzed body in my bed. I wish I had the ability to hold my child the way he could. As far as I could tell, he'd recovered completely. Other than the scar on his neck, you'd have no idea what he'd gone through.

"Don't give up, Holly. You're going to get better," he said firmly. "You will get back to your family one day."

My eyes filled with more tears. It was one thing to hear the doctors say that. Hearing it from someone who'd survived GBS was considerably different, and I felt a tiny sense of hope.

Maybe I could recover from this.

Maybe I would get back to my family as Kit did.

Who knew that someone I'd never met before would be the one to inspire me to keep going.

A few days after the visit with Kit, two local news stations came to the hospital to interview our family and friends. A young, new mom paralyzed so soon after giving birth was a tragedy in my city. I agreed to be filmed for a few minutes in ICU; though I'd spent most of the day feeling like shit, I wanted others to see what happened to me. I wanted people to know about this awful disease most of us had never heard of and how quickly it ruined my life.

I don't remember doing the interview, but when we watched the news that evening, I remember thinking to myself: The world needs to know about Guillain-Barre and what it does to a person. I felt ashamed that I was so naïve and ignorant of the rare diseases people sometimes face.

"We need . . . to call . . . Oprah," I mouthed to Deanne, standing beside my bed. "I need . . . to go. . . on her show."

Deanne turned and smiled at James, then back at me.

I stared, waiting for her response.

She turned to James again with an uneasy look on her face, then back at me again. "It's the last season of the Oprah Winfrey Show, Holly . . . she would have already picked all her guests."

There was no point in calling Oprah.

Looking back, I was pretty high that day. I honestly thought that Deanne would have Oprah by my bedside in a matter of days.

Then things took a turn for the worst.

When I woke up the following morning, the paralysis had spread up into my head and face. I could no longer mouth words anymore or even smile. All I could do was blink. The doctors upped my sedatives again, and I slept most of the time.

When I was awake, though looking close to death, I was cognizant and knew where I was. With the way things were progressing, I figured I'd be in a coma soon. No one came out and said that, but my mom must have thought it too. She called a lawyer to bring in a power of attorney—a document that would give someone the authority to act on my behalf.

I appointed James to make decisions for me. Barely conscious, I scribbled something resembling an "X" at the bottom of the document with a pen in my mouth.

I'm not going to get back to my baby. I'll be a vegetable soon.

Casey was now seven weeks old.

Then what happens? Do they just leave me like this forever?

The thought of being completely trapped in my body, unable to communicate with the world, made me doubt my ability to keep fighting. I had visions of myself comatose, trying to scream out for my mom, her not being able to hear me.

I had no idea what I would wake up to next.

But the following day, a tiny glimmer of hope emerged. Mom noticed my fingertip move for the first time since Day 5.

"Do that again!" she shouted.

James grasped my hand by the wrist and lifted my arm off the bed.

I looked towards my limp hand with my eyes barely open and wiggled my fingers. They fluttered ever so slightly.

The room erupted in cheers; mom wrapped her arms around James.

"You're getting better!" the nurses squealed. "You've finally plateaued! The paralysis will start to fade, and you'll start moving your body again! We told you that you would get better!"

It was the moment everyone was waiting for.

I gazed out the window at the sun shining down on the snow-covered parts of the building, feeling as if I might vomit. The excruciating pain pulsated through my limbs, as it always did. Breaths of air forced their way into my lungs from the machine beside my bed.

I was paralyzed in the ICU. I couldn't feel happiness the way they could. Even if I wanted to smile for their sake, I wouldn't have been able to from the paralysis in my face.

I wanted to keep fighting the way Kit did, but I didn't think I could.

*

On Day 20 in the hospital, doctors told my family I needed to get out of bed and into a chair. "We have to take the pressure off her lungs." An x-ray of my chest showed the upper lobe of my left lung had partially collapsed.

In everyday life, a regular, healthy person stands or sits most of the time, and in this upright position, the heart rests slightly to the left, in front of the lungs. Because I was in a bed all day and night, my heart was resting above my lungs, putting pressure on them twenty-four hours a day.

To get me out of bed, the nurses would use a mechanical lift to hoist my motionless body into the air, then set me down into the recliner my mom had been sleeping on.

"Holly needs to spend at least an hour in the chair every day to take the pressure off her lungs," said the doctor.

My mom looked towards me in my bed. I was half asleep, exhausted from dry heaving the last few hours, but aware of what the doctor wanted. "She's barely moving her finger,' mom said. "I don't think she's ready to get out of bed." Mom was intensely protective of me and didn't like them to do anything that caused me more pain.

"I think she could use a change of scenery," the doctor insisted. "They can take her out of ICU in that chair."

For once, I agreed. I was sure the move would be painful, and maybe I wasn't ready for it, but I wanted to get out of my bed. I needed to look at something other than these four walls.

Three nurses came in to help with the move. They injected me with Ativan to calm my nerves then placed cold cloths across my forehead and thighs to keep me from overheating.

When they rolled my body to the side, I instantly cried from the shooting pains that spread through my body. Minor movements still felt like blows to my limbs. My nurse shoved the massive green canvas sling underneath my hips, then rolled me to the other side to pull it through. Then they attached the hooks of the sling to the small metal contraption beside my bed, a real-life hangman stand. The respiratory therapist took hold of the tube going from my neck to the ventilator. Deanne, visiting that day, stood back with the video camera in her hand at mom's request.

More sharp pain shot through me as my body rose above my bed. From the tips of my toes, up my legs, in my back, then out through my arms, hands, and fingers, every nerve was on fire. My spine felt as if it were being broken in half. The machine beside me beeped like crazy, and I assumed my blood pressure and heart rate were dangerously elevated.

I screamed, but as usual, no sound came out. "My back," I mouthed, again and again.

With my neck paralyzed, my head dropped backward. James rushed to the back of the bed and placed a hand behind my head, as you'd do with a newborn baby. Slowly rising in the air, my immobile legs swung apart in an invasive and excruciating way.

Mom pushed my knees back together, lifting them to a more neutral position. The pain lessened slightly.

"Hurry up," I cried.

"Can you push through the pain for just a few minutes, Holly?" my nurse asked.

"It's gotta feel nice not being in that bed, though," James said.

"No," I mouthed, in pain and desperate to be in the chair already.

Slowly, like molasses, the hoist moved me across the bed. The RT held the tube carefully, trying not to disturb the trach in my throat, which always made me feel sick. Gradually my body lowered, collapsing into the soft material of the recliner that leaned all the way back. My breathing was rapid, my body on fire. Nurses squeezed soaking wet cloths over my face. When I finally cooled down, and once my breathing was under control, James placed Casey on the nursing pillow on my lap.

What an ordeal—just to get out of bed.

"You did awesome," the nurse said to me, then injected me with some meds for my pain. Leaving ICU proved to be just as much of an event. She pushed the chair, the RT wheeled my ventilator beside me, one arm on the machine, the other carefully holding the tube from my throat. My entourage, James, Mom, Dad, Dennis, Deanne, and Jay walked alongside my big blue sofa chair as we strolled through the Grey Nun's halls.

We took the elevator downstairs and went to sit outside the front entrance. The doctor said to stay up in the chair as long as I could handle it. It wouldn't just help my collapsed lung but also help clear secretions, which would make breathing feel easier.

It was early spring that day; the sun was shining, the snow was just beginning to melt. In only my short-sleeved hospital gown that barely covered my thighs, I basked in the cool outdoor air, a treat to my usually scorching body. My family stood around my chair talking, pleased to be out of my room for once. Everyone that walked into the hospital gave me a double-take; it was too cold to be wearing what I was, and with tubes coming out of my throat and nose, I know I must have looked as though I was barely clinging to life.

As much as I liked getting out of my room, the longer we sat outside, the more I felt like a spectacle. Sitting in the chair proved to be much more painful than lying in my air bed, and the muscles along my spine throbbed. After less than an hour, I gave my mom a pained look, and she knew it was time to go in.

I'd wanted to get out of ICU for weeks, but now all I wanted was to go back to where I was most comfortable.

Over the next several days, more small improvements, like the paralysis fading in my face and regaining the ability to move my mouth. I could mouth words and wiggle my fingers a bit more each day, as well as my shoulders. I pointed to letters on the board and could nod my head again. I could communicate with my family. I practiced on the speaking valve; it was a struggle for a while, but eventually, I got the hang of it. On March 21st, mom held her cell phone up to my mouth, and I said, "Happy St. Patrick's Day" to Casey over the phone. While up in my chair, I had my filthy hair washed, which was amazing. I underwent minor surgery (which I have no recollection of) to insert a feeding tube through my stomach. With the hard, plastic NG tube out of my nose, even just existing was a bit more comfortable. Things were moving in the right direction. Mom plastered the ceiling with stars.

Moved shoulders up and down

NG tube removed

But the negatives outweighed the positives, at least for me. I was in so much pain and felt sick all the time. The downfall to the new feeding tube was that I felt every single crushed pill injected into my stomach. The sensation made me even more nauseous than I already was, and near the end of my first month in ICU, I was vomiting or dry heaving twenty to thirty times a day.

I got up in the sofa chair and went outside for a bit every day, which never got easier. Being hoisted up in the bright green canvas sling was torture. Sitting in that blue chair was uncomfortable and being out in the real world was fucking depressing. As soon as I thought I'd been out of my room long enough to make everyone happy, I'd ask to go back to my bed.

It seemed I couldn't catch a break either. From constantly having my catheter changed, I caught an ESBL bacteria, a type of bacteria that produces enzymes resistant to antibiotics, in my bladder. I was only a carrier of the bacteria; with no symptoms, there was no reason to treat it. It would eventually work through my body, but anyone who entered my room now had to wear yellow gowns to ensure no one passed the bacteria on to another patient—which could kill them. Casey was the only one that got away with not wearing one—at first, the nurses bundled her up in a pillowcase—but these days, I barely let her near me. I hardly had the energy to get through each day, let alone focus on my child.

It broke my heart, but I had to keep her at a distance for me to survive.

Now almost a month into this, not knowing what any sort of future looked like, my girlfriends Deanne, Carmen, Lisa, and Jen organized a fundraiser. People donated items to be bid on at an auction, and the money raised would go to our family. On top of our lowered incomes and usual expenses at home, we had costs here too. Parking was fifteen dollars a person per day. My family ate most meals in the expensive cafeteria in the hospital basement. It was impossible to predict how long they'd be visiting me here and how costly this hospital stay would get—hence the fundraiser. Thanks to my incredible friends and Deanne's background in marketing, the event was attended by more than four hundred people and raised our family over thirty thousand dollars. James and I didn't have much money; we mainly lived paycheck to paycheck with very little savings. So, it was a huge relief to know that we didn't have to worry about money on top of everything we were dealing with at the moment.

I was aware of the people rooting for me. Prayers and well wishes from strangers poured in. People donated baby clothes and diapers by the box.

"We're going to get through this," James said, sitting alongside my bed with Casey in his arms. "There are so many people praying for you." He gently pulled Casey's soother out of her tiny mouth and kissed her cheek.

I hadn't had much of a chance to see James as a father yet, but even from my bed, I could see he was a natural. He was constantly bouncing our daughter in his arms, talking to her as if she understood the words he said.

"Say hi to your mommy," he said with a smile and leaned Casey in close to my face. Then he placed her on the bed beside me where I could wiggle my fingers against the skin on her face. I'd usually only let her stay for a moment or two before I'd get nauseous and tell James to take her off.

It was a blessing to have my husband by my side every day, fighting for me while I couldn't. James and I had our challenges over the years; now, I was more in love with him than ever. It was breathtakingly beautiful to see him stepping up to raise our little girl on his own. He was being so strong for both his girls. Even in my fragile state, I knew the situation had already brought us closer and strengthened our bond. That was one positive I could see out of all this.

"When you get out of here, we're getting matching tattoos," James said. With our anniversary and both our birthdays on the nineteenth day of the month (we married in September, James's birthday's in June, mine in November), we'd once talked about getting the number nineteen tattooed on our wrists.

I nodded my head.

Every day was a struggle, but I forged on. I held on to the tiny improvements I made, looking at the stars above my bed every time mom put one up. I truly wanted to believe I'd get better and make it back to my husband and daughter one day.

But on Day 26, we found out that Guillain-Barre Syndrome is often a case of one step forward, then two steps back. After showing signs of improvement, between five to ten percent of GBS patients relapse. Less than a week after my fingers had finally started moving, the paralysis spread back through my hands and fingers, and I was completely paralyzed again.

7

Broken

My mental health deteriorated as the weeks passed. The head-to-toe paralysis remained. Relentless nausea and vomiting rarely let up, making every moment in the ICU more awful. Besides my brother Jay who had to go back up north for work, my family was always by my side. Mom and James studied my limbs day after day, watching for any slight movement, but nothing ever happened.

From lack of movement, the muscles in my fingers were starting to contract, causing them to curl inward—giving my hands a claw shape. The physiotherapy team (also called PTs) fitted me for hand splints made of a thin, stiff plastic mold to keep my fingers straight, with my arms out to the side. The physical therapists also provided foot splints that looked like ski boots to hold my feet at a ninety-degree angle. From lying in bed, gravity was naturally pulling them forward.

I wore both splints on and off every few hours. They were uncomfortable, especially to sleep in. The PTs showed my family how to do passive range of motion (ROM) exercises—to maintain mobility in my body and prevent shortening of the tendons and muscles.

"It's important we keep her muscles moving," the therapists reiterated, "or they will also start to contract.

Contractures will make her recovery longer and more difficult."

My nurses, family, and friends took turns moving and stretching my crippled body in various ways, three times a day, while I lay there looking like I was dead. Sometimes I begged for the therapy that we tenderly called 'range'; it felt good to stretch out my stiff, paralyzed limbs. Other times the slight movements felt like my bones were being snapped in half.

Knowing what I know now, I see how beneficial 'range' was, not just for me but also for my family, who desperately wanted to help in any way they could.

My muscles weren't the only thing affected. So were my eyes, and suddenly, I saw two of everything. The double vision made my nausea even worse as I couldn't focus on anything or anyone without getting dizzy and throwing up. Double vision is a common symptom in Miller Fisher Syndrome, a variant of GBS, but the doctors didn't think that's what I had since my eyes weren't the first thing affected.

The nurses had a temporary solution for the problem and taped a piece of fabric to my eyelid to block my view from one eye, alternating every other day.

I continued getting worse, never better. I felt like a patient in a movie, as close to a vegetative state as you can get (looking like a dying pirate, might I add), kept alive to appease my family. The doctors remained hopeful, insisting we continue moving forward with my recovery.

"We'd like to take the catheter out," one of the ICU doctors said to James and my mom late one afternoon. "We want to see if her bladder is strong enough to work on its own."

My UTI was one of their concerns; that and long-term catheter use can lead to complications down the road such as pain, problems urinating, and sexual dysfunction,

Most of my body was paralyzed. What made the doctors think my bladder would work the way it should? I hadn't felt the urge to pee in over a month. What if the tube had done its damage, and I never regained the ability to pee on my own? What if I was paralyzed in a wheelchair and had to use a catheter forever? Would I be able to have sex again? That was something I'd thought about when seeing people in wheelchairs before, but something I never thought I'd have to think about.

"With the catheter out, you'll use the bedpan again. How about we give it a try," the doctor said with a smile. His optimism kept a very dim light of hope burning inside, and I agreed.

Only a couple of hours later, with the catheter out, pressure built in my bladder, and half a grin grew on my face—adding to my silly pirate look.

"I need to pee," I mouthed, beaming at James through the eye patch. What a relief—I still had feeling down there.

The nurses, who were getting better at handling me, pulled up my white floral gown to my chest, gently removed my brief, then placed the cold, plastic bedpan under my butt. James pulled the bed sheet across my legs for privacy while everyone stood alongside my bed.

I closed my eyes and tried to relax the muscles in my bladder, but the pressure lingered, and nothing happened. I opened my eyes.

"Nothing yet?" the nurse asked.

"No . . ." I tried to say. ". . . but I'll keep trying," I mouthed. The faucet beside me turned on, and the sound of running water amplified the buildup of pressure in my bladder. For fifteen minutes, I tried to pee but couldn't.

"She doesn't have the strength yet. We'll have to do a straight catheter instead," said the nurse.

James left my side to turn off the water, and the nurse pulled the bedpan out from underneath me.

A straight catheter, also known as an in-and-out cath, is a type of catheter only left in long enough to empty the bladder. After the procedure, the nurses remove the tube. A straight cath would allow me to keep trying to pee on my own whenever I had to go.

The sun had gone down, and my room was getting dark by this point. A nurse pulled a rolling lamp up beside my bed, pointed the bright light towards the lower half of my body, which was naked, and forcibly spread my knees apart. Both women leaned in close with their gloved fingers as if they were doing surgery and prodded my genitals. I squirmed as the tube began to shove up into my urethra, the sharp pain lacerating through me.

Tears gushed from my eyes. I tried to squirm; of course, paralyzed, I stayed completely still. I screamed and cried out while James squeezed my hand tight. I couldn't see what the nurses were doing, but it felt as if they were shoving a needle or some type of razorblade up my vagina. I gasped for air with every probe, letting my head fall into the pillow to cry.

"It's okay, baby, it's almost over,' James said. The nurse twisted the tube up inside me again, the slashing pain worsening every time.

"Please stop!" I shouted, though my words were silent. My eyes darted at the people around me, and I made eye contact with my mom.

She leaned close and brushed the hair off the side of my face. "You're gonna be okay," she tried to convince me as she held back her tears.

The piercing pain made my vision fill with spots as I began to lose consciousness.

I closed my eyes, imagining myself passing out, never waking up.

This torture was too much to bear.

Then, the sound of dripping. The tube was finally in the proper position. My bladder quickly drained into the bedpan, and in a split second, the catheter was out, and the unbearable pain dissipated as if it were never there.

It still shocks me that I survived the pain of that procedure.

A few hours later, the pressure built up in my bladder. "Get me a bedpan," I mouthed, holding my head up high. With the straight-catheter procedure now being the most painful experience of my life, next to the ruptured artery, there was no way in hell I'd let them near me without trying to pee first.

The nurse nestled the pan under my bum, and after a long thirty minutes of pushing like I was giving birth all over again, I finally peed on my own. I was so grateful.

I wish I could say I never had to be straight catheterized again. Unfortunately, my bladder wasn't always strong enough. Sometimes I peed with minimal effort; other times, nothing came out no matter how badly I felt like I had to go. The nurse checked to see how much urine I retained using a bladder scanner, a wand-like device that pressed into my lower abdomen, similar to a pregnancy ultrasound. If there was a significant amount of urine still left in my bladder, the nurses had to do the horrific procedure again—each one as painful as the last.

I wailed, not knowing how much more pain I could take.

"It's okay, Holly, you're going to get through this," everyone repeated to me every single day, but I continued to doubt it.

"You are such a strong person!"

"You're a fighter, Holly. You can do this."

I cringed every time someone said that. I wasn't a fighter because, to me, I wasn't fighting. I was just lying there, doing nothing, with very little hope left in me. I couldn't admit to anyone that I had started to wish I would just die already. I was far from strong, and I was ashamed that everyone thought I was.

Despite my hopelessness, Mom and James stayed nauseatingly positive, at least around me. They almost always had smiles on their faces and talked to me as if everything was fine. They stuck to their routine; mom slept beside me every night; James came in every morning with Casey to spend the day with me. Their arrival each morning was signaled by the oooh's and aww's coming from the hallway. Every staff member in ICU, from the nurses and doctors to the cleaning staff and the RTs, adored our baby. I may not have been able to pay much attention to her, but I knew she was gorgeous and that her full lips and bright blue eyes stole every one of their hearts.

Once James was in my room, three or four nurses followed to pry Casey from his arms. I sometimes noticed he had difficulty letting her go, as did the nurses who dubbed him the "baby hog" whenever he politely declined their advances. Months later, I learned from James he was afraid to let Casey out of his sight after everything that had happened to me. My husband felt she was all he had left, and he had to protect her.

"How about you take her today," my mom said, snatching Casey from James arm's then leaning her in towards me on my bed. The walls of the room started to close in on me the second Casey's tiny body approached my face, bringing me back to the MRI machine. A wave of panic and nausea rushed over me.

I shook my head.

Not today.

I'd said that for the last several days.

Mom pulled Casey back from my bed and passed her over to James. "You know you need to bond with your baby," she said with what felt like a slightly judgemental tone to her voice.

I stared back at her in disbelief.

Bond with her?

Was she serious?

Does it look like I can bond with my child right now?

"I know," I snapped back, then turned my head away.

Casey being close to me on my bed not only made me claustrophobic and made me feel sick and nauseous, but it also reminded me of all I had lost. Whenever my daughter was beside me, she stared up at me with her big blue eyes, looking at the tube in my throat and the patch on my eye. I could feel her tiny hand wrap itself around my limp fingers, but I wasn't able to do a thing in return. I couldn't reach out and touch her back. I couldn't scoop her into my arms and snuggle her close. I wasn't her mother; I was nothing but a robot to her, paralyzed in my bed. My baby deserved so much more than I could give her.

"Did you hear?" I overheard two nurses talking later that afternoon. "Holly didn't let Casey on her bed *again* today." As usual, my eyes were closed, but I was awake and heard everything around me. "She isn't even interested in her baby," the nurse later told my mom. "I think she has post-partum depression."

The words knifed through me, and I immediately wanted to jump out of my bed and strangle that fucking nurse. She was wrong—I did not have post-partum. I was obsessed with my baby, like many new moms. All I wanted was for Casey to be in my bed with me so I could hold her close and feel her tiny heartbeat the way I'd felt when she was in my belly. Only a few months ago I still felt her kicks. Now having her near me was too painful, physically to my body and emotionally in my broken heart. I could admit that I struggled to even look at Casey most days, but this was not post-partum depression. My baby was now two months old, and she needed what all babies needed—to be taken care of, to be changed and fed, and rocked and cuddled. I couldn't do any of those things.

I didn't want Casey on my bed, not because I wasn't interested in her, but because I wanted her to be with someone who could give her the love and affection a newborn baby deserves. It was devastating I couldn't be that person, that I had to, selfishly, turn away my own child to survive. I felt guilt and anger that anyone thought I wasn't interested in Casey. You'd think being on your death bed would be a good enough excuse.

Resentment towards everyone around me, especially those that used the term post-partum around me for what I was feeling, built up inside.

"It just doesn't seem like you have any good days anymore," another nurse commented that same day. I took a look around the room, at my daughter in my husband's arms, at the ventilator pumping air through my chest.

What the fuck was she talking about? There were no good days in this hospital.

Trapped in my broken mind, it was hard for me to see good things *were* happening. The aching throb in my neck and back was improving, thanks to the help of a pain specialist who arranged for me to have periodic subcutaneous opioid infusions—basically an injection of pain meds through the fatty tissue in my stomach. My bladder worked like normal again, and I peed whenever I wanted, right into my brief—no more catheters.

Communicating was easier; I articulated my words, making a faint whisper from my lips. I got to spend half an hour on the speaking valve each day, where air passed through my vocal cords. One time I sang along to the song James had playing through the speaker on his phone. My husband also surprised me with a visit from our dogs one afternoon while I sat outside in the chair. It put a smile on my face to see their furry faces again.

I was still paralyzed, but the plan was for me to get out of ICU *one* day—priority number one, to get off the ventilator. To see how strong my diaphragm was, the RTs needed me to breathe into a pressure gauge device—a NIF test. My NIF level needed to be around -30cm H20 before they'd consider weaning me off the ventilator.

With James and mom beside my bed, Mike the RT put the plastic contraption up to my lips, and I breathed in as hard as possible. My chest tightened, and I gasped for air, my lungs feeling like they were about to burst. An overwhelming panic took over me, and my heart pounded. James patted my overheating body with wet cloths as I struggled to catch my breath through another anxiety attack.

Mom held my hand, massaging my fingers. "Imagine yourself relaxing on vacation, somewhere warm, somewhere happy. Anywhere but here."

Since I was a child, I've loved the sun, the sand, and the water. The beach was my favorite place in the world. I also loved swimming in the ocean, at the lake, and in the pool. James and I started traveling out of Canada a few years prior; we'd gone to the Dominican Republic and Jamaica for our honeymoon. Starting a family had put our travel plans on hold for a little while, but now confined to a bed, I made promises to myself that I'd travel more if I made it out of this alive.

Imagining the sound of waves in my ears, the feeling of sand on my toes, and the warm sun on my chest, I closed my eyes. After a few minutes, my breathing steadied, though it was more so from the Ativan a nurse gave me.

My NIF level was at -5—still a long way to go.

The RTs tried to get me to do the test every few days. Not usually up to it, I'd plead with them to come back tomorrow instead. After it had been at least a week since my last one, Mike peeked his head into my room again.

"Not today," I whispered. As usual, I felt like hell.

"We just need to see where you're at."

Anxiety grew in my chest, and I shook my head.

"We need to do the test," Mike insisted as he gowned up, then came up beside my bed with the plastic gauge.

I rolled my eyes, understanding I didn't have a choice. I put my mouth over the opening and breathed in as hard as I could, nearly fainting this time.

I was still at -5. Then I coughed and coughed and dry-heaved on my shoulder.

"Thank you, Holly. Fantastic job. I know this is difficult for you to do. Keep trying. It will get better." He wiped my mouth with a damp cloth. "Thank you for doing the test." Mike walked towards the sliding glass door of my room, then just as he was about to leave, he stopped and turned with a smile. "Because you did this test for me today, when you get out of here, I'm going to let you stay at my vacation home in Phoenix, Arizona."

For the first time in what felt like weeks, I smiled.

"Seriously, after all this, I'm going to *need* a vacation," I whispered.

The room filled with laughter. It was such a wonderful change.

My brother came back into town at the beginning of April, about six weeks into my nightmare in the ICU. After a couple of weeks away, Jay couldn't believe how much better I looked from the last time he saw me. The tube coming out of my nose was gone, and on fewer meds from my pain improving, I was alert and sober. On Day 43, I went twenty-four hours without needing a top-up of medication. I could also handle being up in the chair for longer, which helped keep my lungs clear, so less suctioning and gagging. And I didn't have hot flashes nearly as often. I was still paralyzed, still throwing up every day, but medically, in many ways, I was improving, even if I couldn't see it. I still had my doubts I would make it out of this alive.

James kept Casey at home for four days when she randomly got pink eye, and I missed them like crazy while they were away. I was thankful to have Jay by my side, and we passed the time by watching NHL hockey on the mounted TV in front of me which I hadn't even noticed until now. Once Casey was better and back in her usual spot in her bassinet, she stared up at the TV as if she was into hockey as much as Jay was. She'd stick out her lips or her tongue, wiggle her little feet, and coo at the screen.

I faintly smiled at the thought of Casey as a little girl watching hockey with her dad and her uncle one day. I wondered if I'd be around for that.

Casey spent a lot of time in the clear, plastic bassinet below the window to my right. With me more conscious, I started to see how calm my daughter was. She spent hours in her bassinet, rarely making a peep, while chaos ensued around her. When I thought back over the past several weeks, I only recalled a handful of times when she cried, other than the few seconds before she got her next bottle. James filled up her bottles with pre-packaged formula, and I watched as he shook the plastic bottle in his hands, then held them up to her mouth. I wondered where the bottles came from, as I had been breastfeeding Casey, and those weren't the ones someone gifted us at our baby shower.

I noticed how smart our baby was, too. One day when mom was holding her above my bed to see me as she often did, Casey put her tongue to the roof of her mouth and clucked at me. I was looking away, and she was trying to get my attention. Casey had watched and heard me cluck to communicate so many times, so she did the same thing.

I mustered up the strength to give my daughter the biggest smile I could, and Casey smiled back—the first smile I got to see. Casey had the most precious smile with her big round cheeks and mouth open wide. Staring at her tiny face, I couldn't believe how much she had changed from just a few weeks before. Now two months old, Casey was changing; her cheeks were getting bigger, and she was more interested in things. I still wasn't sure who our baby looked like; she had big lips like the both of us, and blue eyes like mine, but no hair on her little head yet.

"She spends more time on her stomach at home, and her neck is getting stronger," James told me. "And she loves to be swaddled. You should see her, Holly. I'll swaddle her as tight as I can at night, and she passes out in minutes. If she wakes up, it's because she got out of it and needs to be wrapped back up. And she's not eating as much either. She only needs one bottle in the night."

I nodded my head slowly; the ventilator beeps rang in the background. Hearing James talk about our baby was bittersweet; it was amazing to see and hear how great of a father he was, and I was proud of him for that, but I wished I'd get to experience these moments with her, too.

I had less than a month with my daughter before I lost it all.

I thought back to those first few weeks at home, how Casey got hungry every two hours, and how slow of an eater she was. She nursed for thirty to forty minutes at a time, which meant at least every hour of every day I was breastfeeding. Sometimes, it felt like she was attached to my boob all day, which was not easy.

When Casey was two weeks old, I had my first meltdown. "She doesn't stop eating!" I had cried to James. My boobs leaked and throbbed, the kitchen was a disaster, and we had company coming to visit. "This is easy for you; you don't have to breastfeed every two hours."

I gazed at my daughter beside my hospital bed through my uncovered eye, and both eyes filled with tears. I deeply regretted that I'd ever complained about breastfeeding. Strictly on formula, I'd probably never breastfeed my baby again. I'd give anything to have that time back with her. Or the time I was missing out on now. Every Tuesday afternoon, we were supposed to be bonding in Mommy and Me classes. We should be going for walks to the park and having play dates with my girlfriends and their kids. Instead, I was here. A vegetable in a fucking hospital bed. I felt worthless.

I didn't do well at hiding my bitterness. Most of the time, I had a frown on my face and a look of hopelessness in my eyes. Other times my family was able to lift my spirits, like when my mom brought in a stereo to play music, and I found a morsel of strength in the lyrics—specifically in Miley Cyrus' *The Climb*. Like the words in that song of struggle, my faith was wavering, and the voice inside told me I would never reach my dream of being a mother again, but deep down, I knew I had to keep fighting. I had to be strong. It was the only choice I had.

I pushed through, hoping, praying, for the best.

Trying to be strong and think positively was hard, but maintaining that positivity was the real challenge. Especially when people kept telling me things would get better, but nothing ever did. Listening to music helped me for a moment or two, but then my reality would sink back in. Motionless in my hospital bed, I'd watch James and my family walk around my hospital room, pick up my daughter, sip on coffee, and munch on cafeteria sandwiches, going about their days with ease. I'd look out the windows across from me, wondering if the rooms had patients that felt as hopeless as I did. I still couldn't even lift a finger. Most GBS patients hit their plateau after two to three weeks, and it had now been over six.

Thinking clearer, I didn't believe I was being punished anymore. I hadn't done anything wrong in my life to deserve this. I was an honest person, the type of person that always tried to do the right thing. I was a doting and loyal wife. When I was pregnant, I took care of my body by going for lots of walks and eating healthy (not that it was difficult, as my biggest craving was fruit), and once Casey was here, I knew I'd be an amazing mother. I wasn't being punished, everything was going so well in my life for so long; it was just time for everything to come crashing down. I realized something about life, that not every ending is a happy one.

I wasn't going to get this fairy-tale life that I had always dreamed of living.

One morning—Day 45 specifically—James walked into my room with bloodshot eyes filled with tears, and he immediately passed Casey to my mom and sat down in the chair beside me.

"Jeff's not coming to see you today," he said. Jeff was one of James' close friends since childhood and hadn't visited us at the hospital since I'd first arrived. I knew he was supposed to be coming that day.

"Why?" I whispered.

James choked back tears, then cried as he spoke. "He committed suicide yesterday." Jeff was a paramedic in our city, and we later learned he'd been struggling with his mental health.

I didn't reply for a while. James used his sleeve to wipe the tears from his eyes. Mom stood in the corner, wiping hers with a Kleenex that she pulled out of her purse.

I couldn't think of anything to say. James cried and cried for what felt like forever.

"I'm sorry," I finally mouthed with a blank look on my face. No tears came. I was in utter shock of everything that was happening to us, over everything James was dealing with right now. His wife in the ICU, being a full-time, basically single father, having no idea if I'd survive this. Now one of his friends was dead. I certainly wasn't the only one going through hell, and my heart ached for my husband, even if I couldn't show it at this moment.

On one hand, I couldn't comprehend how someone could take their own life, by choice, when some of us were fighting so hard just to stay alive. On the other, I completely related to the feeling of not knowing how to keep going and wanting to give up.

Two days later, I reached my own breaking point.

I woke up on Day 47 nauseous as always and spent my morning vomiting again and again, with zero relief. The nurses tried every med they could until I wasn't allowed any more, but they rarely worked. The room continued to spin, and I threw up into the basin under my neck, gagging and hurling every ten minutes. After several horrendous hours of throwing up on and off, I pleaded with my mother, “Please . . . do. . . something . . . I can’t do this anymore.” I broke down into tears.

“Maybe she has the stomach flu,” my nurse said to my mom. “She seems sicker than normal. Maybe we could empty her stomach. Maybe that will help.” The nurses and doctors did a lot more guessing than I thought they would. They decided to go for it.

“What we’re going to do is put the NG tube back through your nose, into your stomach and pump its contents back out through the tube—into this.”

As the nurse pointed to a clear plastic container beside my bed, my face went white. The thought of something shoved up my nose spiked my heart rate. It sounded horrific, and with my pain finally under control, I was not ready to go through more.

“It will be uncomfortable, but it won’t hurt,” my nurse promised, “and it might help you feel better.”

I nodded and whispered, “Okay.” I appreciated that my nurses were speaking to me more. I guess I looked like I could finally handle a conversation.

“All I need for you to do is swallow. Just keep swallowing over and over.”

I clenched my frozen body and took in a deep breath. Before I had a chance to take in a second, the nurse shoved the tube as hard and as far back into my nose as she could. It was shocking, and she was right; it wasn’t painful but dreadfully uncomfortable. The plastic tube slid its way down my throat one gulp at a time, and I gagged in response.

“Keep swallowing,” she said, so I did.

Eventually, the tube was in my stomach. The nurse stood back from my bed. “How does that feel?” Every swallow I took, the plastic tube rose, then lowered back down my esophagus.

“It feels . . . weird. I can feel the tube,” I mouthed, my eyes tearing up, my heart beating faster. Now I had two tubes going down into my throat.

“How about I give you numbing spray,” my nurse decided, “so you won’t feel the tube.” She came back a moment later, I opened my mouth, and she sprayed.

After only a few minutes, my throat was completely numb. "I can't really . . . breathe," I whispered. I took in another deep breath but now couldn't feel the air flowing through my numb throat. My heart rate spiked again, and panic set in. The machine beside me beeped. My breaths became shorter and faster. I turned to my mom with wide eyes, my lips beginning to tremble as I gasped for air.

"Give her Ativan," my nurse said to another while I hyperventilated.

After the injection, my breathing relaxed, and I calmed down. My stomach drained into the container beside my bed, slowly filling the clear plastic casing with a thick yellow paste. The only thing I 'ate' in ICU was something called 'tube feed,' a yellow, nutritional liquid that came out of a clear plastic bag beside me, going into my belly through a tube.

I tried not to look at the container during the three-hour process—in shock that I was experiencing this, awake and conscious, throwing up throughout.

Was this what happened when drunk people had their stomachs pumped?

When there was nothing else to come out, the nurse pulled the tube out of my nose, which was easier than going in.

"Do you feel any better?" mom asked.

I still felt nauseous and gagged into the basin.

I quickly figured out that pumping my stomach not only didn't help, it made it worse. Now I had nothing to puke up, so instead of vomiting, I dry heaved over and over—and over again. The nurses gave me more meds whenever allowed, and I'd watch them inject whatever they gave me through the IV protruding out of my arm, but it only helped for a little while. I was at my wit's end and cried all day and into the evening.

"Mom . . ." I whispered to my mom. "I can't do this anymore."

"Yes, you can," she replied, grabbing hold of my hand and lacing her fingers with mine. Then her eyes grew wide, and she shouted, "Holly!" Look! Your finger. . . it's moving!

I looked down with my one eye to see the tip of my finger fluttering up and down, the first time it had moved in weeks.

Everyone in the room shouted and cheered. No one expected this to happen, especially with how awful of a day I was having.

"See, you're getting better," James smiled. "You probably hit your plateau again."

I turned my head to look out the window while my mom wrote out another star to add above my bed. My stomach tossed and turned, and I choked back the urge to vomit. In my eyes, I was not getting better. I went to sleep that night feeling worse than ever and woke up throughout the night to puke up the tube feed that eventually refilled my stomach.

"Please," I begged the night shift nurse after fifteen minutes of being awake for more hell. "I need more Gravol. Please!" Gravol was the medication that seemed to work the best.

"I'm sorry, I can't. You just had some not that long ago," the nurse said, as matter-of-factly. This older woman was a nurse I'd never had before, and her tone of voice seemed cold and uncaring to me. She checked my vitals on the machine beside me and said, "Everything looks good. There's nothing I can do for you."

The burning vomit lingered in my throat.

How could she not do anything for me? I felt as if I was dying.

"Please," I whispered again. I didn't know much more of this I could take.

The nurse brought her face close to mine to look me straight in the eye without the patch. "Holly," she said sharply. "You just need to grin and bear it." Then she turned and walked out of the room.

I lay there in shock at what she said.

Grin and bear it? Does she not see what I am going through?

"I am going through HELL!" I wanted to scream.

I couldn't pretend like I was okay when I wasn't. I couldn't push through the suffering like everyone wanted me to. *I'm not a strong person. I can't do this anymore!* I threw up continuously, my mom wiping the puke from my mouth and the tears from my eyes into the early hours of the morning.

"Your finger is moving again, Holly! You're going to get better soon," she said encouragingly.

Any ounce of optimism I had left was gone.

It's not like I had never struggled before. I'd gone through plenty of hard times in my life, growing up with divorced parents, neither of whom had a ton of money. In the city, we bounced from home to home, depending on where mom worked and what her financial situation was. As a teenager, I had my heart shattered more times than I could count, and I'd experienced a fair share of challenges in my relationship with James. I'd gone through financial struggles and had tons of friend and work drama that caused me plenty of stress over the years.

I was always confident in my ability to get through tough times. After my parents' divorce, they put us kids in counseling. When I was twelve, my mom sent my brothers and me to a youth empowerment camp developed by the self-help guru Tony Robbins. My mom volunteered her time with his organization to pay for us to go, and I like to think that both the counseling and this camp played a big part in my ability to overcome adversity. Through the struggles in my life, I tried to be as optimistic as I could, always believing that everything happens for a reason. That's not to say I never got upset over my circumstances, because as a highly emotional woman, I did, but I was great at crying my heart out for hours then picking myself back up—and moving on. I was as strong as they come, I believed. I'd never dealt with severe anxiety or depression—as a child or an adult— nor had I ever experienced suicidal thoughts before.

Until now.

This pain and suffering was too much. Things had never been *this* hard before. My dream of being the mother I wanted to be was crushed, my life ruined. I had no future. There was no reason for me to keep fighting. There was no hope left.

I looked through the darkness of my room at the ventilator beside my bed, the lights shining from the machine keeping me alive. If only I could convince someone to just shut off the machine. Of course, the nurses would try to revive me . . . unless they agreed not to.

"You can have another dose of Gravol," a new nurse said, interrupting my morbid thoughts.

My other nurse was on a break, thank God. Neither mom nor I would have been able to look at her, and mom later requested she never be assigned to me again. After the Gravol injection, I drifted off to sleep at 6 am.

The following morning, sunlight beamed into my room. I looked up at the clock on the wall to see it was almost 8 am, so I'd slept less than two hours. Utterly exhausted, physically and mentally, my body felt as if it were shutting down. I instantly felt the swirling in my stomach, and within ten minutes, I was puking and in tears again.

I didn't have the strength in me to fight any longer.

"Mom . . ." I whispered after she wiped my face with a cool cloth.

Mom tilted her head to look at me with her tired eyes.

"I can't do this anymore," I mouthed. I was ashamed that I couldn't stay strong, that I was letting Casey down, but this was beyond what my mind was capable of handling. "You need to let me go," I carefully mouthed. "Please . . . shut off the machine."

"No, Hunny!" Mom screamed. "We won't let you go!" She started to cry, but her confident words held strong. "Your finger is moving again; we will not let you die when you are finally starting to get better."

I couldn't have cared less that my fingertip had moved.

Mom squeezed my hand. "You need to hold on, for Casey's sake. I promise you're going to get better."

I sighed. My mom wouldn't just shut off the machine and let me die. No mother would. I closed my eyes for a moment, then opened them again. I had to ask someone else for help.

"Get my respiratory therapist," I whispered.

Mom stood up slowly with a suspicion of what I was up to and left the room. She returned a few minutes later with Angela, one of my regular RTs.

"What can I do for you," Angela said with a nurturing smile as she leaned close to my face.

"I want a DNR," I meticulously mouthed, my eyes full of tears. A DNR or a Do Not Resuscitate is a medical order instructing healthcare providers not to do CPR if a patient stops breathing.

Angela took in a loud breath and took hold of my hand.

"I want a DNR . . ." I said to Angela again, watching tears build up in the corner of her big blue eyes. "Please turn off the ventilator and let me die."

"Oh Holly, you can't give up," she said, choking back tears. "You've come so far, and your baby needs you."

I shook my head, not wanting to hear anything about my baby right now.

"Please . . ." I whispered. Let me die. Let me rest from this pain.

"You have to keep fighting," Angela said, rubbing my forehead with her soft hands, wiping every tear that fell from my eyes. "We are all here fighting with you."

I closed my eyes and sobbed uncontrollably, struggling to breathe.

The truth is, I never wanted to die. I just wanted the unbearable suffering to end. I didn't know how I could possibly make it through another minute of this nightmare.

8

Life, Restarted

In the early part of 2013, almost two years after my diagnosis, I got involved with the GBS/CIDP Foundation of Canada, a non-profit organization run by an amazing group of caring and dedicated individuals who volunteered their free time. The foundation's aim was that no one would go through these rare disorders alone. They provided information and resources and connected patients and families with volunteers who'd once been affected by GBS and its variants. Having talked to countless people online over the past year, I wanted to help in any way I could, as did my mother. We both joined as volunteer liaisons, first attending, then later running a support group meeting in our city where survivors and family members talked about what we'd been through over coffee and donuts.

Most importantly, Mom and I visited patients in the ICU, like Kyu and his wife and daughter. I also went back to the stroke and neurology ward at the Grey Nuns to meet patients recovering from GBS—like Rob, a fifty-two-year-old man, and Jill, a woman in her mid-thirties, both of whom were just starting physiotherapy to strengthen their bodies. I spent an hour with most patients answering every question I could and reminding them of where I'd been and where I was now.

It was never easy going back to a place where I'd struggled so hard, but every time I walked out the front doors of the Grey Nuns Hospital, I felt a sense of real purpose, as if I was doing something truly remarkable for the world. I was giving GBS patients the tools I used to make it out alive. This once paralyzed mom was now an advocate for others in a way I could have never imagined. My life had taken an unexpected turn, the first of many.

*

Three years later, five years post-diagnosis, life was drastically different for me. I was big into fitness and in fantastic shape. Casey was five years old; James and I were divorced and in new relationships. Mom and I were heavily involved with the GBS/CIDP Foundation, and I was *Holly After GBS*, the online persona of the woman in my recovery videos that went viral again and again. I had a large following of incredible people around the world—some of whom I had the privilege of meeting at various GBS conferences and symposiums I attended or helped organize. I'd returned to work in Human Resources and was doing well in my career, but my work with the GBS/CIDP Foundation of Canada and inspiring others through my story of survival was my passion. I was getting to carry buckets for others still engulfed in flames from the fire that almost destroyed me.

In the fall of 2016, I represented the foundation at an annual event in our city called the Nerd Run, which raised money for neurology and peripheral nerve research—funding that could help doctors better understand Guillain-Barre Syndrome. The event was a 5km run organized by the Neuroscience and Mental Health Institute out of the University of Alberta—the post-secondary school I'd attended for HR. The foundation asked if I wanted to participate. Heeding the advice received from Jim at my first GBS conference, I now exercised regularly—running and strength training at the gym. I could run five kilometers as I'd done it a couple of years prior for a fundraising race for cancer. I hadn't trained for that event as it was just for fun, and it took me thirty-eight minutes to complete. I wanted to push myself this time. Knowing I was running for a cause so near and dear to my heart, I set a goal to run the 5k in under half an hour. I spent weeks increasing the minutes on the treadmill at the gym until I was ready.

It was late September, and though the sun was shining, the air was brisk, and the leaves had already begun to change colors. Just outside downtown, the Edmonton skyline that I had loved since I was little peered through the trees. Mom and I and other volunteers set up a table with brochures about GBS, CIDP, and the Foundation near the starting line on the grass. Next to us were the Alzheimer's and MS Societies. Five-year-old Casey sat behind the table in a lawn chair, bundled up with Cici, her pink and brown zebra print blankie.

The media was the first to arrive, and their reporters took a few minutes to interview us on why we were here.

"I'm running in support of the GBS/CIDP Foundation of Canada," I said with a smile, then shared a few sentences of my experience with GBS. The reporters were genuinely intrigued to hear how far I'd come.

As more people arrived at the event, they made their way to our table to learn more.

"What is GBS?" asked a young woman who'd introduced herself as a medical student.

"GBS is Guillain-Barre Syndrome, a rare autoimmune disorder," I answered. "Sort of like Multiple Sclerosis, only it affects the peripheral nerves." The majority of medical students are familiar with MS. I gave an abridged explanation of what I went through.

"Wow. That's crazy. What causes it?" the girl asked.

It was amazing to answer her questions and bring awareness to this rare disease that even these medical students didn't know much about.

"It's almost time to go!" Casey shouted from behind the table. After everything we'd been through together, my daughter and I were close, and it was important to me that she be here for this event. I wanted Casey to see how hard I'd worked, and that I'd never given up. I fastened my race number to the front of my shirt with safety pins, laced up my pink runners, and made my way to the starting line.

"Good luck, Mommy!" Casey shouted.

Most of the runners around me were students. Despite only being in my early thirties, they were all much younger than I was, and probably in better physical shape. But I wasn't here to compete; this was about me. I was here to take advantage of the abilities I had regained. My only competition was myself.

When the horn blared, with the words *Guillain-Barre Survivor* written across my back, I pressed my feet firmly into the ground and took off running. Mainly having trained in the gym on a treadmill, the slight pain in my ankles as my feet hit the pavement reminded me of the lingering effects of GBS which still plagued me. My ankles were weaker than normal—a common residual from GBS.

But I kept going. Even with the discomfort, I was fortunate to be able to run like this again, unlike many survivors I knew. I ran alongside the river valley and watched the cars drive by, thinking if they only knew where I started. I thought back to my time in the ICU when my body was paralyzed, and I could literally do nothing, not even reach out and touch my baby girl with my own hands. Here I was, feeling the strength in the muscles of my legs, running in a race in support of GBS.

With tears in my eyes and a sense of gratitude for my abilities, I kept running and running as fast as my legs would carry me. The cold chill in the air was refreshing as sweat dripped down my face. Eventually, I looped around and was almost back to where I started, approaching the end of the race. Alongside the road, a crowd of people cheered. A rush came over me, a burst of adrenaline spread through my body, and I bolted, my aching ankles pushing me toward the finish line.

I had come so far. I was a mother again and was independent. I could walk—I could run! As I crossed the finish line, Casey jumped out in front of me and leaped into my arms. Mom stood back, videotaping this joyous moment.

I had shown my daughter to never, ever give up.

I squeezed my daughter tight with a big smile on my face, then looked up at the large red timer above us. I ran 5km in twenty-eight minutes.

The fastest I'd ever run in my life.

*

One year later, I took my first international trip to visit a patient in another country. A woman named Lisa from Florida had contacted me through my Facebook page. Her sister Puschel, a woman in her fifties, had been diagnosed (coincidentally shortly after the birth of her first grandbaby) and was on life support in intensive care. "We think it would be good for someone that recovered from this horrible syndrome to come see her in the hospital. To give her hope and encouragement. We will pay you to come here."

Casey stayed with James, and I hopped on a plane to spend time with them in the hospital. I had to reassure this woman that life with her grandson was waiting for her as she fought the effects of this debilitating condition.

"You're going to get through this," I told the woman after several hours of travel to be with her and her family in the ICU. "You're going to get back to your life. I was on life support with GBS, too," I reminded her, standing strong and healthy beside her bed.

Paralyzed with a ventilator tube in her throat, Puschel smiled, her pearly whites gleaming back at me. Like me, she had a severe case of GBS. She also had an incredible support system. I met her husband, two beautiful daughters who looked just like her, and her parents. I answered questions and talked about the things I experienced and overcame.

"Please know that once she hits her absolute worst, she'll start to improve," I said to her family. "It's just going to take time. Maybe weeks, maybe months but eventually the paralysis will start to fade, and she will get better." I told them that GBS is often called "Getting Better Slowly" because recovery takes so long. "And that will be the hardest part—the waiting. It's such a long road. Make sure to remind each other that things *will* get better. Celebrate every tiny improvement. Try to stay positive as much as you can. Don't lose hope and never, ever give up. GBS will be the hardest thing you will go through as a family, but one day you will look back, and it will all be a distant memory." Just as it was for me.

"Thank you so much. Like you, our mom is a fighter," her daughter said, grabbing hold of her mom's limp hand on the bed. "She'll do anything to get back to her grandbaby."

Puschel smiled again and nodded. "Thank you for coming and giving us hope," she carefully mouthed.

My visit with Puschel and her family remains one of my favorite hospital trips of all time. Puschel smiled the entire visit, fighting through the horrific pain I remembered all too well. She had a spark in her eye that told me she was going to be okay. I stayed strong the entire visit, but tears poured down my cheeks as I left the hospital.

Later that evening, at the Jacksonville airport, I couldn't find my passport and missed my flight back home to Canada. I was in tears when I called the hotel and my Uber with no luck, realizing I had no way to get back into my country. After pacing the airport for an hour, googling the nearest Canadian embassy (which was four hours away), I found my passport on the floor right next to where I'd initially been sitting. It had fallen out of my pocket. With no more flights to Canada that night, the airline booked me a new one early the following day, thankfully at no extra charge. I took a shuttle to a hotel down the street and ordered room service.

The sun was setting into the horizon as I ate my dinner in bed, casting a beam of light through my window. I stood from the bed and pulled back the curtains, in awe of one of the most beautiful sunsets I'd ever seen. Red, fluffy clouds with bright yellow sunbeams shining through them covered the sky. It was a tough day, being back in ICU and then missing my flight, but I made myself a promise to look at the beauty surrounding me—today and going forward. On a typical day, I would have been furious at myself for misplacing my passport and having to stay another night, but in my newfound wisdom, I knew it wasn't the end of the world. After spending the day in the hospital with someone breathing through a tube in their throat, I knew what I still had, and that was my health—something we all take for granted. I could live my life; I could talk and walk around an airport on my own, which was reason enough to be grateful.

I had nothing to complain about, even when my flight was delayed the next morning, I missed my connecting flight and had to fly to three different US cities to get back to Canada. I sat in one of the cramped flights staring out the window, smiling, hearing the person beside me bitch about how he wouldn't get to bed that night till midnight. All I could think of was how lucky I was to be alive and be out of ICU; to have overcome GBS; to be healthy enough now to fly across the continent and help someone else fighting Guillain-Barre Syndrome.

9

Courage Doesn't Roar

Guillain-Barre Syndrome is an acute disorder with an abrupt onset and rapid progression, but most patients improve eventually, even in the most severe cases. There was proof of my recovery as more of my fingers started to move again after that first flicker. For that reason, amongst others, no one would consider shutting off the ventilator and letting me go. I had no choice but to wake up every morning and carry on. That's the thing about all hard times. You don't get better from the days you feel like pushing; you get better from the days you don't but do it anyways.

I was now able to stay awake an entire day, as the sedatives had been reduced once again. Mom established a routine to help pass the time and ease my anxieties about the day. Mornings started when Mom turned on the TV to watch the doom and gloom of the morning news—a brief distraction from what we were going through. Seeing what was happening in the rest of the world reminded me that there was life outside the ICU.

After the news, Mom brushed my teeth, which always made me gag. At least she used an electric toothbrush to speed up the process. Then she called for the respiratory therapist to come in and suction the mucus out of my trach, which usually set off my nausea for the rest of the day.

"Who is my nurse today?" I mouthed nervously to my mom after the RT finished up.

"I was just about to go ask," my mom said. Still in her pajamas, she threw on a royal-blue housecoat and headed to the nurse's station outside my room.

I stared forward, looking at the photos and feather boas on the wall in front of me, my breathing steadily increasing. After my experience with that awful nurse who told me to "grin and bear it," I was terrified of having a nurse who hadn't yet worked with me.

"Your nurse is Natasha," Mom said when she returned a few minutes later, dressed, hair brushed, and ready for the day.

I sighed in relief.

Natasha, a bubbly French woman near my age, was one of my favorites. ICU management did their best to assign only a handful of nurses to me, ones who understood GBS and my unique challenges. The good ones, like Natasha, knew of the sharp pain I got in my thighs whenever I was turned over, so they log rolled me instead of bending my leg at the knee (how they are trained to do.) The good ones were aware of my skin sensitivity and were extra gentle whenever they touched me. New nurses usually left me in tears with what felt like cruel and harsh movements of my limbs. Most ICU nurses don't see a lot of GBS patients and are used to patients being completely sedated. And they don't understand just how awful nerve pain from GBS can sometimes be.

"How are you feeling today?" Natasha asked when she came in a few minutes later. She placed a thermometer under my tongue and wrapped the blood pressure cuff around my left arm.

"A little nauseous," I whispered. The cuff tightened around my arm.

"Then let's get you some Gravol right away."

My breathing relaxed. Some of the nurses were more sympathetic about my nausea than others. Natasha was one that always tried to get a handle on it before it spun out of control.

"Just so you know, I won't be here next week," she said. "Me and my husband are going to Mexico."

I nodded my head and smiled. I enjoyed it when the nurses shared details of their lives with me. They would talk about their kids, husbands, and vacations, and even though our conversations were one-sided—the nurses chatted for hours while I lay there in silence—it was nice to have people discuss something other than my ill health. I lived vicariously through them.

While the nurse prepared my morning medication, Mom did my range of motion exercises, gently lifting my limbs off the bed—then lowering them ten times in a row. She repeated the same process with my wrists, hands, elbows, and then my arms. Whenever she lifted my left arm off the bed, it bumped the tubing between my trach and the ventilator, which always made me cough and then usually puke. Eventually, Mom stopped moving my left arm up as high so I could get through the exercises without throwing up.

"I can feel a slight push back when I do your arms, now," Mom said with a big smile on her face.

I couldn't *move* my arms yet, but I could *feel* the muscles trying to fire. The movements Mom did every day were becoming smoother, and she could do them with a little less effort on her part, which was encouraging for me. Once she finished my upper body, Mom moved down to my legs, which, in contrast, had zero muscle engagement.

After 'range' came my favorite part of the day—opioids and a sponge bath. The injection into the IV on the inside of my elbow gave me an instant feeling of intense relaxation and took away every slight pain I had in my body. My eyes rolled back in my head as the euphoria spread. Looking back, I know my body was addicted to the drugs I was on. The doctors said they'd deal with weaning later, as managing the unbearable pain was most important right now. To this day, I always advocate for patients to be on as many meds as necessary to get a handle on the horrific nerve pain that is beyond anything even the strongest of adults are capable of handling.

After the injection, my nurse wiped my body from head to toe with warm, soapy water and a cloth. When you haven't had a shower or bath in forever, the feeling of clean skin every morning felt like heaven. The nurses always used Aveeno body wash for babies, the stuff I bathed Casey with back home. James brought it when they recommended that we bring in a familiar fragrance to give me comfort. Between the smell and the coolness on my skin, I was completely relaxed for a moment. The drugs helped, of course too.

Once the intensity of the high wore off, things shifted back to horrendous, with one of the worst parts of my day. First a suppository up my bum, then medication time, the meds injected through the feeding tube in my stomach. My nurse put a handful of pills into a container that looked like the ketchup trays you get at McDonald's, added a bit of water, then crushed it all together. Using a syringe, she withdrew the white, liquid-y paste and injected it into the opening of the tube poking out of my stomach.

I felt the fluid spewing into my gut. Then my nurse grabbed another handful of pills to crush and inject. It was shocking how many different medications I was being given. I was on meds to keep my bowels moving, meds to try to prevent nausea, a blood thinner to inhibit blood clots, a sleeping pill, and antidepressants for my mood and nerve pain. And those are just the ones I remember. Every time the liquid sloshed in my stomach, I cringed and gagged. If suctioning hadn't yet made me nauseous, this was sure to. It was almost clockwork for me to feel nauseous within ten minutes of getting these meds. Then usually, I felt sick for the rest of the day.

After my morning meds, Mom read me my Facebook messages aloud off her phone. From the news stories that had aired, I was getting messages from people all over the province.

Thinking about you, Holly!

We are sending you so much love!

Writing a one-line Facebook post is such a small, easy thing to do, but those people could never know how much it meant to me. Their uplifting words reminded me how many were fighting alongside me.

James and Casey usually got to the hospital around 11 am. Since he spent most of the day here with me, my husband took the mornings to take care of things around the house.

"All the laundry is done," he said, setting Casey in her bassinet beside the window. He leaned in to kiss me good morning, then took off his jacket.

I grinned. In the eight years that we'd been together, James had maybe done laundry once; that was always my thing. My husband cooked, and I cleaned. With me out of the picture and him having to take on the household responsibilities, I was proud of the way he seamlessly fit both roles, on top of taking care of Casey on his own.

"You have an amazing husband," Natasha said, smiling at James. "It's so great that he's here every day with you."

I nodded my head.

Once Natasha left the room, James said he didn't understand what he was doing that was so amazing. "I'm doing what any husband would do for their wife and baby in this situation," he said, squeezing my hand.

I agreed with him. This was typical of James. Before GBS, we were the type of couple that did everything together. I knew there wasn't anywhere else he would rather be than here with me and Casey.

I always waited till James was at the hospital to get up in the chair. Being hoisted in the lift was still quite painful and traumatic, so I made it clear to my nurses that I wouldn't go until he was there to help with the transfer. We'd done it so many times now that he knew how best to minimize my pain.

James held my hand while the nurses rolled my limp body to the side. Their lightest touches were an agony I don't know how I endured. They pulled the sling underneath me, rolled me onto my back, and fastened the canvas sling to the lift. Mom put on my foot splints to stabilize my ankles and keep them from flopping around, yet another thing that caused horrendous pain.

James moved down to the foot of my bed. My RT stood to my left and held onto the tube between my throat and the ventilator. My nurse stood behind me, cupping my head in her hands, so it didn't bobble around. As my body raised in the air, James held his hands under my knees, just below my gown, so my legs wouldn't dangle. I was so anxious and terrified I didn't even bother saying anything when I sometimes realized I wasn't wearing a brief and flashed the entire room.

Mom helped propel my torso upwards and across my bed as we inched towards the blue sofa chair. This process would sometimes cause a hot flash which one time was so severe I fainted. The nurses prepared for this by immediately applying cold cloths across my forehead, chest, and thighs the moment I settled in the chair.

After my temperature cooled, a nurse, RT, James, my mom, Casey, and whatever family member was visiting that day wheeled me out of ICU in my big sofa chair to take a trip to the cafeteria or go outside. The RT was there to roll the ventilator alongside my chair and ensure my breathing stayed under control. The nurse brought along a shot of Gravol, a cold cloth, and a kidney basin for me to throw up in when I inevitably got sick.

Once we were on the main floor, mom stopped at the giftshop window to chat with the lady behind the counter. With her white shoulder-length hair, the older woman would lean her face between the bouquets she was arranging, smile at me, and ask how I felt. I was paralyzed in my chair, my head to the side, breathing on a ventilator, and feeling like death, so I couldn't reply. But her concern was heartening, and I tried to smile back. She always commented on how cute Casey looked. I beamed on the inside as the proud mom I was.

Rolling on through the hospital lobby, we passed kiosks of various things for sale.

"Look at all this cute stuff," Mom said. She stopped pushing my chair to browse through the accessories. "What do you think?" she asked, holding up a sparkly, black purse.

"Or what about these?" James said and pointed to a pair of pink stiletto high heels. My mom and James knew shoes and purses were two of my favorite things to shop for.

It seemed like a strange place to buy fashion accessories. "Let's just go outside," I mouthed, then turned to look out the front doors through my eye patch. The pink stilettos were gorgeous, so was the purse, but I had no desire to shop. I was paralyzed. I lived in a hospital. What the hell did I need purses or shoes for? Seeing things that I couldn't use only reminded me of how depressing my life was.

Back in my ICU bed, after an hour in the chair, we did more range of motion exercises and another round of meds. We spent our afternoons and evenings watching people flip houses and buy real estate in the Caribbean on HGTV, one of the few channels we got.

Casey lay as content as can be in her bassinet or in James' arms while I spent more time throwing up. Sometimes I had a friend or two pop by, though this was becoming fewer and further apart these days. I hated my visitors seeing me heave and in tears and had started to turn them away.

James and Casey left around eight each night. I'd get my evening meds, and Mom would do one last round of 'range,' then she'd brush my teeth. She would chat about how our day went, attempting to bring attention to any positive moments that happened. Sometimes she held the phone up to my ear so I could talk to my brother out of town, which was ridiculous because I couldn't say anything. After that, it was time for bed.

"I hope you have a good sleep tonight," Mom said. She kissed my lips, then tucked the blankets around my paralyzed body. Then she pulled my limp hand into hers, and in a circular motion, she gently massaged each of my fingers, slowly moving down, one joint at a time—just as she did when I was little. It helped calm me for a moment. After Mom finished, she turned off the lights and crawled into the pull-out chair beside my bed.

The sleeping pills did their job well, which I was grateful for. Otherwise, I'm sure my anxiety would have kept me up, trapped with my thoughts for hours. The best nights were those I slept through until morning, but more often than not, I'd wake up feeling sick to my stomach. I'd stick my tongue to the roof of my mouth to cluck to wake up Mom, she'd buzz the nurses, and I'd spend the next few hours vomiting while they held back my hair. Sometimes they'd have to change my brief from a bowel movement I didn't even know I had, which I hated even more than when done during the day. As invasive as it was, now I had two or three nightshift nurses I didn't know shining spotlights between my sprawled legs. They'd clean me, I'd cry, and someone would inject me with Ativan or a top-up of pain meds. When they finished and everyone left the room, I'd fall back into a medicated sleep.

The next morning, we started everything all over again.

To this day, my family says the first weeks in the hospital were the hardest. Unfamiliar with GBS, they didn't know what to expect or if I'd even survive. Now that I was showing signs of improvement, no matter how small they were, the worst seemed to be behind us, at least for them.

For me, this point in the hospital was the hardest. Awake for the entire day now, time slowed to a crawl. Every time I looked up at the clock expecting to see the hours passed, I was met with disappointment and frustration to see it had only been minutes. The ticks of the clock echoed through the room. Every day felt the same as the last. After nearly two months in Intensive care, it was hard to imagine I'd *ever* get out of ICU. Sometimes the thought of lying there for even another hour made me want to scream. Instead, tears rolled down my face.

One morning Mom asked, "Do you want us to do your makeup today? Or Deanne can pluck your eyebrows when she comes to visit later? Maybe that will cheer you up?"

My dark brown eyebrows, generally well-groomed, were growing out of control. But I shook my head. When you are so depressed that you'd rather be dead, you don't care what you look like anymore.

"Mom . . ." I mouthed.

She leaned in close to my face.

"When am I going to get better?" I asked. I just wanted my life to go back to the way it was; to go home and be with my daughter and my husband.

"But, Holly, you are! You're so much better than you were just a few weeks ago."

I leaned my head and puked into the kidney basin resting on my shoulder.

I wasn't getting better. I was living a nightmare I was unable to wake up from. An awful feeling in the pit of my stomach never went away. When you are sick, in pain, struggling, and depressed, nothing matters but feeling better.

Mom wiped my chin, and I looked over at Casey laying in the clear bassinet by the window, kicking her little legs. The bassinet was just like the one from the maternity ward in this same hospital where Casey was born only a few months before.

I remembered being on that ward, where a much smaller Casey lay. On our second night there, our baby began wailing, and I'd crawled out of bed to go to her.

"I'll get her," the nurse said. "You need to rest." The woman gently lifted Casey from the bassinet and into her arms, then slowly rocked her back and forth.

Casey's crying quieted a little.

The nurse made large swooping movements back and forth with her arms.

Casey immediately closed her eyes and stopped crying.

"This little one loves to be rocked," the nurse said with a smile.

Casey loved to be rocked ever since. I watched James rock her back and forth in my ICU room all the time. The larger the half circles, the better.

I took my gaze off Casey in her bassinet to look down at my arms on the bed. Flickering my fingers, I tried to move the rest of my arm, but nothing happened. I couldn't even hold my baby's hand, let alone rock her now. I had no purpose in life except to lay there and be kept alive to make my family happy.

I turned to look at the pictures on the wall, at the person I used to be.

My heart raced. I thought of those people in a vegetative state for twenty years.

My breathing accelerated.

Being on the ventilator was terrifying as it was, but when my anxiety spiked like this, each struggling breath made me claustrophobic. As my breathing shallowed, the walls started to close in on me, and I panicked.

I tried to scream as loud as I could, but no sounds came out as always. Had I not been paralyzed, I would have thrown my arms and legs up in the air, and my body would have gone into violent, thrashing fits. Instead, my arms and legs remained still. I arched my back, or so it felt, then fiercely shook my head back and forth, screaming silently with tears streaming down my face.

"Take everything off the walls!" I tried to scream. Too much was going on around me, with the fuzzy pink feather boas, a massive blue Get Well Soon card, and all the shiny photos on the wall—plus the claustrophobic feeling of everyone in the room at the time.

"It's okay, Hunny," James said, standing up from his seat and taking hold of my hand. "Take deep breaths. You can do this."

Mom started to pull the feather boas off the walls.

"No, I can't!" I tried to shout. *I wish I was fucking dead.*

If only James knew what was going through my mind. I hated that my husband thought I was strong and capable of getting through this. Nobody understood that no, I could not do this anymore.

An injection of Ativan later, and with all the boas off the walls, I began to calm down.

"I'm gonna leave the pictures up if that's okay," my mother asked.

I nodded my head. "Mom," I mouthed. "Can you call Kit again?"

If anyone understood how I felt, it would be him. I'd always been the type of person that fought for solutions to my problems, and despite my anguish, I knew I had to figure out a way to get through this. Maybe Kit could lift my spirits as he had before. Maybe then I could be strong.

The next day, Kit and his wife Tanya graciously came to visit.

"We brought you and Casey some presents," Kit said as he sat down in the chair beside my bed.

Tanya pulled out a baby pink and brown zebra print blankie she'd personally made for Casey. "It's super soft, I made my daughter one too, and she loves it."

Casey was snuggled up beside me in the nursing pillow, and Tanya wrapped the soft blanket around her.

"This one is for you, Holly." Kit held up a handmade sign made of blue scrapbook paper with black words stenciled across it in front of my face. "Angela made me this when I was here."

Like many of the staff in the ICU, Angela, the RT that I pleaded with to let me go, had cared for Kit while he fought for his life in the same room.

I squinted my one eye to read the words on the sign.

Courage does not always roar... It's also the soft voice at day's end, "I'll try again tomorrow.

"We taped it to the wall in front of him for Kit to look at on his bad days," Tanya said. "We want you to have it."

My lip quivered, and I read the sign again.

Courage does not always roar... It's also the soft voice at day's end, "I'll try again tomorrow.

My eyes welled with tears. Kit understood precisely what I was feeling. It was like he knew I needed these words now more than ever. And for the first time in my life, I realized that no, courage doesn't always roar.

Courage isn't always loud and brave. It's not always this superhero of a person eager to face their demons and conquer their battles. Sometimes we *are* terrified. I had to redefine my strength and what that looked like to me. I wasn't weak because I was having panic attacks and wanted to give up and die. I wasn't a phony because I was terrified and skeptical of my future—if I even had one.

I was strong because I was overcoming challenges every day that I thought I never would. I didn't have to *feel* powerful to get through this. All I had to do was get through each day—one day at a time. Sometimes one hour at a time.

And if I couldn't do that, I would just try again tomorrow.

10

Just Breathe

Coming off a ventilator is not what most people think. Patients on life support don't suddenly have the strength to breathe on their own again; respiratory therapists have to gradually wean us off over weeks. About forty percent of the duration of mechanical ventilation is spent weaning. One of the first steps in this process is for the RTs to switch the ventilator to a mode of ventilation called pressure support. Instead of the ventilator mechanically making me breathe, I'd initiate my own breaths, which would trigger the ventilator to deliver support with more air.

The first time I tried it, each breath I took was more challenging than before, and I was terrified I wouldn't be able to breathe— causing a spike in my anxiety. But I persevered and lasted an hour. The second time, my nurse gave me Ativan to take the edge off. It helped a little, and I lasted several hours. Eventually, I discovered that knowing they were switching the ventilator made me anxious, so I asked my RTs to stop telling me when they did. They were always in my room fiddling with the ventilator anyway, so they'd randomly decide to switch me over, then casually leave the room, like they always did. Without knowing, I wasn't as focused on my breathing, and lasted longer and longer until I finally initiated my breaths for twelve hours straight.

After that, I moved on to plugging trials. To do these, the RTs would literally plug the tracheostomy so that I would have to breathe on my own, like normal. To get off life support and have the tube removed from my throat, I had to last forty-eight hours without any help from the machine.

Mike warned me getting to that point would not be easy. “It’ll feel like you’re training for a marathon. These trials over the next several weeks are training to strengthen your lungs.” My respiratory therapists taped a pink piece of paper to the wall with the words *Breathing Olympics* typed across the top, where they’d track how I did.

Even though I was already initiating my breaths with pressure support, it didn’t feel like my lungs were any stronger, certainly not strong enough for this. Breathing was always hard, every minute of every day, and doing it entirely on my own without the help of the machine seemed unattainable to me.

“It will be hard at first. You’ll only last a few minutes, but it will get easier as time goes on,” Mike said. “Let’s give it a try and see how it goes.”

James passed Casey to my stepdad, then stood beside me with my hand in his. Mom stood at the foot of the bed with the video camera in her hand. I wished she would just put the camera away. Most of the time, I paid no attention to it. Other times I hated that my most vulnerable moments, like this, were being filmed.

The RT positioned the valve on my throat, and the machine beside me beeped. “Let us know when you need to come off the valve,” she said while I repeatedly coughed, struggling for air.

I looked forward and took in a deep breath, then another, and another, each inhalation only giving me a tiny puff of air, nothing of substance. A wave of terror washed over me as I gasped for my next breath.

“I can barely breathe,” I tried to say, but like with the other valve, my voice was hardly audible.

"Try to go as long as you can," Mike encouraged.

"What's with your nail polish?" James interrupted, looking down at my feet, trying to distract me.

Mom explained to him how I'd had such severe nerve pain in my right toe earlier that morning, which made me think my toenail was digging into my skin. I'd forced her to take the nail polish off so she could get a better look. My toe was fine.

I took in slow, shallow breaths, fighting for more air from the machine. I felt lightheaded, as if I might faint, but kept breathing in through my nose and out through my mouth. Breathing felt weird and hard to do, but I kept pushing through the irrational fear that I'd die if I didn't catch my next breath. "Hi, Casey," I mouthed to my daughter in Dennis' arms, trying to project my voice and keep my mind off my breath.

Then all of a sudden, my fears started coming true, the air disappeared, and I didn't think I'd be able to take in another breath. "Take me off," I panicked, and the RT rushed to switch the hose. Breathing felt better as soon as I was back on the machine.

Everyone in the room was ecstatic. Mom enthusiastically made a star out of the pink cardstock beside my bed—my first time breathing independently—and taped it to the ceiling. It was hard for me to get excited about breathing on my own for just over one minute, knowing how difficult it was and how much further I still had to go.

That weekend, more improvements came to keep me motivated. The paralysis in my shoulders faded, which gave me the ability to shift my body on my own, making things like switching positions and being changed more manageable, and less painful. The more I could move on my own, the fewer people had to touch me—and the less discomfort I had to deal with. My nausea was less intense that weekend, too, and my nurse took advantage of the fact that I wasn't throwing up to brush out my hair, do my makeup, and shave my legs. I also did my second trial off the ventilator and lasted ten whole minutes. I was proud of myself, even if it was just as hard as before. And not feeling sick for an entire day was an enormous breath of fresh air.

Until Sunday afternoon, when the nausea came back with a vengeance, and I threw up all over myself in bed. I had hoped that *feeling* better was a sign I was *getting* better; feeling sick again was a hard slap in the face saying, see, you're not improving. There's no point in holding on to hope.

My nurses administered as many meds as allowed, but none of them helped, and I vomited throughout the evening.

"I just want to feel better," I cried to my mom. "Can you ask the doctor if I can try another medication?" The next time I felt sick, Kit had recommended I ask the doctors for an anti-nausea med called Nabilone. Kit was a pharmacist who knew all sorts of drugs. Nabilone was a synthetic form of marijuana, usually prescribed to cancer patients sick from chemotherapy.

When mom spoke to the doctor just outside my room about getting different meds, he told her there was nothing he could do for me. He'd already tried Nabilone weeks before when I'd first felt sick.

"Then you go tell her that," Mom had replied. She was tired of always being the one to let me down. I hadn't seen a doctor in weeks, it seemed. I was still in isolation with my bladder infection, so they rarely took the time to gown up and come into my room. Instead, every morning just outside my door, they communicated with my nurses and my mom, who then passed along any new information to me.

The door to my room slid open. "Hi, Holly," Dr. Handsome said as he gowned up and approached my bed. "I know you feel sick, but we already tried Nabilone."

I turned my head to look at my mom.

"One of the other doctors didn't think it was working and took you off," he continued.

This wasn't the first time we'd heard of this happening. The doctors switched off every seven days, so at the beginning of each week, they'd come up with an idea of how to treat me for the various issues I was dealing with.

Then the next doctor came on with a different opinion, and they'd put me on something else.

"Do you know how frustrating this is for us?" my mom told him. "How do we know if a drug will work if we don't let her try it for a while?"

"You're absolutely right," the doctor replied. "Our unit needs to communicate with each other better. I'll talk to the rest of the doctors about working on Holly's treatment together." ICU doctors weren't used to patients being around this long. Because another doctor had taken me off Nabilone, though, he was hesitant to put me back on until they had a chance to speak.

I was desperate and willing to try anything. "Please," I mouthed to the doctor, a tear rolling down my cheek. "I can't keep doing this. Please let me try it."

Seeing me in person must have changed his mind. When I woke up feeling nauseous the following day, the nurse had Nabilone ready to go. She crushed up the pill in the small container, added water, then injected it into the tube in my stomach. I dry heaved immediately when the cool liquid spewed into my body.

An hour later, the sick feeling in my stomach disappeared. Like a dark cloud dissipating and the sun shining again for the first time in forever, I felt peace and calm. I looked at my nurse beside my bed and mouthed, "I think it worked." I felt like a new person. When James and Casey got to the hospital shortly after, I must have had the biggest smile on my face.

"Someone's in a good mood today," James said as he set Casey down in her bassinet.

"I am," I mouthed. "I'm not sick anymore. I got Nabilone."

The nurse rolled the lift into my room, and everyone helped move me to the chair.

"I wanna go outside today," I mouthed. Maybe I'd finally get to enjoy a trip outside, as my vomiting had ruined it so many times before.

"We can do that," James smiled back. It thrilled him to see me in such a great mood.

As we rolled down the ICU hallway, I mouthed "Hi" to every nurse I passed. Each one did a double-take; no one had seen me smile like this before.

We sat outside for over an hour, and I relaxed with the sun shining down on my face. If I had more days like this one, maybe ICU wouldn't be so bad. Sure, I was still paralyzed and struggling to wean off the ventilator, but with my nausea gone, I felt capable of overcoming the hard days and more hopeful about my future. Back in my room, I spent the afternoon in the best mood I'd been in for months.

"It's so nice to see you smiling again," my mom said, placing Casey beside me on my pillow. She bundled her up in the pink and brown blankie Tanya gave us.

I tilted my neck to move my head close to my daughter's. She cooed and wiggled, and I smiled at the funny faces she made. Casey was so adorable; I couldn't believe it. Her beauty was enthralling; I was blessed to have such a beautiful and cheerful little girl. Happiness was something I hadn't experienced in so long; laying with my baby in my bed felt like heaven on earth.

But here's the thing about Nabilone. Even though it's a synthetic version of cannabis, its effects are like the real thing. Because it went through my stomach, it took a while to kick in completely. I went from being happy and smiling to giddy and laughing—as if I smoked too much weed. Hours later, I was suddenly dizzy and paranoid. The vibe was now different, the room sinister like I was in a scary movie.

"I think . . . they gave me too much," I whispered to James, my eyes barely open as the walls spun around me. A wave of nausea rushed over me, and I heaved. "James, I don't feel good. Take Casey off."

Mom pulled my baby off the bed.

"You're probably just sick like you usually are." James nestled the kidney basin under my chin.

"No," I mouthed. My stomach turned, and I gagged again.

What if they gave me too much?

What if I've overdosed?

What if I have to have my stomach pumped again?

My heart rate steadily increased.

"I think it's wearing off," my mom said. "That's why you feel sick again. "We can ask for another dose. It'll help you feel better."

I vigorously shook my head. The drug was not wearing off. I'd only eaten edibles once in my life—a batch of weed brownies James made for us in our early twenties—and this feeling of sick panic was the same. What started innocently with the giggles in our living room ended with my face turning a shade of green and me throwing up all over our kitchen floor. At least this time, I had something to throw up into. Just like last time, my vomit even smelled like weed, though I might have been imagining it.

"But you were in such a good mood today. I think you should try another dose," mom said.

I shook my head. I did not need more. Even though we just convinced the doctor to try this drug again, I didn't like it. "I don't want anymore," I mouthed, turning my head to the side and closing my eyes.

The drug eventually wore off, and I went back to my usual nauseated, sober self. Whenever I was throwing up more than usual, a nurse suggested trying Nabilone again, but I refused every time. The experience had traumatized me.

It took a long time, but we all now laugh about the Nabilone experience—the time I got way too high from synthetic weed.

The paralysis in my upper body continued to fade over the next several days. One day I could turn my hand slightly. The next, I was able to lift my arm above my bed and wave, or at least flap my hand back and forth. The day after, I held my head up on its own, even on the lift transfers to the chair. This made things even easier, and I no longer needed both James and my mom to help with the move.

I was still on a lot of Ativan; between pressure support, NIF tests, and breathing trials, my lungs were getting a brutal workout each day—which made breathing terrifying. But I was initiating my own breaths for over sixteen hours a day and lasting twelve minutes breathing on my own. Things were looking up.

When I look back on those days, though things were difficult, there are some wonderful memories. I remember my girlfriend Karen from high school coming to visit; she had recently had a baby, and when she held him above my bed, he looked at me and smiled his first smile. It melted my heart.

Another significant memory is when two of my nurses tried to cheer me up by speaking in different accents, telling no one in the room first. One spoke with a Scottish accent, the other with a Jamaican one, and I giggled as they went through my range of motion exercises in their thick fake accents. Then they switched to Australian and Indian, then British and French. Some of their attempts were pretty good, but some were terrible, which only made it funnier. I laughed hard, even if it was silent.

That same day, James took a black sharpie and drew a detailed eye, eyelashes, and all, on my eye patch. "You've been missing your other eye for too long," he said. "Let's see how long it takes for your nurses to notice." When James showed me in the handheld mirror, I burst out laughing. I looked ridiculous. The next time the nurses came in, neither one of us said anything.

"We're going to check your vitals," the nurse said, looking straight at the monitor beside me. "How's your pain? Do you need a top of meds?" The other nurse focused on the monitor as well.

I looked at James and smirked. "Pain is at a three. I'm good," I mouthed with a chuckle.

Both nurses turned my way and saw the drawn-on eye.

"What the heck is that?!" the nurse screamed. The other nurse fell to her knees in hysterics. "You have another eye again!" She said from the ground. Laughter filled the room.

When you haven't laughed in months, these moments felt incredible.

As for the eye patch, James tried to encourage me to go without it. I'd been wearing it for weeks as anytime I had it off for even a moment, I'd see double of everything, get nauseated, and ask to have it put back on. Like the range of motion exercises on my left arm that bumped the tube, I tried to avoid anything that might make me sick.

James thought depending on the patch was making my double vision worse, and my doctor agreed. My eyes needed to work together again, so he recommended I take off the patch for small increments each day. I could do it while I did my breathing trials. As I increased my time off the ventilator, I could also increase my time without the patch.

The first time we did it, I was aiming for fifteen minutes.

Mike adjusted the valve on my trach as James pulled back the tape and took the patch off my eye.

Immediately there were two of everything in the room, and my head spun, but I was more concerned with my breathing. I slowly inhaled, then exhaled, then quickly inhaled again. It felt extra difficult today.

"So . . . hard . . ." I whispered to my mom beside my bed, gasping for air.

I inhaled and exhaled again. My heart pounded in my chest.

I don't know if I can do this, I thought.

I struggled for air but kept going, inhaling, then exhaling repeatedly, hitting five minutes, then ten. It felt as if I was running. At the twelve-minute mark, I was so out of breath I didn't think I could go any longer. Mike reminded me my goal was fifteen minutes, so I pushed through the pain of feeling like my lungs were about to burst, constantly looking at the 'Courage' sign in front of me.

As soon as the clock hand hit the quarter-hour, I looked to Mike, and the color quickly drained from my face, alerting him I was done.

He understood and leaned over to take off the valve.

James put the eye patch back on, and I started to cry.

"What's wrong, Holly?" he asked. "You did fifteen minutes! Off both the ventilator and the eyepatch."

"That was so hard . . ." I mouthed. "I can barely . . . breathe." I closed my eyes, out of breath and defeated.

"It will get easier," Mike reminded me. "As your lungs get stronger, you'll last for longer periods. Today was a tough one. Your progress won't be linear. Some days will be better than others."

I understood what he meant, but how was I supposed to last forty-eight hours if I could barely last fifteen minutes now? At this rate, it would be months before I'd get off life support. Even then, would I be able to breathe normally? Or would it still feel like I was sprinting, constantly fighting for more air? In my mind, I couldn't imagine being able to breathe without that machine. I knew the longer I needed the ventilator, the longer I'd be in the ICU.

It was hard to stay optimistic.

After the RTs left the room, I looked toward the sign in front of me that read:

Courage does not always roar... It's also the soft voice at day's end, "I'll try again tomorrow.

With tears in my eyes, I repeated the sentence in my head: I will try again tomorrow.

And the next day, I did.

I was half-hearted about doing the trial when the RT asked if I was up for it. My mom, who rarely left the hospital, went home to nap for the first time in months. Other than James and Casey, I had no other family or friends visiting that day. With my nausea mild, my RT convinced me to go through with the trial, anyway. Every missed session only prolonged my dependence on the machine, she told me. I had to at least try.

The nurse removed my eye patch, James held my hand, and the respiratory therapist put the valve on my trach.

I took in a deep breath, and the RT stepped back from my bed. When I looked over at James, I immediately noticed only one of him standing beside my bed. The double vision was gone. I inhaled, then exhaled, my lungs filling up with a breath of air. I breathed in and out again—another full breath.

Breathing was different this time, already.

It was a challenge, but it didn't feel as unattainable as the day before. This wasn't like running; this was more like a brisk walk.

Maybe they were right. My lungs and my eyes were already getting stronger.

Could I really do this? When three minutes passed, then ten, then fifteen, my achievement shocked me.

"Awesome job, Babe!" my husband said.

"You want to stay on?" the RT asked.

I nodded my head. "I'm good," I mouthed. I wanted to see how long I could last.

James suggested we watch TV to help distract me for the rest of the trial.

"I'll be right outside," the RT said to my husband. "Just let me know when she's ready to come off." The RT slid the door closed behind her.

We watched back-to-back episodes of *Love it or List it*, and for an hour, the beautiful house designs took my mind off my breath. Though I could hardly believe it when it finished, I wanted to keep going on the valve.

"I'm still good," I mouthed to James. And I was barely nauseous, just a little dizzy.

"Why don't you get up in the chair, and we go downstairs. To pass the time," he said.

That sounded like a great idea. Once the nurses hoisted me in, James laid Casey sideways on the pink nursing pillow on my lap, and we headed down to the lobby.

James grabbed a saran-wrapped sandwich from the hospital cafeteria, and we sat at one of the tables. My nurse and RT moved to a table nearby to give us some time alone. This was the first time we'd been out together—our little family of three. Before my hospitalization, other than to meet up with friends and a lunch date with my grandpa and cousin when Casey was first born, we hadn't left the house much.

Without the eye patch on for the first time in the cafeteria, I observed more around me. Doctors, nurses, patients, and their families filled the hall. Many people were looking at us, at me specifically, paralyzed in my chair in a hospital gown—our tiny baby resting on the pillow on my lap. Maybe I was being paranoid.

Did they feel sorry for us? I certainly did. We shouldn't be spending our time together in a hospital. It wasn't fair this was happening when we'd barely begun our new lives as a family. Nonetheless, it was a treat to spend time with James and Casey. Our trip down the elevator and to the hospital cafeteria was our version of the first time going out to eat as a family, and it meant something to me—even if James was the only one eating and did most of the talking. We sat and chatted for a bit longer, then headed back upstairs.

"I still feel fine," I mouthed to my respiratory therapist as James rolled me past her into my room.

"I'm glad you're doing so well," the RT said with a smile. "But we don't want you to push too hard, and it set you back. Why don't we call it a day?"

I was good with that.

"You breathed on your own for two hours and forty-five minutes," the RT said as she removed the valve.

I smiled at James, then looked down at my baby girl cuddled up on the pillow on my lap.

Two hours and forty-five minutes. It wasn't as hard this time.

It was in this moment, I believed I would breathe on my own again. I had faith that I would get back to life with my family. I just had to keep going, keep trying.

After this, I never wore the eye patch again.

*

On Day 60, two months of being in the hospital, Dr. Yousef came by my room to talk about the results of my EMG (electromyography) test. This test measures how fast an electrical impulse can travel through nerves. The results would show how much damage was in my nervous system and could help predict how long my recovery might be. The test itself was done a few days prior and was a horrific experience. Dr. Yousef had stuck needles in my arms and legs that sent shocks through my body as if I was being electrocuted. Even with a heavy top-up of Dilaudid, I cried in pain.

Standing at the foot of my bed, Dr. Yousef glanced down at his notes, then said, "Things don't look very good."

A sick feeling grew in my stomach.

"The nerves in your arms are regenerating, which is why you're regaining movement. But there's no activity in the nerves in your legs,"

My eyes quickly turned to James, and we exchanged blank stares. Then I looked back to Dr. Yousef as he continued.

"In my professional opinion, it will be at least two years before she walks again."

I looked back at my mom with Casey in her arms. I knew how dire my situation was and had plenty of doubts that I'd ever get better again. But deep down, a part of me hoped that one day soon I'd wake up, my legs would be moving again, and I'd just hop out of bed—and leave this place.

Dr. Yousef's words shattered that hope. It felt like every time I'd start to believe I'd make it through this nightmare, something pulled me back into despair, certain I never would.

I stared back at Dr. Yousef in the bright yellow gown that covered his designer suit, not sure what to even say.

He changed the subject and talked about my nausea. "I don't think it's GBS that's making you sick. That's not a normal symptom of GBS," he said accusingly. "I'd like for you to have another MRI, just to make sure nothing is going on in your brain."

My eyes filled with tears, then I broke down.

It wasn't the news that I might not walk for two years that broke me. It was the thought of squeezing into that tiny MRI machine again. I couldn't do it. Hadn't I been through enough pain and suffering already? I was over being traumatized. In the back of my mind, I thought about Kit telling me how he had been nauseous too, possibly from all the meds, and nothing was wrong with his brain.

"No," I mouthed and shook my head.

Dr. Yousef stared back at me without blinking. "And why is that?" he asked, turning to my mother.

She explained how claustrophobic I was; how I had a severe panic attack the last time I went inside the MRI machine.

"I can ask if we can put her under anesthesia, so she's not awake for the procedure." Dr. Yousef turned to me. "In the end, it's your choice if you want to go through with it or not." He stared at me like I was an idiot for not considering it.

I nodded my head and mouthed, "I'll think about it."

Later, my ICU doctor told me it was doubtful they'd put me out for a simple MRI. I imagine the cost and resources to put me under wouldn't have been approved. Something we as Canadians rarely think of, but I suppose, given the amount of time I'd been in the ICU, it would have been a topic of discussion for those who made financial decisions in the hospital.

"Then you can tell Dr. Yousef I'm not doing the MRI," I mouthed to my mom.

I was growing tired of everyone else making my decisions for me.

I wanted to be in control for once.

I later found out that while nausea can be uncommon in GBS, it most certainly does still occur.

Around this time, my pain was at a manageable two to three on the pain scale, and my nausea improved slightly. I wanted Casey close to me again. As soon as James got to the hospital in the morning, I had him and the nurses transfer me into the chair and recline me all the way back. Mom wrapped Casey in the striped nursing blankets friends gave me at my baby shower, then nestled her onto the pink nursing pillow on my lap.

I stared into her eyes and smiled. Casey was a well-fed baby; all that formula was plumping her up now. She had neck and arm rolls, and her cheeks were getting bigger and rounder. My three-month-old was growing. She could hold her head up completely on her own and was starting to make different noises with her mouth. She was smiling more often. Casey was also becoming even more observant than before, and I noticed she loved to stare up at the neon pink stars above my bed as if she were trying to read them.

April 9th – Movement in arms and fingers

April 18th – Lifted head off the bed

Wanting my daughter's attention, I stuck my tongue to the roof of my mouth and loudly clucked. Resting on the nursing pillow on my lap, Casey turned her gaze from the ceiling to look at me. She stared with squinted eyes, looking at the yellow cloth fastened across my forehead with a headband. Then she focused her eyes on the tubes coming out of my neck.

I clucked again, then stuck my tongue out at her.

She stared back at my face, squinting with curiosity, trying to figure out where the sound had come from.

I pushed my tongue out of my mouth again, then watched as her mouth moved around, her lips opening, then closing as if she might try to copy me.

I stuck out my tongue again.

This time, Casey's little tongue poked out through her lips.

"She's doing it!" my mom said with delight.

We did this back and forth for a few minutes, sticking out our tongues at one another. Mom laughed every time my baby mimicked me. Casey was our guardian angel, bringing laughter and joy to such a dark time. Mom, James, and all the nurses were always laughing and smiling at the various things she did, like the time my stepdad Dennis loosely tied a balloon to her foot when she was in her bassinet, and she spent over forty-five minutes kicking her feet like crazy to make it move.

I could tell my mom adored being a grandma—or nana, as she asked to be called just before Casey was born. Mom held her grandbaby in her arms and talked to her all the time. "Your mommy is going to get better soon," she said in her high-pitched baby voice. "Then she will take care of you again."

I wanted that to be true. I wanted out of this hellhole and for us to spend time as a family outside these four walls. My mom had been staying with me at the hospital for two months now. We had hopes and dreams together, too. When I had called my mom just after my ultrasound to tell her I was having a little girl, my mom had cried tears of joy. It meant even more to her that I would have a daughter one day, too, and we couldn't wait to do mother-daughter things, the three of us together.

With Dr. Yousef's comment that I would not walk for two years in the back of my mind, I tried to imagine what my future as a mom would even look like. I thought about my daughter's first birthday, which wasn't that far away. Would I be in a wheelchair for her birthday party? Would I be out of the hospital? Would I even be able to attend?

Then my mind raced. What if the worst happened? What if I don't make it out of this alive? Despite my improvements, I was still on life support in intensive care. People die in the hospital every day. What if I didn't make it? Then what would life be like for my daughter?

I tried to picture Casey as a little girl without a mom, though it was hard to visualize what she would even look like. I knew she'd be in great hands with James. But would Casey know how much I prayed for her before she was born, how much I loved and adored her, even though we weren't together long? I hoped James would explain all that to her. I hoped she'd understand that she meant everything to me, even though I'd only known her a few months.

It broke my heart to imagine Casey growing up without me. I was fortunate to have both my parents. My cousin Spencer lost his mother to lung cancer when he was sixteen; I remembered the pain we all felt for him, especially two years later on his graduation day, when he received his high school diploma without his mom there to see. I didn't want my daughter to go through that. I needed to be there to console her when she had her first broken heart, when she walked across the stage to graduate, and to dance with her at her wedding.

Looking up at the *Courage doesn't always roar sign* in front of my bed, I knew I had to fight to get back to being the mother my baby deserved. I had to be there for Casey's first birthday and her first day of school.

The next time I was up in the chair, with my hands growing stronger, we figured out a way to cock my wrist up against Casey's bottle in her mouth. With her snuggled on my lap, I fed my daughter again for the first time. "I will take care of her again," I said to myself while Casey reached out her finger to touch mine. I fluttered my fingers back. "Who is Dr. Yousef to say I won't walk for two years?" I wanted to prove him wrong and get back to raising my baby. So, for the first time since being hospitalized, I prayed. I prayed to God to please let me get better and walk before my daughter did. I wasn't a religious person; I hadn't attended church regularly since I was a child, but I was spiritual and had a solid connection to my faith. When I was eight, I read my entire Precious Moments Bible and prayed all the time. Since being diagnosed with GBS, I'd been so angry I refused to pray for months. But deep down, I still believed in the power of prayer. I prayed to God I would walk again and get to show my daughter how hard I fought to get back to her.

That same day, for one of my breathing trials, I lasted six hours and forty-five minutes. I sat in the chair for most of it, and it was lovely to have the ventilator all the way across the room from me.

"You are doing amazing," Mike said. "When you can breathe on your own for an entire day, then you'll try doing it overnight. And once you're breathing on your own again, Holly—once you've done it for forty-eight hours straight, the trach will come out, and you will get out of ICU."

His words 'Out of ICU' echoed in my mind.

I knew I had a long way to go, but maybe, just maybe, I was seeing the light at the end of the tunnel.

Mom proposed I set a goal of when I hoped to be out of there by. "That will give you something to work towards," she said.

Still needing to last over forty hours straight, it was hard for me to guess when that might be.

"What about . . . Mother's Day," my mom suggested, as she lifted my right arm straight up in the air for my range of motion exercises. Mother's Day was fourteen days away. "That will give you two more weeks of practice off the ventilator. And getting out of ICU for Mother's Day would be the best gift—for the both of us."

I nodded my head. I wasn't sure I could get there in two weeks, but I promised to keep the date in the back of my mind and work towards it.

"Your right arm is getting so strong," Mom said as I pushed against her with the bit of strength I had. She gently lay my arm on the bed, then moved down to my legs, lifting each one slowly.

I visualized pushing as hard as I could, using every ounce of strength I had in me, as I always did for 'range.'

"One more time," mom said with her hand on my ankle, extending my leg up off the bed.

I clenched my body and pushed.

This time, I felt something different—a flutter.

Mom's eyes grew wide. "Did you feel that?" she asked. She wrapped her hand around the bottom of my leg. "Push against me."

I breathed in, then pushed with all my might.

Another flutter from my leg, a tiny vibration so faint we wouldn't have seen it with our eyes.

But we both felt it. The muscle was contracting in my right shin.

"Holly! Your leg! It's moving!" Mom screamed.

11

Fighting for Happiness

Communication between the brain and muscle is critical when working on regaining strength. Consciously and deliberately squeezing your muscles when you exercise, something called mind-to-muscle connection, gets your nervous system to send signals to call upon more muscle fibers for the task—even though my body was still paralyzed, and the muscles weren't yet able to move. The range of motion exercises we were doing in the ICU was helping, even if it didn't feel like it in the moment. The tiny flicker Mom and I felt in my shin meant the nerves *were* regenerating. Maybe the paralysis in my legs would fade, after all. There was hope I might walk sooner than my neurologist said, and this unexpected blessing brought a smile to my face.

Mom brushed my teeth, washed my face, and then bundled the covers around me that same night. "Why do you think after all this time, after everything Dr. Yousef said about you not walking for two years, that your leg started to move again?" she asked.

Mom was always encouraging me to look for a deeper reason.

"Because I prayed," I mouthed back with confidence. My family and friends had been praying for me for months, but I believe God was waiting to hear from me.

Knowing what I now know about EMGs (from neurologists that specialize in GBS) is that they should never be used to decide whether someone will walk again. EMGs are helpful to understand how the regeneration of the nerves work, but while they may show muscles taking a long time to reconnect, that doesn't mean someone will not walk again.

In my time talking with other survivors over the years, I've learned that many have poor EMG results, like me, yet recovered completely. I've heard some tests showing normal function, but the patient remains in a wheelchair. There is still so much that neurologists don't understand about Guillain-Barre Syndrome, and it's not always possible for them to know what will happen. Doctors do their best, but sometimes they're wrong. I'm glad I took Dr. Yousef's comments with a grain of salt and didn't let it break my spirit. I can't imagine how many people stop fighting because a doctor told them there was little hope.

Something else I learned that I didn't know is that ICU patients can sometimes feel thirsty, despite being sufficiently hydrated from the tube feed through the stomach. Second to shortness of breath, thirst is documented as the most distressing symptom experienced in the ICU. I was lucky not to feel thirsty for the first two months; then, suddenly, I had this intense longing to drink something.

"I need water—" I begged my nurses. "I'm soooo thirsty," I mouthed. Because of the trach in my throat, I wasn't ever allowed to drink anything. Instead, the nurses stuck foam mouth swabs soaked in water in my mouth to dampen my tongue and cheeks. At first, that didn't help until I figured out I could suck on the swab, and a tiny drop of water would trickle down my throat.

"Again," I'd mouth to James. He handed me swab after swab, and I sucked out the water from the foam, the refreshing droplets only making me want more. "Again, please," I asked. Eventually, I convinced James to dip the swabs in Sprite, the syrupy sweetness tasting like pure bliss on my tongue.

"She can't be sucking on those," one of my ICU doctors said when he learned what I was doing. "It's fine to dampen her mouth with the swabs, but because her throat is obstructed from the trach, swallowing fluid is dangerous. If she accidentally breathes in the liquid instead of swallowing it, it can go into her lungs and lead to aspiration pneumonia." I was doing so well on my ventilator trials—pneumonia would limit my ability to do them. "If she can't do her trials, it'll lengthen her time in the ICU."

I nodded my head and agreed to stop. That is until the feeling of thirst came back. When you feel like you're in a desert about to die, you'll do anything for a drink.

"Please . . . water . . ." I pleaded with my family. My parched mouth needed fluid to flow down my throat and rejuvenate my body. To me, it was a matter of life or death.

Mom, standing beside my bed, shook her head. "Not until your trach is out."

I stared at her in disbelief, my eyebrows furrowed. Getting off the ventilator was weeks away—if I was lucky. It was ludicrous for her to expect me to survive that long without drinking anything. Though my voice of reason tried to remind me, I'd already lasted eight weeks.

Feeling desperate, the next time Mike came in to see me, I asked him if he could do anything for me. "If I promise not to swallow, can I have a popsicle to suck on or ice chips to chew?" I carefully articulated my words, so he'd understand. I knew there were ice chips here, somewhere. I'd munched on them when I was in labor with Casey.

"No, I'm sorry," Mike said beside my bed.

Frustrated, I looked down. "If you expect me to run a marathon, I should be allowed to have a drink," I mouthed.

He tried not to laugh at my reasoning. But he could not help me. Both a popsicle and ice chips could still cause fluid to get in my lungs if I breathed them in. "It's not worth the risk," he said.

Maybe to him, it wasn't. I continued to beg my mom and James for swabs to suck on, convincing them every so often when no one else was around. The two of them were nervous about the risk, but I knew they'd do any small thing to make me happy. After my mom brushed my teeth, I also realized that she used a hose, similar to a dentist, to give me water to swish around my mouth. Previously, I'd spat it out into a cup, but I decided to swallow it instead with how thirsty I was. When the refreshing cold water dripped down my throat, my mouth curled into a grin.

"What did you just do?" Mom asked, holding the cup close to my mouth. "Did you swallow the water?"

I smiled mischievously, showing my teeth without saying a thing.

Mom burst out laughing and set the cup down on the tray beside me. "Your smile looks as guilty as a Cheshire Cat," she laughed. "But you can't be doing that," she changed her voice to sound stern. "You don't want to get fluid in your lungs."

I nodded my head again, pretending to agree. I was stubborn, in my twenties, and figured the worst would never happen to me (even though it already had), so I continued swallowing small amounts of water whenever she rinsed out my mouth. Though I'd save just enough in my cheeks to spit out into the cup, I'm sure she knew what I was doing, considering I asked her to brush my teeth several times a day for a while. My mom would do anything to make me feel better.

*

The days passed, some slower than others, and before we knew it, it was almost Easter. Mom insisted we do something different, something special. Traditionally James and I got together with our families for turkey, so with the help of the ICU staff, Mom planned a dinner in one of the hospital courtyards. She invited James' parents and his aunt and grandma to join my parents and brothers for supper. I'd get up in my blue sofa chair in my finest hospital gown, and everyone would bring a dish. Mom was excited about the dinner and couldn't stop talking about it in the days leading up to it.

"It's going to be a perfect day."

I was nervous. My nausea was so unpredictable, and I had no idea how I'd be feeling. Fortunately, I woke up on Easter Sunday and felt okay. Once the nurses hoisted me into my chair, Mike set me up on the valve to not have to wheel the ventilator downstairs. My breathing trials were going well, and I now lasted more than half the day without the ventilator. With Casey on the pink and green checkered pillow on my lap, we rolled down to the cafeteria, then outside, where picnic tables were on a concrete pad. My parents, brothers, James's parents, and his aunt Connie and grandmother arrived a little while later. It was a gorgeous day, the sun was shining, and although the exterior hospital walls surrounded me, I smelled spring in the air.

"I hear your leg is starting to move!" Connie said to me with a smile. She scooped Casey out of my lap and took a seat at the table. "Don't worry, Holly. You'll be kicking your legs again in no time."

I smiled and watched her squeeze my baby's cheeks. I sure hoped so.

But the thing about going through hard times is that your view on the situation can flicker between positivity, skepticism, and disbelief from one moment to the next. Some days I convinced myself I was strong enough to get through this. I'd already survived so much. Other times I'd lost all hope.

When my mom unwrapped the homemade turkey and mashed potatoes that looked exactly as I remembered from years past, the smell instantly made me gag. Not that anything ever smelled good to me; some days were so bad I made James take his food and eat in the cafeteria. I don't know why I thought this would be different. My stomach twisted at the smell of rotten food that wasn't rotten, and I immediately turned my head to vomit on my shoulder. My nurse rushed over and placed the kidney basin under my chin, and I threw up again. Mom came over to wipe my face while my nurse injected me with Gravol.

"Hopefully, that will tide you over for dinner," my nurse said—and the medication did help for a little while.

Mom sat back down at the table and thanked everyone for coming. Every person took the hand of those next to them, and James put mine in his." Holly is showing signs of improvement," Mom said. "And we are so grateful. It means so much to have everyone at the hospital together for Easter," she continued. "Now, let's eat! You guys start first. I'll take Casey."

James' aunt passed my daughter over to my mom, and she bounced her up and down on her knee. Casey smiled her big happy grin—and everyone beamed. I looked down at my limp arms which could hardly stay up against Casey's bottle. I wished I could bounce my baby like that. All I could do was sit paralyzed in my chair and watch the two of them bond. Then everyone passed the various dishes around the table, pouring soda cans from the vending machines into Styrofoam cups the nurses had supplied. Even if it smelled gross, what I wouldn't give to enjoy food and drinks again.

My lip quivered. Yeah, a muscle in my leg had moved, and I was pleased about that, but right now, I couldn't do anything with what felt like a tiny twitch in my shin.

My eyes filled with tears, and I turned my head to hide my growing sorrow.

I sat in my usual silence while the conversations flowed around me—mostly about my daughter and how much she'd grown. Then halfway through everyone's dinner, nausea returned. My nurse held back my hair while I threw up into the basin, again and again, the bile burning my mouth and nose. I caught Connie's eyes on me out of the corner of my eye, and she quickly turned away. I sensed her pity, an emotion I felt from most people when they looked at me. I knew people felt terrible for me, but they couldn't possibly understand. People always surrounded me, but I was deeply alone. My emotions hit me like a wave, and tears welled up in the corner of my eyes. This time I couldn't stop them from falling down my cheeks.

"Take me back to my room," I mouthed to my mom while my nurse wiped my chin.

Mom stood from the table and crouched beside my chair. "But you haven't opened your Easter presents yet. And we're almost done eating," she stated.

"I don't care. Take me back, now." I couldn't sit any longer and pretend to be happy. I couldn't watch everyone eat their meals as if nothing was wrong when everything was. Tears poured down my cheeks.

James set his plastic cutlery on the paper plate in front of him and stood from his chair.

"I'll take her upstairs," my mom said to James. "You guys' finish eating."

Along with Mike and the nurse, we rolled back up to the ICU on the second floor. I know my mom was only trying to cheer me up, but the meal had done the opposite. We hadn't even made it to the doors of the ICU when another wave of nausea rushed over me. I vomited in the kidney basin, and Mike pulled my chair to the side as people walked by.

Was this what my life had become?

Me throwing up again and again while everyone else walked on by, living their lives? Would I ever get to enjoy a meal again? A drink? Time with my family? Would I ever bounce my daughter on my knee? My tears turned into hysterical sobs.

"Things will get better," Mike said, leaning down in front of my chair. "It's just going to take a bit more time."

I was so sick of people saying that to me. Maybe because time was taking forever, or perhaps because a part of me struggled to believe it.

When we got back to my room, while the nurses hoisted me with the lift back in bed, Mom ran downstairs to finish her meal and help tidy up. When she got back, she said everyone was done and would come up and see me. "That should cheer you up, "Mom said.

"No," I mouthed sternly and shook my head. "I wanna be alone."

"Okay . . . how about just your dad and your brothers then?"

"No," I repeated. I had turned away many friends over the last few weeks, even Deanne once or twice, but this was the first time I turned away my family. A few minutes later, James came into my room, and I again burst into tears.

"I can't do this anymore!" I silently screamed. My husband came close to my bed and intertwined my hand in his.

Mom slid the glass door closed for privacy while I sobbed. "Tell us what's on your mind."

I explained to her and James by mouthing words that the meal was not fun for me. I couldn't enjoy it the way they could; it wasn't the same experience. They smiled, and they laughed while I vomited and cried.

"Okay, what else," Mom asked, the way she always did when trying to get me to open up.

I told them how angry I was at what my life had become, that my chance at being a mother, something I had wanted my entire life, had been stolen away. It was torture for me to watch everyone around me hold my child in their arms. She was *my* baby. I had grown her in my belly for over nine months. She was mine. I was growing resentful of my family—that they could raise my baby, walk around, eat and drink and live their lives while I was stuck wearing diapers and fed through a tube.

James and my mom stood silently at the side of my bed while I cried.

"I just don't understand what I did to deserve this," I whispered, looking down at my limp body on the bed.

"But your breathing is getting stronger, Holly," Mom said. "You're so close to getting the trach out. Then you'll get out of ICU. Things will get better."

I slowly shook my head back and forth. 'No," I mouthed between sobs. "You don't understand. Getting the trach out isn't going to solve my problems. I'll still be sick and throwing up all the time. I won't be able to walk. And I won't be a real mother to my baby girl." Saying it out loud, though I couldn't actually say it, made me realize that the goal of getting out of the ICU didn't mean much to me.

I'd still be in the hospital. I still wouldn't be raising my child.

My cries intensified, and my breathing quickened into a full-blown panic attack. I wanted to scream, but I couldn't make a sound. I wanted to thrash my body, to punch and kick and jump out of bed and just run away. Of course, my body defied me and stayed completely still, my heart rate spiking. I arched my back and violently shook my head back and forth, the only thing I could do.

"Let's put her back on the ventilator," Mike said when he came in to check on me; the nurse must have called for him. Mom and James stepped to the side, and he removed the valve to change out the tube. The nurse injected a dose of Ativan into my IV, and I stopped crying, at least out loud.

After Mike and my nurse left, Mom sat down beside my bed and held my hand. She massaged my fingers, slowly moving down each joint. At first, I stared at the 'Courage' sign on the wall in front of me, then I closed my eyes and sighed, feeling Mom's comfort and love.

I wish I knew how to keep going, how to just try again tomorrow. But at this moment, emotionally shattered, I couldn't do it anymore.

It's hard to keep going when you are in the darkness of life's challenges, more so if you're dealing with depression. It's challenging to acknowledge when you're actually making progress along the way. We tend to focus on our end goals, telling ourselves we won't be content until we achieve that goal. I think subconsciously, I had already decided that I wasn't better until I was back at home with Casey. Until that happened, I could not be happy.

It didn't help the situation when the mild tingling pain in my body intensified, sending electric shocks through my limbs. Dr. Yousef said the increase in nerve pain (also called peripheral neuropathy) was likely because my nerves were regenerating—this was a good sign.

"We're going to put her on a drug called Gabapentin," my ICU doctor said to James and my mom.

Gabapentin, and a similar medication Lyrica, are the two most common drugs used to combat neuropathy pain in GBS. While generally quite effective for pain relief, they have various side effects, including drowsiness (and dizziness, nausea, and weight gain). Shortly after my 9 am injection, I fell into a deep sleep, napping through my exercises and not even noticing when James and Casey arrived just before lunch. The nurses still got me up in the chair, during which I briefly opened my eyes while they got me in and out of the lift, then promptly fell back asleep for the rest of the day. I woke up for a minute or two that evening after they moved me back into bed. James kissed me goodbye, and then I slept until morning. Mom was a little worried as I hadn't been that sedated since the beginning, but the drowsiness diminished after I slept for nearly twenty-four hours straight. Gabapentin worked well for me, and the neuropathy improved over time.

Shortly after starting the medication, though not related, my respiratory therapist noticed increased secretions coming through whenever she suctioned my trach. They explained it meant I might have an excess of mucus stuck in my airways and lungs that would need to be cleared. A physical therapist used a small vibrating machine against my chest in hopes of releasing the mucus. My doctor ordered an immediate bronchoscopy—a procedure that allowed them to examine the inside of my lungs to see how bad it was.

"We'll insert a thin tube with a light and a camera on the end through your trach to take a look," Dr. Yang said.

They wanted to shove a tube into the hole in my throat and down into my lungs. Flashbacks of the NG tube being rammed up my nose to pump my stomach came rushing back, which then triggered memories of the plasmapheresis tube slicing through the vein in my thigh. I'd become terrified of all medical procedures, fearful of further torture and pain.

"I don't want to do it," I mouthed to the doctor with tears in my eyes. The thought of the bronchoscopy spiked my heart rate.

"Don't worry. It will be uncomfortable, but it won't be painful." Dr. Yang rested his hand on mine. "We'll give you plenty of Ativan before."

His reassurance did not help. By the time he came back that afternoon for the procedure, my anxiety had skyrocketed even after a heavy dose of Ativan. I could hardly catch my breath, and my body shook in fear. When the doctor leaned in towards me with the tube in his hand and saw my teeth chattering, he finally understood how petrified I was.

"Alright," he said, placing the tube down on the tray beside my bed. "Let's just get you some anesthetic and put you under."

I sighed a breath of relief that I wouldn't be awake for the procedure. At the same time, that made it even more frightening.

"You're gonna be okay, Babe," James said. "It's a minor procedure."

That didn't ease my worry. A minor procedure had almost killed me.

When the nurse returned with the drugs, James and my mom moved toward the end of the bed. "We'll be right here when you wake up," said Mom.

As soon as the anesthesia surged through the IV in my arm, my eyelids felt heavy, and I readily closed them. I reopened them to quickly look at James and my mom at the foot of my bed. I was scared, yet they stood there with big smiles on their faces.

"That wasn't so bad, was it?" Mom asked.

I turned my head to look at the doctor.

He smiled and backed away from my bed. "Your lungs look pretty good," he said

The nurse tidied the tray beside me.

"It's done?" I mouthed.

"That's it," he said. "You did great." Dr. Yang left the room.

It felt as if I'd literally blinked, and the procedure was over. It turns out I'd been out for fifteen minutes.

*

Though still dealing with pain from time to time and unpredictable nausea and vomiting, the strength in my body improved a little every day. Whenever my mom did my range of motion exercises, she felt my legs pushing back a tiny bit, even if they weren't moving yet. My arms were moving a lot, albeit flimsily, but I was figuring out how to better position my palm against Casey's bottle. Feeding her was the one thing I could do for her now, which made me proud.

To help strengthen my hands, my physical therapists brought me various items to play around with—a pink foam block, similar to a stress ball, to squeeze as hard as I could, and small, plastic orange cones to stack. I could barely do either. The foam felt like rock-hard cement in my hand, and my arm shook as though I had Parkinson's, so I couldn't even get the cones on top of each other. At first, I tried to do the exercises every day but eventually gave up. All they did was discourage me.

My lung strength, on the other hand, improved drastically. My NIF's were at −20cm H20, close to the −45 that would be considered normal for someone my age. And on Day 68, when I lasted thirteen hours straight breathing on my own, something profound inside told me, "You've got this now. Keep going." I may have said that getting out of ICU wouldn't improve things, but it seems a big part of me wanted to fight and see.

The following day, before the sun was even up, I mouthed the words "Get my RT" to my mom. With only so many hours in a day, and if I wanted to last off the ventilator as long as possible before bed, I had to start early. "Put me on the valve," I instructed the therapist when she came into my room.

"Your determination is so inspiring," she said with a smile, fastening the valve to my throat.

I smiled back with a level of confidence I hadn't felt for a long time. I imagine the RT was used to my usual sour mood.

"We have a surprise for you today," she said. "Give me a couple of minutes, and I'll be right back."

I couldn't imagine what the surprise might be.

She returned with a brand-new ventilator—a crisp new monitor on wheels to go beside my bed. "Look at the side of it," she said.

I tilted my head to read the label.

'Holly' was written across the machine.

The respiratory therapists named all the ventilators in the ICU, most of them after movie or book characters, such as Obi-Wan-Kenobi, Megatron, Mulan, and Pocahontas. There was a special one, named after Kit. They decided to name this new one after me.

"One day, this ventilator, named Holly, will help someone else breathe until they are strong enough to do it on their own," she said.

Incredibly honored, I smiled again—a real, genuine smile.

Just when things were going well, the nausea returned two-fold. Every little thing made me feel sick. Whenever the RTs suctioned my trach, I'd get nauseated and throw up. When I did my NIF tests, I'd feel sick and then throw up. I vomited whenever the nurses rolled or changed me, when they got me up in the chair, and every time they gave me my meds. Eventually, just moving down the hallway made me dizzy, and I'd puke again. With relentless nausea back with a vengeance, my determination diminished once again. My smiles disappeared, and I started to kick my daughter out of my bed again.

"Take Casey," I mouthed to James, then turned my head to look out the window. "I feel sick." It was so frustrating that things felt so hard all the time.

James picked Casey up off the bed and held her in his arms. "You know you still have so many reasons to smile," he said.

I glared back at him, then shook my head. The room was spinning so much I couldn't think straight.

"Holly, you are leaps and bounds ahead of where you were even last week. You're going to keep getting better," he said.

I shook my head again, then dry heaved while my nurse injected me with meds.

James was trying to lift my spirits, trying to remind me that good things were happening. He was doing the right thing, but it was hard for me to see that while violently gagging.

"I just can't keep doing this," I whispered and cried. It was impossible to stay positive.

"Why don't you just pretend to be in a better mood," he said lovingly. "For your Mom's sake. You don't know how happy your improvements have made her. It would make things even better if she could see you happy, too."

I turned back to the window beside my bed. Being nauseous made me feel hopeless, as if I had no reason to smile. No reason to be happy whatsoever. Even though I most certainly did.

"Have you heard of sea-bands?" my nurse piped in, a woman I'd never had before. It was normal for nurses to be in my room and me not even notice.

James and I looked at each other, and I shook my head.

"What are those?" he asked.

She explained that sea bands help ward off seasickness. They are knitted elasticated bands with a small button sewn in them that push into the P6 pressure points on the inside of your wrists. "I've worn them every time I've gone on a cruise for the last fifteen years," she said. "They drastically reduce my motion sickness. They might be worth trying."

"Awesome, thank you so much. I'll try to find some tomorrow," James said, quickly writing it down on a piece of paper.

I didn't think much more about it. At this point, nothing worked long-term, and I found it hard to believe anything would.

Later that afternoon, Mike came in with news that brightened my day. He said, "Tonight will be your first try without the ventilator."

I turned to James, and we both smiled. It was finally time.

"There's no pressure to stay on the valve all night, but how about we see how long you can last," Mike suggested.

If I needed to come off, no matter what time it was, we just had to let him know.

I was excited but nervous about my body's capability to breathe on its own while I slept. I counted down the hours until it was time for bed.

"You got this, Babe," James said to me before he left for the night. He leaned Casey above my bed, and I kissed her warm cheek goodbye. There was nothing to be done with the ventilator; I was already off for the day. They would just leave the valve on overnight for as long as I could handle. Thankfully, with the help of the sleeping pill, I fell asleep quickly, but in the middle of the night, I woke up and was wide awake.

Mom was passed out hard beside me. I tried to close my eyes and go back to sleep, but I was too focused on every breath going in and out of my chest.

"Everything okay?" my nurse asked when she peeked her head in my room and saw my eyes wide open. "Do you need to come off the valve, Holly?"

I shook my head. My breathing felt normal, just as it did during the day. I wasn't wide awake out of fear or from struggling to breathe. I was awake because my heart was pounding with excitement. Lasting off the ventilator overnight was a huge step for me—if I could keep it up.

"Can I have some Ativan?" I mouthed. I wanted to go back to sleep, and Ativan always made me drowsy. "I think I'm going to have a panic attack," I fibbed.

"Of course," the nurse said, then injected me with a dose.

I felt guilty for being dishonest to get medication, but I was desperate to fall asleep so that I could last off the ventilator all night. If I didn't sleep tonight, I knew I'd feel like shit in the morning and would probably have to go back on. I was eager to see how my breathing would be tomorrow. Would I be exhausted and need to take a break off the valve for a day or two more? Or would I be able to keep going, and going, until I reached forty-eight hours? The Ativan took effect. My eyelids grew heavy, and I drifted off to sleep.

When I woke up the next morning, sunbeams stretched across my blankets, casting the room in a warm, golden glow. I immediately noticed that each breath in and out felt as natural and strong as it did the day before. I'd now lasted more than twenty-four hours straight without the machine and felt my determination growing again.

"Good morning," my RT said to me and my mom when she came into my room. "How's your breathing? Do you want to stay on the valve, or do you want to save your energy for next time?"

"Stay on," I mouthed.

Mom smiled, half asleep from her bed.

I was halfway to forty-eight. "If I last another twenty-four hours, my trach can come out tomorrow morning?" I enthusiastically asked. It seemed unrealistic I could be that close.

Mom turned to hear the therapist's response.

"Hmm, it's hard to say," she replied. "Tomorrow is Sunday, and I'm not sure the doctors will do a procedure like that over the weekend. And with everything you've been through, they might want to be extra careful. I imagine they'd give it another twenty-four hours and wait till Monday."

Though I was eager and usually an impatient person, I was okay to wait one more day. It felt surreal that my trach might potentially be out in days.

My RT took the opportunity to explain to us that once the trach was out, they'd first replace it with a small button to keep the hole open in case I struggled to breathe again, and they had to put the trach back in. But if everything went well, then after another forty-eight hours, the button would come out. At that point, I'd no longer need to stay in the ICU, and I'd move back to the neurology ward

I might actually get out of here.

Feelings of excitement for life again rushed through me. If I recovered from this disease, I could finally be a mom again. I could go out dancing with my friends. I could live!

I promised myself to be a new person when I got home. I would enjoy every day; I would try new things and visit new places. I wanted to experience everything the world had to offer.

I have to keep going, I told myself. Sometimes I was overcome with feelings of being overwhelmed, other times full of determination. Either way, I always kept going. I stayed on the valve for the rest of the day.

On my second night off the ventilator, I woke up nauseous in the middle of the night. I tried to go back to sleep, but my stomach churned. I stuck my tongue to the roof of my mouth and clucked to get Mom's attention.

"I feel sick," I mouthed when she woke up and asked what was wrong. With one eye barely open, she leaned over to buzz the nurse. Even after Gravol that helped, then Ativan that I once again lied to get, I stared up at the ceiling, wide awake.

The nausea was gone, but my heart pounded; I was too excited to sleep. I'd been that way since I was little. In the weeks leading up to Casey's birth, I'd barely slept. I noticed my mom had already drifted off. After several long minutes alone in silence, I clucked to wake her up again. She opened her eyes slightly.

"I can't sleep at all," I mouthed.

"Okay," she replied. "Why don't you watch TV?" She fumbled with the remote beside her chair and turned it on. The timing was perfect; while she clicked through the channels for something for me to watch, we discovered the royal wedding between Prince William and Kate Middleton was being aired live from London. "How about we watch this," Mom said, opening her eyes a little wider and sitting up in her chair.

We spent the next couple of hours watching the impeccably dressed wedding guests arrive at Westminster Abbey—the breath-taking castle that resembled something from a fairy-tale. We watched as the gorgeous Kate walked down the aisle with her dad, her beautiful white dress trailing behind her.

"Oh my God. Look at those hats!" Mom said, laughing at some of the guests at the wedding.

"Yeah but look at her dress!" I mouthed. Captivated by the beauty of the wedding ceremony, I almost forgot where I was. Eventually, I looked over at my mom, then up at the clock on the wall to see it was three in the morning—and I was wired. I looked back at my mom, who rubbed her bloodshot eyes and yawned.

I knew my mom loved sleep as much as I did and would rather be sleeping. Instead, she'd stayed awake for hours, so I didn't have to watch TV alone. She did that for me. She'd do anything for me. Before all of this, my mother was developing her career as a speaker. She had put her dreams on hold to be with me at the hospital. Having my mom there by my side when I was at my sickest meant the world to me.

I thought about the last couple of months here in the hospital and how close my mom and I had grown. Growing up, we had our differences, fighting over curfews and chores. I was independent and strong-willed, traits I got from her, and our personalities often clashed. Our relationship improved once I was an adult and out of the house. Mom became my confidant and the person I went to for advice. Then, becoming a mother myself strengthened our bond. Now, she had spent almost every minute of the last two and a half months by my side. Through every horrific procedure, every painful experience. If there had been room, she would have climbed into my bed to snuggle me, like she did when I was little. Each time I cried, she was right there to hold my hand and reassure me. If she ever worried that I wasn't going to recover, if she ever felt like giving up, she never once showed it.

Months later, Mom told me that her faith had wavered. At one point early on in ICU my doctors told her my case was so severe, I'd probably be in the hospital at least a year. I'm glad she decided not to tell me that.

I thought about how devastating it must be for her as a mother to see her daughter fighting on life support day after day. Yet, she usually had a smile on her face and held her head up high. My mom stayed optimistic, trusting that everything was going to be okay.

I was in complete awe of her strength.

I thought about what James had said the day before, about how even though I didn't feel happy, I should try and smile for my family's sake.

That's all they were waiting for.

When Mom noticed I was staring at her, she smiled, and instead of giving her my usual blank expression, I smiled back.

"What a great night," she said once the wedding was over and turned off the TV. "One of our best nights in the hospital."

She was right, and it was all because of her.

As I lay in my paralyzed state and Mom fell back to sleep, I knew I needed to be more like my mother. Strong and positive. The strength and courage my mom had for me made me realize I had to do the same for my daughter.

I had to keep fighting as bravely as I could. Closing my eyes, I made a conscious decision to wake up tomorrow—and be happy.

12

Welcome Back to the Real World

I didn't see it coming, but my medical team agreed to take out my trach on Sunday, May 1st, after nearly ten weeks in the hospital. I had reached my goal of breathing on my own for over forty-eight hours. Though nervous, my adrenaline, excitement, and a little Ativan kept me calm while they removed the tube from my throat while fully awake. The respiratory therapist replaced the trach with a small white button in my neck. Once the button was out, I'd be able to eat and drink again. All my anxiety was for nothing; the process was completely pain-free. When we did my NIF test, I inhaled -45cm H2o.

"I'm finally a normal person," I whispered to James and my mom from my bed. "I got the seal of approval." My voice was hoarse and quiet as if I had a severe case of laryngitis, but I grinned from ear to ear. I could finally talk again. I'd been communicating just fine by mouthing words the last several weeks, but it was incredible to know I was physically using my vocal cords again.

"In time," the doctors told us, "Her voice will get stronger. It'll eventually go back to normal."

"What do you want for your first drink?" my mom asked.

Thinking back to my days of intense thirst, I remembered the fizzy taste of Sprite on my tongue.

"Sprite, for sure," I said. "Or—wait. Maybe an iced tea," I hadn't had an iced tea in years. "Or should I do a Coke? Or ginger ale . . ." Mom and I giggled. I wasn't even a pop drinker, but the thought of the sugary sweetness sounded delicious, and I craved every soda I could think of. "Let me get back to you on that."

"And what about to eat?" James asked. Whatever I wanted, he'd get for me.

Hmm. I hadn't thought about that one. I never once felt hunger, even on a liquid diet of tube feed for two and a half months. Unsure of how my stomach would handle it, I settled on something light and one of my favorite snacks, a bowl of strawberries, raspberries, and blueberries.

Before I'd be allowed to eat or drink anything, I had to pass a swallowing assessment first, scheduled for once the button was out. Because the nerves in the throat are affected, many GBS patients have difficulties swallowing throughout their journey. To ensure I could swallow properly, I had to perform a barium swallow exam, where I'd have to take in barium sulfate, a metallic compound with small bites of food. The metal would show on a fluoroscopy (similar to an x-ray), and they'd see if what I swallowed went down my throat or into my windpipe. I was nervous about the test as I knew that if my muscles weren't strong enough, I wouldn't be able to eat or drink yet—and probably couldn't leave the ICU until I could.

For the next two days, we waited—waited to see if my breathing was strong enough on its own. I slept with oxygen tubes in each nostril, which was uncomfortable and chafed my nose, but I didn't mind. The ventilator was finally gone from my room, leaving a large space beside my bed. James also found Sea-Bands for me and fastened them around my wrists. I'll never know if that's what helped or if it was because the trach was finally out of my throat, but I never felt nauseated again. This was a turning point in my recovery.

Then, after proving I could breathe independently for another forty-eight hours, the RTs took the button out. Exactly like the trach removal, it was fast and painless. My RT covered the circular hole in my neck (called a stoma) with a thick white bandage. She told us that the hole would close on its own in a few days. I was amazed by the human body and the fact that this hole, where a thick plastic ventilator tube went through, could heal without stitches so quickly.

Once I was out of bed, and up in my big comfy chair, a young man that worked for the hospital wheeled me to the speech therapy department for my swallowing test.

This was the first time I remember leaving intensive care without my family. I wasn't used to being able to speak and didn't say a word the entire elevator ride down.

In the lab for the fluoroscopy, nurses fed me bits of crackers with the metal compound spread on top. I thought the barium would taste worse; it was just a bit metallic-y on my tongue. My swallow felt normal to me, but things that felt normal often weren't.

"Things look good," the speech therapist said with a smile when I'd finished. "We just need to have your doctors review the video of the x-ray to make sure. I'll come let you know in ICU as soon as I get confirmation."

The same porter wheeled me back up to the ICU.

An hour later, the therapist was in my doorway. She said, "So, we have a little problem."

I was still up in my chair, patiently waiting for the results. My heart sunk into my chest.

Did I fail the assessment? Was I not strong enough to eat or drink yet?

"The video didn't work. Nothing was recorded, so the doctors had nothing to watch."

Did this mean I'd have to do another test? When would that be? It seemed everything in the hospital had to be booked well in advance.

She continued. "It's not an issue. I saw enough to know that your swallowing was great. You're good to go." She left to inform my ICU doctor, and he gave me the go-ahead to drink and eat. After what felt like being in a desert for two months straight, I'd finally get to drink something. I couldn't have been more excited.

James cracked open the can of Sprite I'd decided on and poured it into a Styrofoam cup, my mouth watering in anticipation. When he held the cup to my mouth, the sweet Sprite tasted like sweet, sugary lime on my tongue. I gulped down the cold, fizzy liquid.

"More," I said to James, and he tipped the cup back toward my mouth. I took in another big gulp. "More." James refilled the cup again and again until I'd drank the entire can. Everyone laughed when I let out a huge burp.

"I caught that on film," Mom giggled with the camera in her hand.

Then I moved on to the bowl of berries. I was glad I picked fruit for my first thing to eat. My taste buds went crazy for their sweetness as I devoured each spoonful.

Later that evening, James fed me my first meal. The hospital food was chopped into tiny pieces of mashed-up turkey, corn and peas, and potatoes, and despite looking disgusting, it was delicious. Anything would have been at this point. I just wished I could have fed myself. Though my hands and arms were moving again, I couldn't do much with them. Just like my baby Casey's, they were too flimsy and weak to hold anything. This meant that someone else would have to help me every time I ate or drank. I was breathing independently, no longer felt sick, and was getting out of ICU soon. But I was a long way from being independent again.

That same day, my toes wiggled for the first time—another sliver of hope to keep me going. I knew this meant the nerves in my legs were regenerating quickly. Every GBS case is unique, and some people recover at a faster rate than others, and this movement in my toes excited me.

"Once you're back on the neurology ward," my doctor explained, "You'll be assessed and placed on a waiting list for the rehabilitation hospital. You're going to the Glenrose."

The Glenrose Hospital was on the other side of Edmonton and was the same place Kit had gone for his rehab. I was familiar with it only because a friend whose husband had been hit by a car did his recovery there. Once at the Glenrose, I'd do intensive therapy to strengthen my muscles, and I'd learn to walk again. The wait to get into this hospital could be anywhere from a few days to several weeks. I crossed my fingers that it wouldn't be long. The sooner I finished therapy, the sooner I'd be able to go home. Then I could finally return to my life of being a wife and mother.

I thought I'd have more of a heads-up, but Mom and I woke up the next morning to a nurse telling us I'd be moving to the neuro ward within the hour. In a blur, Mom pulled the stars off the ceiling and took down the photos and Get-Well cards from the wall. Then with me in my bed, we rolled out of my room and down the hallway.

After almost seventy days in intensive care, I was finally leaving. I'd reached my goal of getting out by Mother's Day. We waved to the staff we passed down the hall like we were on a parade float, but most nurses were in rooms dealing with patients. I was disappointed I didn't even get to say goodbye to the people that felt like family to me now.

When we rolled through the entrance of the new ward up on the fifth floor of the hospital, I was excited about this new chapter but nervous about what came next. Almost all the ICU nurses knew me by now; some had worked with me since that very first day. Many of them treated me as if I was their sister, their daughter, their friend. They understood how to care for someone with GBS. They knew to handle me gently and raise me in the lift without causing me pain. They knew how to put me at ease on my bad days. I was nervous about having new nurses with no experience treating my extremely specific needs.

When James and Casey arrived at the hospital that morning, we were already settled in my new room. Multiple nurses had lifted me out of the ICU bed by grabbing hold of the sheet underneath and transferred me to a bed on Unit 52. I was in a private room again because of the bladder infection. I was still only a carrier with no symptoms, waiting for it to work through my body. Even still, I was on contact precautions, meaning everyone donned a gown and gloves to enter.

The room was a lot smaller than my last one. Casey's bassinet and my big comfy chair, which doubled as mom's bed, took up most of the floor space. On the upside, we had a massive private bathroom with a shower. Now James and my mom didn't have to use the public washroom in the hall. Still mostly paralyzed, I used a bedpan and adult diapers.

When my nurse came in to introduce herself for the day, I was pleasantly surprised to see someone I knew, a girl James had gone to school with. Charlene was one of the nicest girls I'd met; friendly, bubbly, and caring—the perfect qualities for a nurse. My nervousness about being on the new ward subsided with her presence. The day was made even better when a girlfriend stopped by with a gorgeous bouquet of daisies. I wasn't allowed flowers in the ICU, and even though before GBS I didn't care for them much (I thought they were a waste of money for something that just died), now I appreciated them and their beauty so much more.

After a wonderful day with Charlene, things took a turn for the worst when my new nurse came on shift.

"Can I get a bedpan?" I asked the woman after she'd checked my blood pressure and heart rate. She nodded, left the room, then returned with another nurse—and the lift.

James and I looked at each other, both confused. Why did she have the lift? I wanted to go pee, not get up in the chair.

"We want you to try peeing on a commode," the nurse said.

A commode is a medical chair with a hole in it, used by people who struggle to sit on or get up from a toilet. It's considered a step up from lying in bed and peeing in a pan under your bum. The patient is lifted on the commode, and the chair is rolled over the top of the toilet. But I'd never been on one. I'd never even heard of one before this. My limbs were barely moving again; I wasn't sure my torso was strong enough to hold up my body. I'd sat in my big lazy boy plenty of times, but I was laying back in a recliner, not sitting upright in a chair.

I looked to my mom as I bit my lip.

"Holly has never used a commode," Mom said to the nurse. "She still has a lot of paralysis. She's never even sat up." My mom explained precisely what I was thinking.

"Why are you speaking for her?" the nurse snapped at my mom. "She can speak for herself." She turned to look at me.

I was so used to my mom being my voice in the ICU, I hadn't realized that I instantly looked to her whenever asked a question, expecting her to answer for me.

"Try the commode," the nurse said sternly.

My eyes welled with tears. I was sure this would cause excruciating pain.

"I don't think she's ready," James said.

"You all need to step outside," the nurse interrupted. "There's not much space to use the lift in here." She ushered James with Casey in his arms out the door.

He kept eye contact with me as he exited the room, and I started to cry from the fear of the pain this might cause.

"I'm not going anywhere," my mom said, standing firmly beside my bed. She knew I wasn't like most patients; I had to be log rolled and held carefully while being slung up in the air. She grabbed my legs as the nurse put the green sling under my body.

"You don't need to help. We can handle this ourselves," the nurse said.

Mom stepped back as she slowly lifted my body in the air.

Lacerating pain shot through my thighs, and I screamed as loud as possible, shocked by the sound escaping my mouth.

Mom jumped forward and straightened my legs. The pain stopped, and we continued.

Once I was lifted in the air, and down to the chair, I used all the strength I had in my core to sit up straight. It wasn't painful, just challenging, but once I was in the bathroom, I peed into the toilet, my first time since back in the emergency room months ago. When I finished, the nurses, with mom helping, used the lift to hoist me back into my bed, no one saying a thing.

"I'm really not happy with what just happened," Mom finally said to my nurse once James and Casey were back in the room. Mom's voice was louder than usual. "I don't think Holly was ready to do that yet."

"That's the way things are done on this ward," the nurse quickly replied. She turned to look at me. "You better start toughening up. Physiotherapy will be a lot harder than what you just had to do." Then she turned and walked out of the room.

My tears returned.

When mom came to my bedside to comfort me, she also had tears in her eyes.

"It feels like we're starting over," she said.

With GBS being so rare, we knew we'd have to educate the nurses about my hypersensitivity. It did feel like we were starting over.

"I don't want to do physio," I sobbed. The thought of going through more pain was terrifying. And how would I learn to walk if I couldn't handle the suffering?

"We'll get through this," James said to Mom and me.

Unfortunately, more pain came quicker than I anticipated. A couple of hours later, slight discomfort in my back, a two on the pain scale, quickly escalated to a piercing nine. After my mom buzzed the nurse, I lay suffering in my bed for ten more excruciating minutes. In the ICU, I don't think I ever waited for more than two. I was in tears by the time the nurse arrived.

"Things are a lot different here than where you came from," she said to the three of us as if she sensed the agitation in the room from her tardiness. "We have lots of patients to care for, not just one like the ICU nurses. We can't rush to every call like they can. I'm really sorry. Now, what do you need?" she asked with a friendly smile.

I didn't like the woman, but I understood where she was coming from. The nurses were busy, constantly getting called for while in my room. Next time, I wouldn't let my pain get that bad before calling my nurse.

After I told her about the sharp stabs in my back, she said, "No problem, I'll be right back with your pills."

I looked at James from my bed, confused once again.

"Pills?" I asked before she left the room. "I always get my pain meds through my PICC line." I pointed to the IV sticking out of the inside of my elbow.

"That's something they do in ICU. Not on this ward," the nurse replied. "You're not on a ventilator anymore. You can swallow the medication."

When she left the room, my face reddened. How dare she tell me I can't have it that way. A pill would take at least half an hour to work. A needle in my arm provided instant relief and a rush of euphoric pleasure that spread through my body, making me feel glorious. When I tensed at the thought of no longer getting my meds in my arm, I knew my body was addicted to that feeling. Hopefully, weaning off these meds wouldn't be too hard.

I didn't have a choice of how I got my drugs—the nurse made that clear. Everything was different on this ward. I had to swallow my pain pills and pee on a toilet. I would have to do grueling physiotherapy. What if the therapists were like this nurse; what if they pushed me to do things that caused horrible pain? I missed the nurses who understood me. I missed my old routine and the comfort of knowing what to expect next.

For a moment, I wished I was still on life support, back in intensive care.

*

Not everything was bad on Unit 52. The following day, I discovered that no longer having a trach meant no more medication pushed through the feeding tube in my stomach—no more feeling of fluid splashing around my insides. I got to swallow the pills instead. At first, mom gave me them one at a time with juice, then three or four in a spoonful of apple sauce. It was a challenge to down fifteen pills in a row, but better than through the tube in my stomach.

"Good morning! You must be Holly!" a blond woman in the bright yellow gown everyone wore said cheerfully as she stepped into my room. Behind her was a younger woman who looked to be about twenty.

"I'm Samantha, your physiotherapist." the older woman said with a smile. "Call me Sam." She turned to the girl with curly blond hair. "This is Jerilee. She's a student at the University of Alberta. We'll be your PTs until you move to the Glenrose."

These women didn't look scary.

"And I'm Marilyn," my mom said, extending her hand to each woman. "Everyone just calls me Holly's mom."

"Very nice to meet you both," Jerilee said with an eager grin on her face. "This is my first experience with a GBS patient." She was excited to hear all about my case, starting with my first symptoms and my time in ICU. After I filled them in, Sam grabbed a clipboard. She'd worked with GBS patients before, she told us, and she'd helped get them back on their feet.

"Let's assess you to see where you're at. That'll tell us where to start for physio. How does that sound?" Sam asked, placing her hand on mine.

I smiled, feeling hopeful. "Sounds good to me."

"Let's start with your arms. Put them out in front of you and raise them as high as you can."

I slowly lifted both limp arms up, something I had yet to try doing. My arms shook with weakness as they rose, my left stopping parallel to my chest, my right continuing above my head. No matter how hard I pushed, my left arm stayed stuck in one spot parallel to the floor.

"Okay, you can put them down," Sam said.

I lowered my arms, looked down at my bed, and sighed. I knew why my left arm was like that. From all the times we'd avoided moving it when we did the range of motion exercises in ICU. I never let them lift my left arm as high because it always bumped the tube in my throat and made me sick. Now my arm was frozen because I hadn't worked on it.

How would this affect my ability to do therapy?

"Don't worry about your arm," Sam said, putting her hand on my shoulder. "We'll stretch it out and get it moving again." Her confidence made me relax.

My PTs noted other issues, like how my fingers were stiff and curling inward, giving my hand a claw shape. I had minimal fine motor skills, like my daughter, I couldn't grasp much in my hands. But when Sam asked me to, I was able to lift my right foot about an inch up off the bed, a massive progression from my toes wiggling a couple of days before.

"I'm sure you'll be lifting your other leg soon," Sam said.

Movement usually comes back symmetrically after GBS. Sam promised me we'd work through everything—together. To start, she said I needed to wear my hand and foot splints more often to keep everything stable, something that we should have done from the beginning.

"This will help with your drop foot." When she noticed the orange cones sitting on my windowsill, she pointed to them and said, "Those are a great way to improve your hand-eye coordination."

Oh, crap. Those stupid cones. They were impossible to do back in ICU. I could hardly hold them, and my arms were so shaky, but I promised Sam and myself that I'd practice with them again. I knew I had to at least try.

When I told them about the shooting pain in my thighs whenever my legs were bent, Sam said my quad muscles were likely tight, and they too would need to be worked out and stretched. I tensed my body, nervous about the pain that might cause, and looked at my mom from the corner of my eye.

Sam moved closer to me. "You don't have to do anything you don't want to," she said. "You're in complete control of your body, Holly. If something we do is painful, you tell us to stop."

Thank God. I was so afraid of being pushed beyond my pain threshold. Her words reassured me I'd be okay. These ladies were in my corner. And when I told them about my back pain, they immediately ordered me an air bed like the one I had in ICU.

"Your sensory nerves are affected. You need to be on an airbed—a normal bed will be too painful." Samantha may not have understood what it was like to have GBS, but she made me feel like she did.

"How about a wheelchair? Have you sat up in one yet?" Jerilee asked.

I shook my head. "Only the recliner." I pointed to the comfy chair beside my bed.

"Okay, that means your torso is probably pretty weak from laying down for so long. We'll just need to work extra hard to build up those trunk muscles." Sam said.

"She has been up on a commode," my mom quickly added. "The nurses had her on one last night."

Sam looked at my mom, her eyes widening. She turned back to me. "We need to see if you're even strong enough for a commode. For now, stick to using a bedpan until we're sure you're comfortable sitting up on your own."

I relaxed again. I didn't feel ready for the commode. It was reassuring that my therapists wanted to take things slow.

"Let's have you sit up alongside your bed and see how long you can last," Sam said.

Another thing I had yet to try doing. I was always on my back, whether in my bed or the sling or reclining in my chair. Sam rolled me onto my side, remembering to bend my legs at the knees, then the two of them held my hands and pulled me upright. My weak legs dangled over the side of the bed. My body shook as I tried to hold myself up. Then sharp pain penetrated my lower back. I wobbled and thought I might fall over.

"Your spine is curved, like a C," Sam noted, with Jerilee observing.

The pain intensified. After less than sixty seconds, I asked to lie back down.

"Your core is extremely weak, Holly, weaker than I thought it'd be. Did you have a c-section with your baby?"

"She did," Mom said, "And emergency surgery on her stomach."

I lifted my gown to show my scar.

Sam nodded her head as I explained what happened with my ruptured artery.

"And you were pregnant." She explained that going through the body changes of pregnancy, then having two major surgeries, one where they likely cut my abdominal muscles in two, would drastically weaken my core. "It will take a bit more time and effort to rebuild those muscles—more than the average person. But as your core gets stronger, you'll be able to support your back for longer periods. Sitting up will get easier. And moving your arms and legs will, too." The plan was to do therapy twice a day, once in bed and once up in my chair. "We'll start next week. It'll be hard at first, but you'll get stronger. One day, we'll get you walking again. It's just going to take time."

I smiled, then chuckled to myself. As if I hadn't heard that before.

To help motivate me, Sam suggested I set a goal each week. With her input, we decided my first goal was to sit up in a wheelchair. With a few exercises this week, she was confident I'd be able to do it. After my PTs left, I felt great about my physio—excited even—a drastically different feeling than I had the night before. It made me realize how much of an impact a medical professional's attitude can have on a patient. Sam made me believe I could do the therapy—or that I at least had to try. She planted the seed deep within me that with hard work, I would walk again.

My second time up in the lift went much smoother. When Mom offered to help my nurse, this one graciously accepted. Mom showed her the easiest way to get the sling under my body and how to hold my legs without causing me pain. The nurse nodded her head, impressed my mom knew so much.

"This isn't my mom's first rodeo. She knows what she's doing," I told the nurse.

She and Mom laughed as they hoisted my body over into my chair—a new one, so mom and I no longer had to share. Once my body was positioned, I immediately noticed this chair felt different; maybe it was much more comfortable, or maybe my body was stronger already and could handle things better. I lasted hours sitting up in it.

Life improved over the next couple of days. I got my new air bed, which eliminated the back pain. I found out my hands were just strong enough to push the call button on the remote on my bed, a huge accomplishment that meant I could page the nurses on my own.

The littlest things made my entire day. Like when James' parents brought me my first food from outside the hospital, a chocolate frosty from Wendy's. James spooned the thick ice cream into my mouth, and it tasted ten times better than I remembered. Every new thing I ate was a treat for my taste buds. When a friend brought me giant homemade chocolate chip cookies, I decided to try and eat one on my own. It was difficult to grasp because of my strength and hard to get it into my mouth because I was shaky, so pieces of it crumbled everywhere. I didn't care. The small bites I got were worth it. For the rest of the day, my nurses kept finding chunks of cookies in my bed, and I laughed every time. "Sorry about that!" I kept saying. It felt good to laugh again. I noticed I no longer had that awful feeling in the pit of my stomach and hadn't felt sick in days. With my nausea gone, I felt positive and happy again. I was smiling all the time.

"The Holly we know is finally back," Mom said cheerily.

When James asked me what I wanted for Mother's Day, I said, "My eyebrows waxed."

James smiled. I was starting to care about myself again.

I wanted to get out and do things—if you can call venturing through the hospital, something to do. Partly because of my newfound freedom now that I wasn't attached to a ventilator anymore, James or my mom could just wheel me wherever I wanted to go, but mostly because I was getting bored. Mom went and picked up a cake, and we brought it down to the ICU; a thank you to the staff for taking such incredible care of us while we were there. One of the respiratory therapists surprised me with a scrapbook she had made with Casey's photos, and I almost cried as I flipped through the cute pictures I'd never seen. We couldn't have asked for a better team to nurse me back to health and support us through it all.

Feeling great again helped my determination grow. My first weekend on the new ward, I asked James for my cell phone to attempt to text. My lack of motor skills made it nearly impossible to push the right buttons on the phone, but after ten minutes of trying and failing, then trying again, I typed the word, Hi, and sent it to my mom, who had gone home for a few hours that day.

"Is this James or Holly??" she quickly replied, as the text would have come from my phone.

I carefully ran my fingers across the tiny keyboard. H-o-l-l-y, I slowly typed. Using my hands was difficult. But not impossible.

"OMG," Mom wrote back. "How exciting! I'll be back soon."

After that, I navigated to Facebook, which wasn't easy, as this was before mobile apps existed, and we had to go the old-fashioned route through our phone's browser. I used all my strength to push down the buttons (again, this was before touch screens), and after many failed attempts, I updated my status.

"My first update. I'm alive. Doing well."

Messages immediately poured in. I'd been MIA on social media for months. I went back and read the hundreds of messages I'd gotten in the last seventy-five days. It was almost hard to believe the number of people out there rooting and praying for me—from my best friends to strangers, friends of friends, and people I hadn't talked to in years. I'd finally be able to write back. Before GBS, my phone was a big part of my life; I texted my friends all the time, so I was eager to communicate with the outside world again. I spent hours in my room, either lying in bed or reclining back in my chair, texting everyone I could think of. It took three times as long to type out a message, but all I had was time. Plus, texting was basically physiotherapy for my hands.

When Mother's Day rolled around, Mom planned a do-over meal. Easter was a bust, with me throwing up halfway through it, then having a panic attack, and not allowing my family in my room.

"Let's try another dinner," Mom suggested. "You pick the food this time."

I recently graduated from mashed everything to solid food but was still living on plain hospital meals. I was ecstatic about getting to choose. At my request, James whipped up a shrimp stir-fry and a Greek salad, and Jay made pineapple delight for dessert—three of my favorites.

In the hospital cafeteria downstairs, we met my mom and dad, Dennis, James' parents, and brothers Brett and Jay. Not able to hold a fork yet, my mother-in-law fed me while I sat pulled up to the table in my recliner chair. I could have been upset for not being able to feed myself or not getting to hold Casey in my arms the way everyone else did, but I was just grateful to be so much better than the last time we were all together. I was off the ventilator. I wasn't nauseated. I could eat my favorite home-cooked meals, surrounded by the people I loved. It was important to focus on the good things. After dinner, James surprised me with a gift card for the spa.

"You deserve to be pampered once you get home, after all the shit you've gone through," he said.

He had also arranged for someone to come to my hospital room to wax my brows. I was so thankful for him.

Mom snapped some pictures on her camera, and when she showed them to me, I barely recognized myself. On the tiny screen was a disheveled person with out-of-control eyebrows and hair.

When Mom opened my Mother's Day gift from my brother, I immediately burst out laughing. A ceramic figurine, a Cheshire cat that grinned from ear to ear. I remembered back in the ICU when I swallowed the water when I wasn't supposed to.

"I heard you smiled with a guilty Cheshire cat grin," Jay said with a smile, and Mom and I laughed.

This was back when I felt as if I was dying of thirst. It was crazy that we were already looking back and laughing about it now.

Things had changed so much in the last few weeks. I was breathing on my own, something I'd once deemed impossible. Maybe impossible things aren't impossible after all. I felt optimistic about my recovery and more determined than ever to see myself through it.

First, I needed to put on some weight. When a patient is bedridden for a long time the way I was, it's estimated they lose one percent of lean muscle mass each day in bed. After spending seventy-plus days completely immobile, surviving on a liquid diet, my limbs were skin and bones.

A nutritionist came by to examine me in my bed. She squeezed the muscular tissue on my arms and legs, and when she grabbed where my calf muscle should be, her fingertips practically touched. The skin was hanging off me. I knew I'd lost weight, but I didn't think it was quite that much because of how swollen my face and stomach were from all the meds. While lying in my fancy new bed that could weigh me while in it, I found out I'd lost almost thirty pounds over the last ten weeks. Thankfully, I'd come to the hospital heavier than normal due to the pregnancy weight.

"I'd like to see you gain back fifteen pounds," the nutritionist said, which would bring me back to my typical weight of a hundred and forty pounds. "I'll also get the nurse to do some bloodwork to see what nutrients you're lacking."

My stomach sank a little from her comment. I didn't want any more needles. It seems funny that I went through the most horrific pain of my life, and a tiny poke to the arm made me afraid. I was just so done with going through any more pain. Though in the end, it wasn't that bad.

The bloodwork revealed I was extremely low on potassium and magnesium. I needed to take supplements to bring my levels to a healthy range. I'd take daily pills for potassium but had to get the magnesium through the PICC line in my arm for two hours every day, and they'd test me again in a few days.

"I'll also get your nurses to add protein powder packs to your meals—to help build back the muscle you lost."

Mom mixed them into my morning smoothies and afternoon soup. On this new ward, I was getting to do so many new things. And I noticed how quickly my mobility and strength were improving. Within days, I lifted both legs an inch up toward the ceiling. When my nurses put the head of my bed on a sharp incline, I didn't fall to the side; I was strong enough to keep my body upright.

Mom set my pink nursing pillow on my lap so Casey could sit against it facing me. It was a little embarrassing that the whirlwind of the last couple of weeks had distracted me from her. Once again, sometimes, I don't even remember my daughter being in the room. Which was a testament to how well-behaved she was. She knew she needed to stay quiet and be calm in her bassinet while we navigated through all of this.

With my baby in front of me, I reached out my arms and intertwined my clawed fingers with hers. The nausea was gone, and the pain under control. For what felt like the first time, I could get to know my daughter. With nothing but free time now, we could finally bond. "I love you so much, Casey," I said with my scratchy voice and leaned to kiss her tiny heart-shaped lips.

My daughter smiled, her chubby cheeks rising and her mouth opening wide. It meant everything to me that I was able to finally speak the words, "I love you," to my baby girl. We spent hours cuddling up in my hospital bed. I'd kiss her over and over and over again. Being able to speak and reach out to touch her, it felt that I was finally something that resembled a mother to her.

Casey had changed so much from when I was first admitted. She was no longer this little potato that did nothing but poop and pee. The corner of her zebra-print blankie was always in one hand. Her personality was bubbly and cheerful. Her exaggerated smile made everyone beam. Now four months old, she was starting to hold her bottle independently. With her bottle in her mouth, she looked at me like she knew who I was, and I felt unbelievably fortunate I was finally coherent enough to watch her develop and grow.

"You know, the two of you are both learning how to do things," Sam mentioned one time she came by. Casey was lying with me in my bed, her finger wrapped around mine. "You'll both learn how to use your hands, how to grasp objects, how to sit up independently and stand. Eventually, you'll both learn how to walk."

It was wild to realize I wouldn't be the only one learning how to do all these things. I wasn't alone in this. And that motivated me. I knew that if my four-month-old daughter could do this, so could I.

It was time to work hard and get my life back.

The next step was being assessed by the doctors at the Glenrose, the rehabilitation hospital I'd eventually move to. A man in a white coat stood beside my bed and had me squeeze his hands, then tested my reflexes. This brought instant flashbacks of doing this with the Ed Helms doctor back in the ER before I knew what GBS even was. That felt like an eternity ago.

The Glenrose doctor then tested the sensitivity in my skin by dragging what felt like a serrated knife against the bottoms of my feet. I stared in shock to see he was only lightly brushing the tip of a safety pin along my foot. The tingling in my body had faded quite a while ago, but my feet were still hypersensitive, and gentle touches felt like cuts to my skin.

"You're the perfect candidate for the Glenrose," the doctor said after testing my limbs' strength and motor function. "We've had many GBS patients over the years. I can't tell you when a bed will be available, but you're on the waiting list. Probably a few weeks from now."

I thought I'd move to the Glenrose sooner than that. Kit didn't wait long before he was transferred. Ready to dive into my therapy, I wanted to go now.

"I know that sounds like a long way away, Holly," he said. The stunned look on my face must have given away my thoughts. "But a few weeks will give you more time to get stronger before starting physio. And you need to be a bit healthier and come off some more meds, anyways."

Since leaving ICU, I hadn't used Ativan or any anti-nausea medication, but I was still on antidepressants, morphine, blood thinners, laxatives, and many other pills.

The doctor continued about the Glenrose and what to expect once I got there. Since I still had the ESBL bladder infection, I'd be in a private room, but since the patients there were not as high risk as here, I'd get to go to multiple therapy classes each day.

"And how long will I be there?" I eagerly asked, mentally skipping to the part where I was strong enough to go home.

"It depends on how fast you progress."

I knew Kit was there for a few weeks. Hopefully, my stay would be around the same.

"Once you're strong enough, we'll get you set up with equipment for you to use at home. Things like ramps for getting in and out of your house in your wheelchair, a seat for your bathtub, and anything else you might need for mobility."

Again, I said nothing, sitting quietly in shock. What was this talk of a wheelchair? I thought I was going to their hospital to get better, strengthen my legs, and learn to walk. Did he not think I'd recover enough to walk again?

"Just because you go home in a wheelchair," he quickly added, "doesn't mean you'll stay in one. Most people recovering from GBS finish the last bit of their recovery at home."

My fears were calmed.

"After you leave the Glenrose, you'll finish the rest of your therapy as an out-patient, coming back for a few hours, a few times a week. In the meantime, you get a little a bit better, and we'll call you as soon as we have a bed."

Mom and I set the goal to be home by June 19th, James' birthday. Now the second week of May, this would give me five weeks to improve my strength. My PTs later agreed this was a reasonable target, which kept my flame of determination burning. I couldn't wait to be strong enough to be back home with my family.

I started physiotherapy with Sam and Jerilee the next day. They stood alongside my hospital bed, and I pushed against their resistance using my frail hands, arms, and legs. Every tiny movement felt like I was pushing against a cement wall, not a person, and my muscles vibrated from my efforts. Once I finished a few different exercises, the girls lifted me upright to sit up in bed again. Sweat dripped down my arms and chest.

"Try for longer this time," Sam said.

After a few minutes, my core was on fire, but I did it.

"Amazing job. That's all we'll do this morning," Samantha said once I was lying back down. Sweaty and red-faced, she could tell I was beat after only ten minutes of movement. Plus, we had another session later that day that she must have wanted to save my energy for. Because when she came back that afternoon, Sam rolled an empty wheelchair in front of her with a big smile across her face.

"What is that?" I nervously smiled back, knowing very well what it was.

"You want to try sitting up in the wheelchair for your therapy this afternoon?"

I stared nervously at the metal contraption, then over to my mom. When I'd set a goal of sitting up in a wheelchair for the week, I didn't think we'd be doing it on my first day.

"You did really well, sitting on the side of the bed this morning," Sam said. "I think you're ready."

I looked at the stiff, black wheelchair, then at my oversized, plush, comfy recliner. It felt like looking toward the future, then back at my past. I barely knew my therapists, but I trusted them. "Let's do it," I said.

With Mom's help, the nurse got me up in the lift and then lowered me down into the hard seat on the chair. My abs immediately burned as I held my torso up. Pain radiated in my lower back and butt.

"How's that feel?" Jerilee asked.

"It's a little painful, but I can stay in for a bit." I knew if I wanted to progress, I had to push through the pain.

"Well, how about we leave you be, and your mom can get us whenever you're ready to come out of the wheelchair," Sam said. The PT room was directly across the hall from mine, so they could be back in a snap of a finger if needed.

"Sounds good to me," I replied.

Once they were out of my room, I impulsively did what I think most able-bodied people do when they sit in a wheelchair—I put my hands on the wheels and tried to roll. Unlike normal people, I was not strong enough to do it. I pushed my hands as hard as possible to move the chair forward, but the wheels didn't budge.

I sat in the chair and chatted with my mom for some time. The hard, thin seat was uncomfortable, and it took a lot of effort to sit upright. But I lasted for almost thirty minutes before I had Mom grab Sam and Jerilee from across the hall.

"You should be proud of half an hour," Jerilee said.

And I was. It was short but sweet. I'd already reached a goal.

"Now, you'll get up in the wheelchair instead of the recliner. You'll try staying in it for longer each day. Then you can do your exercises sitting in it," Samantha said.

She also suggested we set another goal—transferring into my wheelchair. I'd use something called a transfer board, which would slide under my hip while sitting in bed then shuffle my body over to the chair. Once I could transfer with it, I wouldn't have to use the lift anymore.

If I wasn't even strong to move the wheels yet, moving my whole body out of bed seemed unlikely. But if I did it, that meant no more being hoisted up in the lift, so I was excited to try.

On my second day up in the wheelchair, I lasted for over an hour. I asked Mom to wheel me into the bathroom so I could look at myself in a mirror. I'd seen a picture or two from back in the ICU, but I was pretty out of it at the time.

Mom rolled my wheelchair into the dark bathroom, then flicked on the light like a grand reveal.

"Wow . . ." I whispered. Sitting in front of me was someone I didn't recognize.

My blue eyes were sunken in. Dark shadows rested underneath my lash line. My brown hair was all frizz and grease, my skin a sickly pale grey. My face was swollen like I was having a slight allergic reaction, as was my belly—I looked six months pregnant again. Acne peppered my cheeks and jawline, worse than I ever had in high school. My eyebrows were bushy and out of control, making me look unrecognizable. And to top it all off, I had a ghastly wound on my neck that looked as if someone stubbed out a cigar on my throat. But despite that, I was impressed that the trach hole had already healed and closed completely.

Though my appearance was shocking, I told myself that what I looked like did not define the type of person I was—a fighter that wanted to focus on something far more important—my rehabilitation.

On that same day, with my weak hands vibrating, I held a cup to my mouth and drank water without anyone's help.

I was more determined than ever and remembered who I was. The girl that went after the things I wanted. Everything I had in my life I'd worked my ass off to get, my career, my car, my family, our home. I could do the same for my recovery.

"I heard you held a cup today, Miss Holly," said one nurse, who wasn't assigned to me that day, from outside my door.

Word traveled fast around the ward. The nurses popped their heads in to congratulate me whenever I accomplished something new. I was proud of myself, like a child showing off what I could do.

A neurologist visited almost every day (while back in ICU, they came to see me every week), and when Dr. Clark, the Ed Helms lookalike, walked into my room, I was thrilled just to show off that I was alive.

"You're looking very optimistic and happy," he said as he stood beside me in my wheelchair. I'm sure I looked a lot better than when he last saw me, probably just before I was getting rushed to the ICU to be intubated.

I *was* optimistic and happy. My nightmare was finally over. I felt like *me* again.

The doctor turned to James and my mom. Doctors always seemed to do that when filling us in on my condition. "Holly's magnesium levels have already improved, so she won't need IV treatments anymore."

I looked down at the tube that stuck out of the inside of my elbow. With no other medications administered through the catheter in my arm, my PICC line could come out.

"A nurse will take it out for you in the next day or two. It'll just take a couple of minutes."

"What about the feeding tube?" I asked, eager to get these things out of my body.

"That one's a bit trickier," he replied.

Because of the complications resulting in my artery rupturing, the hospital didn't want to take any risks. Someone higher up decided that the surgeon who'd put the feeding tube in had to be the one to take it out. I'm sure they were afraid I'd sue them for their mistakes, though I wasn't that type of person—accidents happen, even in the hospital.

"The surgeon is all booked up right now and won't be available for another week or two."

Though I cringed whenever I bumped the tube protruding out of my stomach, I could handle waiting. "How about the antidepressant," I asked. "When can I come off that?" I was up for staying on the pain meds, laxatives, and blood thinners but didn't want to be on any drugs I thought were unnecessary.

"Just because you're feeling a lot better doesn't mean you're ready to come off." The drug I was on, Cymbalta, wasn't something that could be dropped quickly anyway. I'd have to be gradually weaned. "And don't forget, Cymbalta helps with neuropathy, so I think it's probably best for you to stay on it for now."

With my nerve pain finally under control from a perfect mix of pills and the random injections in the stomach, I didn't want to mess with a good thing and agreed to stay on them.

"I encourage you, Holly, to do anything that helps you feel like yourself again. As you rebuild your life, your mental health will be just as important as your physical." It meant a lot to me that he cared about how I was doing. "At some point, we'll give you day passes, then weekend passes, where you'll get to go home for short periods of time."

I jolted my head to look at James and smiled. My heart began to race. I had no idea hospital weekend passes were even a thing. I'd get to go home much sooner than I thought, at least temporarily. I pictured myself snuggling with my husband and daughter on the couch, watching Disney movies, and having my girlfriends over for a glass of wine.

"When I go home, am I allowed to have a drink?" I asked. Being pregnant before coming to the hospital, it'd been almost a year since drinking alcohol.

"We'll see what meds you're on at that point," he said. "But it should be fine. Again, I encourage you to do anything you need to help you feel more like your old self."

I smiled and said to my mom and husband, "Life is starting to go back to normal."

*

We quickly established a new daily routine on Unit 52. I usually woke up to a nurse coming in with my breakfast I'd eat on a tray from my bed—my version of room service. Samantha gave me specialty utensils, adaptive forks, and spoons designed for people with a weak grip or limited range of motion. The silverware had large, round handles that were easier to grasp, and I used them to feed myself. Like a messy toddler, I struggled to get the food to my mouth, spilling bits of eggs or pancakes all over my gown. But it was better than being fed by my mother or my husband. I wanted to do things myself.

After breakfast, Mom brushed my teeth, and sometimes I had a sponge bath if my nurses had time. Even these were different than what I was used to in the ICU. The nurses used warmed-up baby wipes to wash me down—versus hot water, soap, and a washcloth in the ICU.

"We probably won't get to wash your hair," one of my nurses had told me.

They were busy; it was apparent how often they got paged each time they were in my room. My nurses in ICU, it seemed, were always around, but then again, I was on life support, so they had to be. Here, I only saw my nurse a few times a day.

My mom came up with the brilliant idea of rolling my wheelchair into the bathroom, propping the back of my chair on the lip of the shower, and leaning it back. Using the handheld showerhead, she washed out the greasy flakes from my hair, then spent hours attempting to brush out the tangle of rats' nests gathered at the nape of my neck. Mom was afraid she'd have to cut it off, which I refused to let her. Thankfully, with a lot of patience, Deanne got the tangles out using a fine-tooth comb. We learned from this day forward to always French braid my hair to keep it from tangling, something we should have done from the beginning.

Sam and Jerilee came in at ten o'clock every weekday morning. With their bright, upbeat attitudes, I couldn't help but feel excited about my recovery around them, again realizing the importance of having such a supportive team. I pushed and pulled my limbs against their body weight for my physio—they felt like the strongest two women in the world. Even though the exercises were challenging and sometimes a little painful, I enjoyed doing them. I was moving my body in a way I hadn't been able to in months, and the exercises helped loosen my tight muscles. I always felt more comfortable and relaxed after our sessions.

When my therapy finished, Mom turned on the TV, and we watched music videos until James and Casey got there. *Born This Way* by Lady Gaga, *E. T.* by Katy Perry, R*olling in the Deep* by Adele, and *Get on the Floor* by Jennifer Lopez were in the Top Ten at the time, so their videos played constantly. These songs will forever remind me of my time on this ward.

Once Casey and James got to the hospital, he and Mom strapped me into the lift and hoisted me from my bed over to my wheelchair. With all my hard work, I'd be able to transfer on my own soon. In my chair, I ate my lunch again with the help of my adaptive cutlery. After I finished eating, we left the room. The wheelchair was getting easier to sit in, and I loved being rolled around with Casey resting on the checkered pillow on my lap. It was nice to go whenever we wanted, without a posse of nurses and RTs following behind.

My first trip outside around the hospital grounds felt bizarre. When I was first admitted to the hospital, it was February, the dead of winter. Now into May, the snow was gone, the trees were budding, flowers bloomed. With a blue sky and shining sun, the outside world was breathtakingly beautiful. On one of our subsequent trips outside, we weren't so lucky with the weather, and as we rolled up the hill back toward the hospital, Mom and James struggled together to push my chair against the wind. We laughed and laughed as I attempted to shield Casey and I from the gusts of wind with her blankie. After being somber for so long, laughing at the silliest things was so refreshing.

I had more physio at two o'clock every afternoon. Sam showed me how to exercise my arms and hands and improve my fine motor skills with various things they brought. Sitting in my chair, I tried to fasten buttons on shirts, clip safety pins together and open and close jars. I stretched out my fingers in putty that felt like cement. Everything was near impossible at first, and it was frustrating and challenging, but as the days passed and I remained consistent, each task got a little easier to do. Eventually, I was strong enough to move the wheels on my wheelchair, though it wasn't pretty. My right arm was much stronger than my left, so when I pulled the wheels back, I turned to the right—going in a complete circle—another thing we laughed hard about.

After physio, I got back into bed and had James set Casey down on the nursing pillow to face me. She had started to giggle recently, mainly for James, so I'd make faces, stick out my tongue and play peek-a-boo in an attempt to get her laughing. Whenever Casey touched my hand, I laced my fingers with hers and smiled with gratitude for being able to do something so simple. Casey looked at me like she loved me. My heart felt as if it were going to burst. I cherished every single minute with my baby girl.

I spent more time practicing my eating skills over dinner. Sometimes I'd get frustrated over my shaky hands, and James would offer to feed me, but I was determined to get it right and always turned down his help. Eating on my own was a challenge and took me three times as long, but I reminded myself that it was not impossible. I had to keep at it. After dinner, Casey came back into my bed, and the four of us watched whatever we could find on TV that evening. James headed home with Casey at the same time every night, around eight o'clock. Mom and I chatted, she brushed my teeth, put on my hand and foot splints, made her bed, and we went to sleep.

The following day, we started all over again.

After just a few days of this routine, things felt monotonous, like I was living the movie Groundhog Day—waking up to the exact same thing again and again. I looked forward to any visitors that stopped by, like when Jay came back in town for his four days off, and we talked for hours while he helped me with my exercises, NHL hockey playing in the background.

"Why don't you read?" Mom suggested after my brother was gone again. "It'll help pass the time." She handed me a small booklet, a handbook we'd been sent by the GBS/CIDP Foundation of Canada back in Intensive care. This was the first time I'd seen it. Strong enough to hold things in my hands, Mom reminded me I could now read all about Guillain-Barre Syndrome on my own.

I knew a bit about GBS beyond what I'd experienced. Despite the heavy sedation in ICU, I remembered hearing the conversations about what was happening to my body. I knew I had an autoimmune disorder; my own immune system attacked my nerves and paralyzed me. I knew my case was possibly triggered by childbirth, the epidural, or c-section—or maybe all three. But that was about all I knew, and I was eager to know everything.

Awkwardly flipping through the pages with my curled hands, I skimmed the book and discovered many startling facts about Guillain-Barre. Like how, on average, one to two out of every hundred thousand people get GBS a year—not one in a million like I thought I'd heard in ICU. In some areas, it's more than that; in others, less. That meant that, on average, ten to twenty people could get it in a city the size of mine in a single year. It was a rare illness for sure, nothing compared to the number of people diagnosed with cancer each year but knowing that other people in my city had GBS made me feel much less alone. Back in ICU, it felt as if I was one person in the world fighting this fight.

It shocked me to read that five percent of GBS patients die. Not from Guillain-Barre per se, but from complications, like not getting on a ventilator soon enough or the patient having a heart attack from all the stress on the body. Other things, such as blood infections and clots, can also cause death in GBS. I immediately felt blessed to have made it to the hospital before my breathing stopped, considering how fast the symptoms progressed. And after all that had happened in those crucial first weeks, I understood how lucky I was to be alive.

I read more about how GBS can affect breathing, how the breathing muscles, most specifically our diaphragms, weaken, and fatigue, so we go into respiratory failure. Surprisingly, mechanical ventilation in GBS only happens in some cases. I knew, like Kit's, my case of GBS was severe, but I assumed most cases were. It turns out those ending up on ventilators only make up about thirty percent of cases. The rest don't end up in intensive care; they just stay on a neurology ward like the one I was on now.

Why did that have to happen to me? Why did my breathing have to be affected? What a difference not being on a ventilator would have made. Maybe I wouldn't have been throwing up all the time and could have had Casey on my bed every single day. Maybe I would already be home by now. But there was no point dwelling on the past.

I turned the page to learn about recovery and what to expect. My heart sank when I read that not everyone recovers from GBS. About twenty percent of survivors will have a long-term disability requiring an assistive device to get around—either a wheelchair, a walker, or a cane. Not walking ever again was a possibility I was aware of because of how bad things were in the ICU, even if no one ever came out and said it. Understanding now how severe my case was, I couldn't help but worry I'd be in that percentage that doesn't recover.

My strength improving almost daily tempered that worry. I could lift my legs a little higher off the bed. I decided to ignore what I read and instead crush my goal of transferring without the lift. I had extensive work ahead of me. If I was going to strengthen my body, I needed to get out of bed. Samantha, Jerilee, and Mom all felt I was ready, too. James was still at home when we decided to go for it. They wheeled me across the hall to the physio room, beside a hospital bed set up along the wall.

"We're gonna take off one of the armrests from your wheelchair," Sam explained as she grabbed a large wooden board that resembled the deck of a skateboard. "Then I'll put the transfer board under your hip, between you and the bed, and you're just going to shuffle your body across it."

Jerilee wrapped a thin cloth belt around my waist so they could help shift my weight.

It sounded simple enough.

Sam unclipped the armrest, Jerilee put the end of the board under my butt, then placed her hand on my back over the belt for support.

I tried to move.

The bottom half of my legs shifted a little.

I tried again.

My hips and thighs didn't respond. I kept trying to thrust my body over, using all my strength in my arms, sweat suddenly pouring down my chest. My body was too heavy for me to lift, even a little. I started to topple forward.

Jerilee held the belt strong to keep my body upright. Sam saw I wouldn't be able to get across the board, so using the belt as a lifting strap, the two of them helped toss me onto the bed. My frail body flopped onto the mattress.

I lay there for a few seconds on my side, catching my breath. Sam and Jerilee were out of breath, too. I was skin and bones but complete dead weight. There was no way in hell I'd be able to move on my own.

"You're not quite ready for transferring," Sam said woefully as if she, too, was saddened by my inability to reach our goal. Grabbing another nurse to help with my legs, my PTs lifted me back into my wheelchair. "For now, we'll keep using the lift," Samantha said as Mom rolled me back across the hall. "Don't worry. We'll try the board again soon."

I stared down at the floor, disheartened.

Back in my room with just me and Mom, I stayed quiet in my wheelchair for a few minutes, staring at my legs. I could not believe how hard the transfer was. Not just hard, impossible. My week had been going well in physio, but this made me realize I still had a long way to go. I was supposed to be going to a rehab hospital to learn to walk soon. How was I supposed to do therapy and learn to walk if I couldn't even transfer? I'm sure everything I'd do there would be much more challenging than that. This was the first big thing I'd attempted to do.

I had failed.

Is this a sign that I will not recover? My eyes filled with tears.

"You okay?" Mom asked.

I turned my head to look out the window. "What if I can't do anything in physio?" I whispered. "What if I'm too weak to do the exercises? How am I supposed to learn to walk if I can still barely move?" Tears trickled down my face.

What if my progression stops here? What if I never get out of this wheelchair?

I wouldn't be able to help my daughter take her first steps. I wouldn't be able to run and play tag with my little girl. No more dancing with my friends in the club. I wouldn't get to run and jump into the ocean like I loved doing on vacation or hike to the top of a rocky mountain like I'd always wanted to do. My stomach sank thinking about being in a wheelchair for the rest of my life. I wasn't even thirty yet.

"I just want to walk again," I cried to my mom. "I just want my life back."

What would my life even look like in a wheelchair? How would I do things? How could I play with Casey, take care of her, clean the house? What about driving? What about more kids?

How will I function? It all sounded overwhelming.

My breathing sped up. My heart rate skyrocketed as I cried uncontrollably. The surrounding air became thinner, and I struggled to breathe again.

A panic attack took over my body.

13

The GBS Reset

The year or so that followed my release from the hospital was incredible, to say the least. I was home with my husband and daughter. I was walking again. The pieces of my life I'd lost for months were back. Getting to be a mom again, of course, was the biggest blessing of all; simple things like being able to lift Casey in my arms, putting her in her pink polka-dot jammies, and leaning down to tuck her in her crib every night felt extra special. Being there to witness and record her milestones in her First-Year calendar—when she first waved, drank from a cup, got her first tooth, and when she first said "mum"—was a gift. We wore matching costumes as I'd always wanted to do for Halloween—we went as ladybugs. I'd once felt doubtful I'd experience these moments with her, and even though we lost out on so much time together, I felt deeply connected to my daughter. Casey was my guardian angel—my life support. I survived because of her.

James also had a strong bond with Casey. He'd spent so many months taking care of her on his own. You could tell how close they were by how he seemed to read her mind and give her exactly what she needed. Most men don't get alone time like that with their babies. I saw it as a blessing from our tragedy.

In my first few weeks at home, I expected to pick back up where I left off—as the person I once was and back to the life I had before. But I quickly discovered that everything was different. Or maybe I was different. My near-death experience had moved me, shaken me up, and changed my perspective on life. I now understood what people meant when they said, "Things can change in the blink of an eye." We are all a diagnosis, a car crash, or a traumatic event away from our lives being shattered. I'd lived through it. Now, I had healed into someone else.

Like a caged animal finally set free, the world around me was much more beautiful. The sun seemed to shine brighter; trees were greener and more lush. Food and drinks tasted sweeter. I was grateful every day I woke up feeling well to be able to get out of bed on my own and take on the day. For years I had taken my health for granted.

I appreciated my husband and daughter more than I thought possible. My marriage with James flourished. We were both on a high with me alive and home again. We got our matching tattoos like we wanted to—the number nineteen, our wedding date, on our wrists. Our journey through hell and back brought us closer. We were able to let the minor annoyances in life go. We made a point of spending more time with those we cared about; going camping with friends, then taking a trip to visit Spencer in the mountains. The following year James and I went to Mexico with some of our siblings.

We adored being parents to Casey, who continued to be the most amazing little girl, always laughing and smiling. By seven months old, she was sleeping through the night. James and I were both thankful to be living our lives again—the way we originally planned.

With the leftover fundraising money, we paid off our extensive debt, set up retirement funds for us and an education fund for Casey, then put the rest away in savings. For years, James and I struggled to make ends meet. If it weren't for the fundraiser, we would have been tens of thousands of dollars in debt. I was overflowing with gratitude for what my friends and family had done for us. I had to go through something horrible to get there, but for the first time in my life, I wasn't worried about money.

Although there were days I no longer thought about my time in the hospital, my every decision was colored by what I went through with GBS. I had been trapped in my body for months, with no agency or options to improve my life. Now, I'd been given another shot. I became observant, taking everything in and thinking about how I wanted to spend my time. Before having GBS, after becoming a mom, I figured it was time to cut back on partying and going out with friends. Now, going out to dance was something I promised I'd do more of. It was liberating to know I was free and healthy enough to go after anything I wanted. After all that I'd accomplished—breathing on my own, walking again, climbing stairs—I felt powerful and strong, capable of conquering the world.

These were some of the happiest times of my life.

Wanting to be around others who understood how I felt and what I'd gone through with GBS, I joined a Guillain-Barre Syndrome support group in my city. The people in my group were the strongest human beings I'd ever met. A few of them dealt with severe weakness in their limbs, like one man in his sixties named Izy, still in a wheelchair and diagnosed a year before me. I learned that recovery looks different for everyone. I wasn't one hundred percent yet, but I was darned close. Knowing this enhanced my feelings of gratitude for being able to walk again.

After seventeen months off work, in the middle of 2012, I returned to my job in Human Resources at the casino. Despite how much I loved my time at home with Casey, I felt that going back to work was the final puzzle piece to getting my life back. Career-oriented and an extremely hard worker, the stay-at-home-mom life was not something I planned for long term. I loved my first few months back at work.

"We're implementing a new policy," I remember my manager explaining to our HR team after I'd been working again for three months. "We aren't allowing employees to wear nail polish anymore. We want our dress code to be streamlined and simple. We don't want to bring attention to our staff on the casino floor."

Sitting in the board room of our office, I glanced down at my long acrylic nails that, at the time, were painted zebra print.

"This policy applies to us in the HR office, too," he concluded—probably talking directly to me.

That night I drove home and felt oddly bothered. This new policy meant I'd have to leave my usually acrylic nails, sometimes sparkly pink or bright, neon yellow, bare. I was torn, there was no reason for me to be upset over something as minute as the color of my nails, but thinking back to my time in the hospital when I couldn't take care of myself, the simple act of getting my nails done was a big deal for me now. I never had bare nails, even on life support. They represented the agency I had over my own wellbeing. I started to question whether I wanted to work there anymore.

It wasn't about the nails, of course. It was the need to have control in my life. I needed to do the simple things that brought me joy, such as getting my nails done. As I dug deeper into my view of my job, I realized I did not love it. I had only taken the job because I'd been laid off from a drilling company just before our wedding and was desperate for work. My current company was becoming more concerned about things that had nothing to do with how well someone did their job. And I wasn't as challenged as I could be. The casino was also a far drive from our house, which meant more time on the road and less time with James and Casey in the evenings.

This new policy, as insignificant as it seemed, changed my view. After all that I'd been through, I wanted—and needed—more in my life.

Weeks later, after interviewing for new positions, I accepted an HR Advisor role for a large manufacturing company back in the oil and gas industry. This new job was closer to home, had better pay and hours, and let me do whatever the hell I wanted with my nails.

My job wasn't the only thing I looked at differently. My view on people changed, too. I became more empathetic to strangers I'd see, often wondering what was going on in their lives at home. I thought back to when I was in the ICU and pictured James going shopping with Casey at the grocery store. No one around him would have known just how horrible things were for him at that time. To this day, when I see a stranger in a bad mood, I empathize that they could be going through something awful, doing their best not to fall apart, fighting to survive. My experience taught me to take the time to show kindness to strangers.

My relationship with others also changed. I first noticed that my friends filtered negativity out of our conversations as if I'd been through enough shit—I didn't need to hear more. Then as time went on, the negativity trickled back in. When friends complained about the guy that cut them off on the freeway or how a server screwed up their order, it seemed like minor inconveniences to me—especially when I'd spend time with other GBS survivors who talked about real problems, like still not having the energy or strength to walk five feet.

I no longer related to negative people that had the ability to fix their problems or change their lives—but chose not to. I'd been paralyzed on life support with no way of improving my life, and I knew that most people have options in the majority of situations. If you are unhappy, change something. Life is too short for complaining; it's time to go after what we want—now. I wanted to live my life free of conflict, drama, and intensity. I tried to stop taking things so damned seriously and have more fun.

Sometimes bad things happen to show us the world in a whole new light. My life was drastically different. I was the closest I'd ever been with my mom. My friends and family meant the world to me. Appreciating the support they gave me in the hospital, I made a point of working on those connections and living life to the fullest. James and I even started to talk about having another baby—though I was terrified of getting GBS again, it was worth the risk to continue with our lives the way we planned.

I felt older and wiser from my trauma. This pause in my life made me want to aspire for more, to grow, and to be a better person. I immersed myself in writing *Happily Ever After,* the first edition of this book. I didn't want to take my life for granted like I used to. I started running and volunteering more with the GBS/CIDP Foundation of Canada.

I wish I could say this honeymoon phase—this portion of my life that was so carefree and joyful—lasted forever, but sadly, it did not. Things often go back to the way things were before a tragedy. In early 2014, three years after my diagnosis, problems arose in my relationship with James. It certainly didn't happen overnight. We weren't blissfully happy one day, then miserable the next. Like many long-term relationships, everyday stresses in life started to affect us. Our busy toddler took up all our energy. We both worked full-time. With less time as a couple, we gradually stopped showing each other the love and appreciation we both deserved. Little things bothered us again. We started to argue over everything, from chores to parenting, money, sex, and how we spent our free time. Our fights went from sporadic to daily. I didn't understand how we could even argue after everything we'd been through in the hospital together.

This was not the first time we had relationship problems. It was no secret that our relationship was sometimes dramatic in the seven years leading up to me getting pregnant. Our friends and family who knew us best had seen us at our worst.

"Me and James got in a huge fight," I cried to my mom over the phone many times before my time in ICU. "He told me it's over."

"Oh, don't worry, Holly, you know he doesn't mean that," my mom replied. "He always comes back around." Known for our explosive fights, for breaking up 'for good this time,' then getting back together, no one believed we'd ever split up.

Now we were parents. We'd gone through GBS together and managed to avoid fighting for the last few years. I thought we'd outgrown the immature bullshit. Faced with relationship struggles once again, we found ourselves behaving exactly as we had all those years ago.

Every issue we ever had in our relationship emerged. Minor disagreements turned into full-blown fights that escalated beyond our control. We would scream and fight and yell and cry. Arguments from one issue that we should have resolved in a conversation turned into a zillion other things, causing the fight to last for days. Each time we argued, we swore our relationship was over for good this time.

For a time, we would always apologize to one another after we calmed down. We loved each other too much to end our marriage. We knew what was important to us, and that was each other. But with our issues never getting resolved, we fought again and again and again. Over time, the apologies stopped. It was easier if we just pretended as if nothing had happened. I was left emotionally drained a little more after each altercation. I'm sure James was, too.

In my early twenties, I'd justified how our relationship was. All relationships struggle. The screaming, name-calling, and constant threats of breaking up were normal—a part of being in a passionate long-term relationship, or so I believed. The person I was now, older, wiser, a mother of a little girl, was starting to see our relationship for what it was—an unpredictable emotional rollercoaster. Most things I said, James took a different way, and vice versa—we were oil and vinegar. Things were chaotic.

The hardest part for me was that I knew we didn't lack love for one another, only respect. So, was our love enough to keep us together? People can care for each other but still hurt their feelings, too. These days we were hurting each other more than we were loving each other—and now we had a little girl witnessing it all.

In June of 2014, after one of our worst fights the weekend of our tenth anniversary, I packed a suitcase and went to Deanne's for several days. I thought it might be over for real this time. I just couldn't take it anymore. The emotional torment of our relationship was exhausting. But alone in the spare bed at Deanne's, I felt torn. How could I walk away? Even though I'd grown up with divorced parents, I always believed you work through marriage problems; you never, ever leave. I felt guilty for even considering it. I understood that marriage wasn't easy; it was hard work. Ashamed my marriage was struggling after everything we'd been through just a few years before, tears filled my eyes.

This wasn't just my husband or the father of my child—this was *James*. The man I'd grown up with. The man beside my hospital bed. The one caring for our newborn as I fought for my life. James had gone above and beyond what was expected of a husband, exceeding the definition of 'in sickness and in health.' We had overcome a tragedy together. And our relationship was not all tears and pain. We had a past full of beautiful memories, a life full of joy. James was my best friend, always by my side. He was faithful and loving and an incredible dad. We had a life together, with friends and family that adored us, who were rooting for us to stay together. I loved and cared for my husband so deeply. We had to make the necessary changes to make it work.

"Things will get better. Our relationship can improve," I told myself as I unpacked my bags back at home after just a few days away. "Everyone fights." But were other couples' struggles as tumultuous as ours? Could we change our toxic behaviors to save our marriage? I wanted to, and I know James did too. But the fights continued once I returned home, even with the help of a marriage counselor. Doors were slammed. Resentment grew. We went days without speaking to each other and spent more time apart. As soon as we'd tuck our toddler into her big girl bed and kiss her goodnight, I'd lace up my runners and head out the door for a run, or he'd leave to a friend's place to play video games—our way of escaping each other and our problems. As the months on the calendar flipped by, our relationship deteriorated even more.

I wrestled with my emotions almost every night, crying myself to sleep—James passed out soundly beside me. Some days I knew I had to leave, others I was convinced I needed to stay. My experience with GBS made things that much more complicated; on one hand, I couldn't just walk away from the life I worked so hard to get back to. On the other, after all the trauma and pain of ICU, I could not allow for more chaos in my life.

I didn't know what to do. But by the fall, we slept in different beds, and when we fought, we talked about me moving out.

We continued to shout the meanest, cruelest words to one other, things that you should never say to someone you love. Some days I didn't care that the harsh words came out of my mouth. Other days I couldn't recognize myself and hated the person I was becoming.

On the outside, my relationship with James was picture-perfect. We'd just celebrated a decade together. We'd overcome GBS, had a beautiful little girl, and an amazing group of family and friends. We had our matching tattoos, a home, and two dogs. While our relationship struggled, friends questioned why we weren't getting along after all that happened in the hospital, even going as far as saying I was the problem and most likely suffering from PTSD. They had no idea how vicious our arguments were.

I was physically and mentally exhausted from trying to make it work for so long that I just couldn't do it anymore. It made me sick to my stomach, but I knew something had to change.

After everything we'd been through together, we—Casey included, deserved better.

Just before Halloween, the morning after one of our final screaming matches, I said to James, "I'm getting my own place." I'd reached my breaking point. "I want to keep working on our marriage and going to counseling," I said. "But I can't live here anymore." We needed space. I needed time to process our relationship and to get honest with myself about how I played a part in its breakdown. I had to figure out what I wanted for my life because I truly did not know.

James helped me move to an apartment I found fifteen minutes away, still on the south side of Edmonton. I signed a three-month lease, unsure how long I'd be there. We agreed to switch off with Casey every other day, so she didn't have to miss either of us too much. James put his anger and hurt aside to unload boxes from the SUV he purchased for our growing family back when I was pregnant. Casey went to my parents for a couple of hours while we unloaded my things.

"Well, that's everything," James said, standing in the spiderweb-infested doorway of my main-floor apartment. He looked down at his shoes, avoiding eye contact with me.

"Thanks for helping," I said. Was I making the right decision? What if our relationship problems were just a normal part of marriage, that this just happens after ten years together, and it was up to us to do the work to make it through.

"No problem," he muttered.

My heart was breaking in two. Our love, it conquered something together. How did we get here?

Just before James turned to the door, I dove into his arms.

"I love you," I said.

I don't know if he said it back, I didn't hear him say it, but he was crying as he pulled away from my arms and walked out the door.

As soon as I closed it behind him, I sat on my couch and sobbed harder than I ever thought possible.

Now what? Where do we go from here?

Maybe some space would be good for us, and we'd realize how much we needed one another. Maybe this time away would strengthen our relationship and be the best thing to happen to our marriage, like GBS was. But how do we work on things when we don't even live together?

What the hell was I doing?

Maybe something was wrong with me. Perhaps I did have PTSD.

If my husband and I ended up separating, I'd have to rebuild my life for a second time, all before I was thirty. I left with practically nothing, just the bed from our spare room and our old couches from the basement. Mom and Dennis lent me an old dining room table and chairs and box spring and mattress for Casey to sleep on. Having been with James since I was eighteen, I'd never lived on my own before.

Deep down, I knew leaving was the right thing to do, even if it meant walking away from the life we'd built together and breaking up the family I'd fought so hard to get back to. I'd miss my husband's smile and the way he made me laugh, but I couldn't fight with James for even one more day.

If we didn't get back together, would he forgive me for leaving? What about our family and friends? How would this affect Casey? Did I really want my daughter to grow up with divorced parents? Would I even be able to survive on my own?

Despite the paralyzing fear of having no idea what my future looked like anymore, I knew from conquering GBS that I was capable of moving forward. Capable of taking the next steps and overcoming the darkest, most challenging of times because I'd done it once before.

No matter what lay ahead for me, I knew I would survive.

14

One Step at a Time

My mother, Marilyn, worked in social services for years, but her side hustle and passion has always been singer/songwriter. In 2004 she put out an album under the name Marilyn Rose, with titles such as *One More Mile to Go* and *I Surrender*. In the months leading up to my GBS diagnosis, Mom was working on her career in inspirational speaking. A highly empathetic and sensitive woman, my mother had an incredible way with words.

Four years before I would break down in sobs in my newly single apartment, something I would have never predicted, I sat in the wheelchair of my room in Unit 52—about to have a panic attack from the unknowns of what my future would look like. Mom crouched beside me and took my hand in hers.

"Holly," she said softly, as she gently massaged my fingers. "We need to focus on one obstacle at a time. You don't need to worry about walking right now. You're not there yet. Focus on your physio, on strengthening your legs in your bed. One thing at a time. One day at a time." She reminded me of all I'd accomplished the last several weeks, including getting off the ventilator, holding a cup, starting to feed myself—holding Casey in my arms. There was a point where I struggled to breathe on my own for just a few minutes and look where I was now.

She wiped the tears from my cheeks. Looking into my mom's confident brown eyes, my breathing steadied, and my heart rate relaxed—the first time without the help of Ativan.

I nodded. I'd been through hell and back. I was so much stronger than I gave myself credit for. Just because I couldn't do the transfer now didn't mean I wouldn't at some point down the road. I just had to keep trying. Like Mom said, I needed to stop worrying about all the things I'd have to learn to do and instead focus on right now.

I wiped the last of the tears off my face, dispelled my negative thoughts, and said, "Okay. One day at a time. I can do this."

Sometimes we must let go and allow ourselves to fall before we can build ourselves back up.

I busted my ass in physio and celebrated every new triumph, like when I was strong enough to push the button on the remote control to change the channel and when I finally stacked the orange cones on top of one another. My motor skills were improving; I could hold the toothbrush and brush my own teeth. I could clutch Casey's soother to put in her mouth. On Day 80, my nurse carefully pulled out my PICC line, and now that I was finally free from the thirty-centimeter-long catheter that spanned from my elbow up to my heart, I said to James and Mom enthusiastically, "I'm pick-less!"

No matter how small, celebrating every accomplishment was key for me. The nurse covered the tiny hole on the inside of my elbow with a large white bandage.

There were more bumps along the road, like when out of nowhere, I struggled to pee. I'd feel the pressure build in my bladder—I knew I had to go, but with the pan under my butt, I'd push and squeeze, but nothing happened.

"It could be from the bladder infection or from having a catheter for so long back in ICU. Or the muscles in your bladder might still be weak," nurse Charlene proposed as she unwrapped a sterile tube. It didn't matter what was affecting my ability to pee. What mattered was that it meant I'd have to have another in-and-out catheter to empty the urine out of my bladder.

A lump grew in my throat, and my heart rate began to rise. The lacerating pain in my genitals from the last time was something I'd never forget.

While in bed, Charlene pulled up my gown and began to insert the tube into my urethra. Perplexed by the fact this was someone I knew and that I'd been to a few parties with the girl currently face down in my vagina, I didn't notice the pain. The inflammation in my nerves had calmed, and the procedure ended up being no more painful than a regular pap. Thankfully, it would be the last in-and-out catheter I'd endure—though I struggled with my bladder and bowels for many months to come.

Mom wanted to help me feel more like myself again and did my makeup every morning. As the type of girl that felt my best all done up, she figured it would help lift my mood. She picked up cheap sun dresses from Goodwill and changed me into them every morning after my bath. At first, I was hesitant about the dresses. When you're bedridden, it's nearly impossible to get anything on or off. There is a reason hospital gowns tie up in the back. Mom, the genius, sliced the backs of each dress with scissors, so she could drape them over me and then tuck them behind my back. When I looked at myself in the mirror, this sickly young girl, a stranger stared back, but with a bit of mascara and a cute floral dress, at least I felt less like a hospital patient.

My first trip off the hospital grounds was on a gorgeous sunny day when mom took me in my wheelchair across the street and around the corner to Tim Hortons—her favorite coffee shop. She didn't tell anyone on the ward we were leaving. She figured it would be our little secret. Though I'm sure if she had, they would have warned us how tricky things might be. My chair couldn't roll over curbs easily, so every time we crossed the street, we had to go to the corner of the sidewalk where it slanted into a ramp, though not every path had one.

When we got to Tim Horton's, my wheelchair barely fit through the entrance. Mom struggled to maneuver me through the doors and around the tables full of customers. Some people kindly pulled their chairs out of the way, others sipped their coffee completely ignoring us. Many looked at me with what felt like pity as we rolled our way to the till.

"I'll get an iced coffee," I said, looking up at the woman behind the counter. Something cold seemed like a wise decision since I was still experiencing hot flashes from time to time, and it was so warm out.

The woman leaned closer. "Can you repeat your order," she asked.

My vocal cords were still weak, and it was hard to project my voice.

"She'll get an iced coffee," Mom spoke for me once again.

I looked up at the people towering over me in my chair as we trudged through the busy café with our drinks.

"Sorry, just need to get past you," Mom said to a group of teenagers who thankfully moved to the side to let us out the first of two doors. One of them held the second open for us.

"Thank you," I whispered. I wanted them to know I was new to all this—being disabled and out in public. My heart broke thinking about the people that deal with this daily, how difficult it must be to be confined to a wheelchair, trying to maneuver through a world made for those able-bodied. Despite the challenge of being wheelchair-bound, I was still grateful to be out in the real world again.

I may have been in a wheelchair, but Mom wouldn't let me forget how far I'd come. Back in my room, she pulled out her laptop and brought up all the photos and videos she'd taken over the last few months. I remembered her snapping pictures and recording me here and there—me wanting to scream, "Get that fucking camera out of my face,"—but didn't realize how often she'd filmed me. Clicking through the photos and videos, I stared back at the screen, at this person on life support I couldn't recognize. My face was swollen and appeared slightly bruised. The ventilator tube, first in my mouth and then later down my throat, was a stark reminder of how close to death I was.

One video was especially hard to watch—James held up my paralyzed hand as I lay in my bed in the ICU, me trying to move my fingertips and nothing happened. Still wearing the eyepatch and in so much pain, I remembered how broken and depressed I'd felt in that moment. How utterly hopeless I'd been.

Then I watched the first time I breathed on my own. Then the first time I lifted my arm off the bed. And finally, when the trach was out, Jay pushing me down the hall without a tube in my throat, my arm clumsily waving in the air. It still seemed like yesterday I was paralyzed from head to toe and I'd cried to my family, "Am I ever going to get better?"

Seeing my journey from the ICU right in front of me showed me I *was* getting better. My family tried to tell me, but I didn't believe them until now. I was improving, even if it felt like slow motion. I smiled as I watched the rest of the videos—playing with Casey in my bed for the first time, eating with cutlery, and drinking from a cup.

When the surgeon was available to take out my feeding tube from my stomach, the nurse told us the procedure would be done right at my bed.

"I don't have to go to an operating room?" I asked nervously.

"Nah, it'll take less than a minute," she replied. "The surgeon will be by shortly." It was morning, so James and Casey were still at home. This meant I'd only have Mom by my side. The idea of the tube being removed was terrifying.

"Is it going to hurt?" I asked the surgeon when he arrived in my room. I wondered if he remembered me from inserting the tube back in ICU or if was this just a work task he'd check off from his day.

"Yeah, it's gonna hurt," he said rather abruptly.

I was taken aback by his honesty. Most nurses and doctors tried to placate me and say it wouldn't be that bad, but it always was.

"I'm not gonna lie, it will be extremely painful," he warned, "but very fast. Whenever you're ready, let me know."

My heart rate sped up as I pulled the sheet down on my bed and then lifted my gown to reveal the thin plastic tube poking out the side of my belly. "I'm ready," I said with shaking hands, making eye contact with my mom. I wanted this over with.

Standing beside my bed, the doctor squeezed his hand around the tube and grabbed tight.

"One . . . two . . ." he counted.

I took in a big deep breath.

On three, he yanked as hard as possible, his face going red—that's how hard he pulled.

Lacerating pain shot through me as if I'd been stabbed from the inside of my belly with a screwdriver. I screamed as loud as I could, my voice cracking.

"All done," said the doctor, standing with the detached tube in his hand.

In a split second, it was over, leaving me in shock. I said nothing. The insufferable pain was now completely gone as if it never happened.

The surgeon covered my wound with a sterile bandage, then wished me all the best before hurrying out of my room. Even though the tube had reached all the way into my stomach, I didn't need stitches or staples, or even medical glue. Like the hole in my neck, it would heal and close on its own, leaving a tiny circular scar beside the giant gash down my torso, another disappointing scar to add to my haggard body. At least now, I was completely free of all medical tubing.

With my nerve pain managed by just Gabapentin, I came off all narcotics. My pain dulled to more of a tingly, numb sensation, like when I was first diagnosed. Being off the hard drugs helped the swelling in my stomach finally retreat. Mom finally left the hospital for more than a few hours at a time, and sometimes she'd take Casey—allowing me and James some time alone. Finally thinking straight, I was ready to talk about everything that happened over the last few months. I wanted to have real conversations again, mostly with my husband. James and I had been through a lot in our relationship, but nothing as traumatic as this. Our families had always been healthy.

"Can you tell me about the first few days?" I asked. Having been so heavily drugged, those were the vaguest, and I wanted to know things from his perspective.

James told me everything, how he sat beside my bed in the same ward I was on now. Dr. Yousef saying the words Guillain-Barre and how it might take months for me to recover. When I was having trouble breathing, and when I was rushed for emergency surgery.

"The doctor told us you might not survive." James looked down at the ground, the corner of his eyes filling with tears. "I called my dad while we waited," he continued. "He asked me what was wrong, but, Holly, I couldn't even speak. I tried to make out words, but nothing came out. How do you tell your dad over the phone that your wife might be dying?"

By this point, tears were rolling down James's cheeks, and I, too, started to cry.

I couldn't imagine what must have been going through his mind. James was twenty-five years young, a brand-new father. He wasn't prepared for this sort of trauma. He was so close to losing me, his wife, the woman in his life for eight years, and the mother of his newborn daughter. He would have had to raise our baby on his own.

"I was a fucking mess for months," James said.

The two of us cried for several minutes without saying a word. Going over the fine details of everything was a lot, but it had to happen. We needed to release the pain we'd been holding in.

Finally, I composed myself and spoke. "It's all going to be okay, now." I reached out to hold James' hand. "I made it," I said, smiling with pride.

James smiled back then wiped the tears from his eyes with his sleeves. "Yes, you did," he nodded. "And you're still getting better!" We talked about how I'd wheeled myself from the hallway into my room earlier that day, a huge step forward in gaining independence. Hopefully, soon I'd be able to move my wheelchair more independently.

"But what if I don't fully recover," I blurted out. I was doing a great job maintaining the positive attitude I desperately needed to make it through each day, but this fear always existed in the back of my mind. "Did you know, not everyone recovers from GBS?" I told him what I'd read in the booklet. "What if I don't get strong enough to get out of a wheelchair?" How would we function? How could I be a mom?

James paused for a moment, then said with certainty in his voice, "If that happens, we'll deal with it. And we'll be fine. Things might be hard, but we will get through it—together." He reminded me that the chance of me walking again was high. "Don't even worry about the future right now."

I nodded my head, but there was more than just that on my mind.

"I hate the sound of my voice," I said. The doctors told us it would be back to normal after about a week. It had been two, and it was still hoarse and scratchy as if I had a bad cold.

"Your voice is fine. No one is going to care what you sound like after everything you've been through."

I had to agree. I once had a tube down my throat, a valid explanation.

"But my scars . . ." I stuttered, tears forming in the corners of my eye. I'd have those ugly things on me for the rest of my life. "Every time that someone meets me, the scar on my throat is going to be the first thing they'll see." Not my blue eyes, not my big smile, but the scar. I started to bawl. "I don't want to be known as the girl with the ugly scar on her neck."

James told me I was beautiful, and that no one would be distracted by my scar. "And it's only been two weeks, it's gonna fade."

It *was* still healing.

"The scar on my stomach won't, though." Three months later, it had healed, leaving a jagged beige line going down my torso. You could see the tiny marks on either side where the thirty staples had been. The scar on my inner thigh was just as horrific. "I'll never be able to wear a bikini again," I cried. It felt stupid to cry over something so trivial, but it still hurt like hell.

"Yes, you can," James interrupted. "You don't have to hide your scars. You should wear them proudly, after all that you've been through."

I smiled, encouraged by his support.

"What you should do, is make up some crazy story for anyone new that meets you. You could say that you were bitten by a shark in the ocean and lived to tell about it. Or wait, no—" James laughed. "You should say you were in a bar fight and stabbed and cut up by a bunch of girls. That sounds bad-ass."

I laughed at his recommendations. He was always trying to make me laugh.

"Or—maybe you could just tell the truth. That you survived something that almost killed you. Which is something you should be proud of."

James was right. I had nothing to be embarrassed about. If anything, I should be proud of all that I'd overcome. I knew I needed to learn to accept the scars on my body. They were there to remind me what I'd gone through and that my body had healed.

*

Weekends at the hospital were quiet. Without physiotherapy, my days were long and drawn out. I had plenty of time to think about my circumstances, confined to my wheelchair. I tried not to worry about my future, instead only imagine.

What would happen if I didn't walk again? I wondered what life would be like in a wheelchair, raising my daughter, and hanging out with my friends.

What would my mental health look like?

Would I be sad and miserable and furious at the world for my circumstances, like I was in ICU?

Would I fall back into that deep state of depression I'd fought so hard to get out of?

I'd been through hell and couldn't go back to that place again. I had a daughter who needed me in her life. Could I not just accept the cards I'd been dealt, figure it out, and live the best way I could?

The truth is, I had no idea how my recovery would look. But I knew where I was now, breathing and talking and using my limbs again, was better than where I was. I wasn't in pain and never felt sick. I could talk to my family. I could tell Casey I loved her and hold her in my arms. If this was the best I would get, I had to be okay with that. I would adapt. Why? Because I could never give up on myself again, the way I'd wanted to in the ICU. I was stronger than that now. I made a promise to myself to move forward as best as I could with what I had. Even if my future would look a bit different, I'd be with my daughter, which is all I ever wanted.

I asked to be lifted into my wheelchair as soon as I woke up on the weekend. I figured I might as well get used to being in one. Other than the coffee shop down the road and the hospital cafeteria downstairs, there was nowhere to go, nothing to do. I had no idea how a day pass home would even work, but I was hopeful I'd get one soon, just to get out of here for a bit.

"The thing is you don't have a commode or a lift at your house," the doctor explained when I asked him when I'd be able to go home. "You won't have any way to go to the washroom." The joys of being wheelchair-bound, I couldn't just get up and go when I wanted. "But . . . if you use the washroom before you leave the hospital, technically, you could go home for a couple of hours at a time."

My heart fluttered. Realistically, I was wearing a brief for emergencies anyhow.

"But how would she get home?" Mom asked.

I couldn't shuffle over to a bed, let alone into a vehicle.

"You'd have to call for a cab and ask for a wheelchair-accessible one. They can take you in your wheelchair and bring you back." He paused for a moment and looked up at the clock on the wall. "You know what? You don't have any physio today. If you want to go home this afternoon for a few hours, you can."

Mom and I jerked our heads to look at one another, our mouths open wide.

"I can go home? Today?!" I shouted. It was so unexpected. I could go be with James and Casey.

My doctor nodded and smiled. "I'll get the nurses to get you your lunchtime meds, and you can call a cab now."

Mom already had my cell in her hand. I was so excited to call James and give him the fantastic news but decided to surprise him by showing up instead. Mom called my stepdad Dennis who intended to stop by the house before coming to the hospital that day and asked James if he'd like to take the dogs for a walk to get him out of the house. Mom got me dressed, had me lifted into my chair, and wheeled me down to the lobby.

When the taxi-van arrived, I waited in my chair on the pavement outside while the driver folded down the back seats. He set up a ramp, rolled me into the back of the van, and buckled my chair with different seat belts anchored to the floor and alongside the doors. It was strange being in a wheelchair inside a vehicle, and I tried not to think about getting around like this in the future.

As we made our way to our home, the outside world quickly distracted me from my worries.

James and I bought our house less than a year before when I was four months pregnant and barely showing. It was the second place we owned together; we bought our first when we were nineteen. This house, a two-story detached home with three bedrooms, was where we'd raise our family—we wanted two kids. An older home that needed some work, we'd hoped to remodel the kitchen and bathroom after the baby was here.

When we pulled up to the house on our quiet street, it looked exactly as I remembered, though the last time I was here, the big cherry blossom tree in the front yard was blanketed in snow. Mom rolled me to the backyard, where the sun was shining, and the trees were starting to bud. She parked me next to the BBQ. "I'm gonna go grab us a drink," Mom said, heading toward the back door.

On our drive over, we'd remembered the three concrete steps into my house would make it impossible for me to get inside, but I was happy to just sit in my yard soaking in the sun. Mom came back with an ice-cold beer and said, "This calls for celebration."

I wasn't a beer drinker, but this one tasted like the best one I'd ever had. Minutes later, the back gate opened. Pushing Casey in the stroller, James stopped frozen in his tracks when he saw me casually sitting in the backyard, beer in hand.

"You're home!" he finally said, leaning down to give me a hug.

Day 82 and almost three months since I'd barely walked out the same back door and left for the ER. I smiled, so grateful to be here. Our dogs were just as excited to see me as I was them, they whined and tried to jump up on my lap—this time, I could reach down and pet them.

James remembered I was supposed to get my eyebrows waxed at the hospital that day and called to have the woman come to our house instead. He also phoned a few nearby friends to drive over and say hi. No longer attached to any machines, wearing a floral dress and a bit of makeup, I looked somewhat healthy again. It was nice to see people away from the hospital. When the woman arrived to wax my eyebrows and mentioned she'd need me close to a plugin to heat the wax, my friends didn't hesitate to grab a corner of my wheelchair and lift me up the steps inside.

Being inside was weird. There were baby toys scattered everywhere: toys I had never seen before, as some had been donated to us. But it was still my home, and many things were exactly the way I'd left them—our black, leather couches, the photos on the walls, and items along the kitchen counter. I was quickly brought back to the life I once knew and loved. Back when I could walk.

After my eyebrows were waxed, I looked in the mirror and saw a glimpse of my old self for the first time in months. James and I had been laughing about how crazy thick my dark eyebrows were getting; he'd jokingly started to call me Oscar the Grouch. With my brows groomed and shaped similar to how I'd had them the last ten years, I felt much more like myself again.

A couple of hours later, we called for a taxi, and Mom and I headed back to the hospital. Leaving was hard, as was waking up in my hospital bed the following morning. I wanted nothing but to be at home with Casey and James. I couldn't wait to go back again. When I told the doctor how well everything had gone the day before, he said there was no reason I couldn't go back today if I wanted.

Half an hour later, we rolled out of the hospital and made our way back to my house in a cab.

This time mom had a friend meet us to drop off a ramp so I could easily be rolled inside. James and I talked about what I wanted to do for the day, and I decided to call Deanne over. It had been forever since I had time alone with my best friend.

"I'll let you girls be," James said and snuck away to the golf course across the road—probably one of the first times he felt he could relax.

Mom had Dennis pick her up so she could also go home. Casey stayed, with Deanne's assurance she'd take care of us both.

It was surreal being back in my living room, chatting with my girlfriend like we used to do all the time. I didn't mind that I was sitting in a wheelchair.

Deanne cuddled with Casey on the couch. About an hour later, she quickly stood up and set my daughter in her swing. "I'll be right back," my friend said, then ran up the stairs. She came down less than a minute later with my straightener in her hand.

I smiled, thankful for my friend and how thoughtful she was. Deanne knew that I always straightened or curled my wavy hair.

"I want you to feel more like you again," she said, then proceeded to do my hair. If I'd realized anything over the last few months, it was what an amazing friend I had. When my husband was at the hospital with me, Deanne was often at our place helping tidy up. She babysat Casey when James ran errands and came to the hospital at least every other day. She had filled in the months on Casey's First Year calendar, documenting all the new things that Casey did since I wasn't able to. I had an incredible support system, not just Deanne but all my friends who came by whenever they could. My friendships were important to me, and I promised to spend more time with those I loved as soon as I was home.

That night, in my own kitchen, I ate my dinner with regular cutlery (it was all I had) for the first time on my own. Even in a wheelchair, it was a fantastic weekend.

*

When my physio team found out I'd gotten day passes over the weekend, they decided it was time to attempt the transfer again. "We have to keep trying," Samantha said. "'Cuz once you master transferring from your wheelchair to a bed, then a commode and back, you might get weekend passes to go home."

If my doctor agreed, I could potentially sleep in my own house two nights a week—at least on the couch for now. Talk about motivation. I was enthusiastic to try again.

My legs showed progress in physio, and I was starting to figure out how to move them around, so Sam suggested we try to transfer without the board. Samantha removed the arm from my wheelchair, wrapped the same fabric belt around my waist, then with Jerilee, grabbed hold of it.

"On the count of three, you'll push yourself up as hard as you can with your legs. We'll lift you off the chair, then shift you over to the bed."

My feet were tingly and numb as if they were asleep, so I wasn't sure how this would work. But I tensed up my legs, hoping to keep them stiff and strong.

"One . . . two . . . three," counted.

I planted the bottoms of my feet deep into the floor, or at least I think I did. I couldn't feel anything. Sam and Jerilee pulled my body up and helped me fly over to the bed, using all our strength.

I made it.

Although I was out of breath, and it was hard, but not as difficult as last time. We did it a few more times, back to the chair, then back to the bed again. Sam showed James and my mom how to wrap the belt around me so they could help, too. That way, I could get in and out of my chair whenever I wanted.

"Now you can stop wearing briefs, and we can help transfer you to the commode." I'd get to go to the washroom on my own again. Finally, a piece of my dignity back.

*

My body continued to strengthen. From wearing my hand splints more often, my fingers were starting to straighten out, making it easier for me to grip things. I started doing some of my makeup on my own, just my foundation and blush, as my hands were still pretty shaky. Mom did my mascara. I wasn't strong enough to lift my arms back above my head either, so I couldn't put my hair up on my own; Mom did that for me, too. But I was getting better at using the wheels on my chair to move myself around.

One day while practicing rolling myself in the hall, I noticed Samantha with a group of geriatric patients exercising in the physiotherapy room, doing things I couldn't do in mine. I wondered why I'd never been invited to this group class. Sam later told me I couldn't attend the sessions because of the bladder infection. The bug wasn't harmful to the average person but dangerous for the older patients on my ward—almost everyone but me.

Samantha saw how disappointed I was that I couldn't exercise the way they could. She ordered me a monkey bar that hung on the ceiling above my bed so I could practice pulling myself up. This would help strengthen my upper body even more. She also gave me more leg exercises to do in my spare time—things like laying on my side in bed and lifting each leg up in the air. My hip muscles were so weak I could barely lift them more than a few inches.

On May 19th, Day 87 in the hospital, Samantha said we were going to try standing in PT. The day was special to me; on this day, the year before, I'd found out I was pregnant with Casey and had fallen in excitement on the bathroom floor. A moment I'd forever cherish, it was hard to believe how much had changed over the last year. I had to get back to being a mother to my daughter and knew that attempting to stand was the next step to reaching that goal.

Samantha had Mom bring me a pair of shoes from home, something I hadn't worn since I walked into the hospital back in February. Sitting in my wheelchair near my bed, mom squeezed the shoes on my feet, the material feeling like little knives to my skin. My feet were so sensitive.

Once my shoes were on, Samantha rolled me up to face the side of the bed, then had me hold on to the arm rail for support. Jerilee attached the belt around my waist. Like the transfer, I'd push off with my feet, this time, I'd try to push my body weight up on my legs—with the help of the girls, of course. I was doubtful I'd even be able to do it.

"You're just going to try to push your bum up," Samantha said. On her count of three, I once again tensed my leg muscles, then pushed up with all my might.

My body shifted off the wheelchair and raised into a standing position.

Jerilee's mouth opened wide.

"Show off," Samantha smiled. "See, I told you."

"You stood right up, Holly!" Jerilee said.

It was an odd feeling, planting my feet without being able to feel them on the ground, and my body felt as if it weighed five hundred pounds. After fifteen seconds, my weak legs swayed and wobbled, and I sat back down. We did this three times in a row, each for fifteen seconds. It was hard work but incredibly empowering to be standing again, and the smile on my face showed how proud I was.

Later that evening, after clearing it with my nurses, James and I headed over to the mall. It wasn't far, just past Tim Horton's, and I knew the way to get there in my wheelchair. Now that Casey was a few months old, we wanted to get her ears pierced before she could grab at them. James had been the one who suggested we both take her; he knew I wanted to be there for this. I was thankful there was somewhere nearby we could go.

Once Casey was sitting on James' lap at the salon, I moved my wheelchair to face her. James held her close, and I tried to distract her with big smiles. But as soon as the technician pierced her ears, Casey wailed in pain. James shoved a bottle in her mouth, and I gave her kisses. Her cries gradually stopped.

The salon was busy that day, and the ladies helping us were enthralled with how cute Casey was. She quickly forgot about her pain. I hardly noticed when people looked over at me in my chair. My daughter was so beautiful in her new pink flower earrings. Casey's bald head sometimes made it hard to tell if she was a boy or a girl, these earrings now made it clear. I gave my baby another big smile, and this time—she smiled back.

"You look so pretty," I told her. "Your first earrings." It was amazing to be a part of her milestones instead of always hearing James talk about them while stuck in a bed. Other than the first few weeks at home, Casey and I hadn't done anything together. Being there as her mom while she had her ears pierced was a big deal for me.

James pushed my wheelchair through the mall with Casey resting on the wheelchair tray above my lap. I wondered what people thought when they saw me. I knew if I saw someone my age in a wheelchair, I'd naively assume they were paralyzed in a car accident. I had no idea there were rare diseases out there, like GBS, that incapacitate you. Most people don't.

We took a different route on the way back to the hospital. Ending up at an intersection without sidewalk ramps, James continued to push me down the road hoping to find a place to cross—but nothing came along. He eventually decided to cross and hop the curb on the other side. Unfortunately, just as we crossed the road, a car turned, heading straight toward us. James bolted with my chair and then tried to get me up on the sidewalk as quickly as he could. But the curb was too high.

My heart pounded as he struggled with the chair.

The car slowed down, then stopped to wait.

As did the several other cars that came up behind us. James couldn't maneuver the wheels to get them over. Someone honked, obviously frustrated that we'd jaywalked and were now in the way. My face was red with embarrassment as people in their vehicles sat there and watched us struggle.

"Get me off the road!" I shouted at James, though I knew he was trying. He eventually leaned the chair back enough to get it over the curb and lifted me on the sidewalk.

My eyes filled with tears. Something as simple as crossing the road was such a hassle now. The thought of dealing with this for the rest of my life was stressful.

But it made me even more determined to get out of that wheelchair. I knew my legs needed to be as strong as they could possibly be if I wanted to walk again. With the help of my PTs, I got up on a stationary bike every day in physio. At first, my ankles were so flimsy Samantha had to strap them to the bike pedals with resistance bands to keep them in place. I wasn't strong enough to do it on my own, so Samantha and Jerilee each took a leg and helped me push the pedals. But every day, my ankles grew stronger. By the end of the week, I was peddling the stationary bike for ten minutes at a time. We were masters at the standing transfers, with the help of two other people, and I moved from my bed to the chair and commode all the time.

I was ready to go home for a weekend pass. We called a cab, and James followed behind in his truck. Sam sent a commode so I could use my washroom this time. Since I couldn't get upstairs, I'd sleep on the sofa.

My mom went home for the night; her first sleep in her bed in weeks. "Let's transfer straight to the couch," I said to James. "We can watch TV, and I'll just stay on the couch all night." James agreed and settled Casey in her bouncy chair on the floor.

After rolling my wheelchair up to the side of the couch, my husband wrapped the belt around my waist. Then on the count of three, I used all my strength to stand. This time, though, without the help of a third person, my legs started to buckle. My body began to crumble.

Maybe we should have kept my mom around for a little longer.

James pulled up on the belt hard and pushed my limp body over, so I tumbled forward on the couch. Our assumption that we'd be able to do the transfer easily just the two of us was wrong. But at least I'd made it to the couch.

We agreed to move me as little as possible. James popped out the footstool on the recliner and pulled my weak legs in front of me. I reclined back in the leather couches we'd had since we were eighteen, the first purchase we'd made together. James put Casey on a blanket on my lap, cuddled up on the couch beside me, then turned on American Idol to watch all the episodes I'd missed.

I glanced up at the photo of us and our bridal party above the TV. I instantly felt calm and at peace. So suddenly, it seemed, I was here with my husband and baby again. Even if it was temporary, this was all I'd wanted for months. It felt so good to be home.

But being there partially paralyzed was not easy. Every time I had to pee, which was often because of my bladder infection, James had to help transfer me to the commode and then back to the couch. We figured out how to do it, but it was a challenge that took triple the amount of time and effort. Each move was this whole big thing that left us exhausted and out of breath for a few minutes. I had to pee twice in the middle of that first night, and then in the early morning, when I woke up, I found I had shit myself—all the meds my doctors had been giving me finally worked, when I was at home. I cried when my husband had to take off my pajamas and wipe my body clean. So much for getting my dignity back.

James thought it was hilarious and not a big deal.

Casey had woken up in the middle of the night, too, which James had to tend to. He couldn't just nap during the day when he wanted. My husband had to do everything for the both of us: the cooking, cleaning, transfers in and out of the chair, Casey's diaper changes, and bottle feedings. It's not that he couldn't handle taking care of Casey; he just wasn't used to taking care of me at the same time. We had my mom, my nurses, and Samantha and Jerilee's help at the hospital. Here, everything was on him.

I felt useless in my wheelchair while he scrambled around the house with a frantic look on his face.

James ended up calling some friends and inviting them over for dinner. We needed the distraction and a little help. He thought I'd feel better around my friends. Unfortunately, I just felt uncomfortable. I'd tried to do my hair but learned my arms weren't strong enough to hold the straightener up, so my hair was a mess per usual. I couldn't do my eye makeup on my own yet, either. I didn't feel like I looked like me, especially in the shorts and tank top I had James put me in. It turns out from all the weight I'd lost; I was swimming in my own clothes. Making matters worse, watching my friends pick up my little girl in their arms, something I couldn't do yet, was emotionally tough.

But later, James and our friends surprised me with a cake that read *Welcome Home Holly*. With the sun setting behind us, we sat around the patio table in our backyard, and with my closest friends, my husband and daughter, and me with a glass of wine in my hand, I was home. Something I'd dreamed about for so long. I needed to enjoy my time here, it had been months since I'd been together with friends, and I'd be going back to the hospital before I knew it. Talking, laughing, and drinking the night away, lost in the moment, I forgot I was paralyzed in my chair.

We spent the rest of the weekend watching movies on the couch. It was too much work to transfer me on and off the commode, we quickly found out, so I wore a brief, which was easier on the both of us. The only other hiccup we had was when I tried to go home Sunday night. Because it was the May long weekend, there weren't any wheelchair taxis available. Mom had to call the hospital to tell them I couldn't get back till morning. I felt like a kid breaking curfew, and we laughed, wondering if I'd get in trouble for not being back on time.

It ended up being a blessing. That night I got to witness Casey rolling over for the first time. Still weak, I wondered when I'd be able to roll over again.

Back at the hospital during physio that week, with Sam and Jerilee holding on to my belt, I stood three more times, each for one whole minute. My improvements were small, but improvements, nonetheless. Getting a taste of my freedom on the weekend made me even more determined to get back home where I belonged. Our next goal was to get my legs strong enough to be able to transfer into a vehicle. That way we wouldn't have to depend on a cab.

"I have an idea," Mom said early one morning before anyone else came into the room. My nurses were still doing sponge baths in my bed every day, and every few, Mom leaned my wheelchair into the back of the shower to wash my hair. She figured she could help me transfer to the commode, which was just a plastic chair, and roll me into the shower—so I could bathe on my own. And it worked.

Once I was sitting in the shower, Mom helped me take off my gown. She turned on the water above me, handed me the showerhead and a loofah, then closed the curtain behind her. "Enjoy!"

For several minutes I sat holding the hose over me, the hot water trickling down my body. It felt like that first shower after a greasy camping trip with no running water, only this time I hadn't showered in three months. I soaked in every second, with no desire to get out anytime soon. Looking down at my naked body, at my scars, at my loose skin, at the unruly hair on my legs, armpits, and pubic area, I chuckled. "Jesus, do I need to shave." Eventually, I grabbed the shampoo to wash my hair. But I found I couldn't squeeze the bottle; my hands were too weak to get anything out. I had to call my mom to help. When I finished my shower, I felt like a brand-new person.

I was basking in my independence and wanted to try to shave my legs. "Hey, do we have a razor here?" I asked my mom after I was dressed in a bright pink dress cut up the back.

"We do, but I don't know if that's such a good idea. You're still pretty shaky."

I still had tremors in my hands when using my fine motor skills. I assured Mom it was fine, and she handed me a pink shaver. Leaning forward in my chair, I proceeded to run the razor up my legs, still wet and dripping from the shower. After several strides, a slight tingle. I must have nicked myself—very lightly as it barely hurt. Then, teeny tiny droplets of blood dripped down my legs.

I nervously looked up and smiled at my mom.

"Holly!" mom shouted, then pulled her hand to cover her grin. "You're still on a blood thinner!" Excessive bleeding is the most common side effect of blood thinners. Even though it didn't hurt, more blood poured down my legs.

Mom grabbed a roll of toilet paper from the bathroom. "I'm not asking for band-aids," she laughed. "The nurses will know I gave you a razor. I don't want to get in trouble!" She rushed to cover each cut with TP.

By the time she finished, me and Mom were laughing hysterically. I had over twenty tiny pieces of toilet paper all down my legs.

"Like that's not obvious," I laughed.

"I love how you told me you were fully capable of doing this, and not even two minutes later, you're bleeding everywhere," she laughed again.

The situation was hilarious. Laughing was something I'd craved for so long; now, every time I did, it was like therapy for my soul. It truly is the littlest things that make such a difference in life.

Caring more about my appearance and style again, I gave up the Goodwill dresses and started to wear my own clothes again. Mom helped me out of my gown and into tank tops and sports bras since none of my bras fit anymore from all the weight I'd lost. While I sat in the wheelchair, Mom slid each of my feet into a pant leg, I was able to push myself up with my arms, then mom pulled my pants up to my waist.

Just like everyone had told me, I was getting better. Even my fingers were finally straight from the splints, making it even easier to do things. Every morning that week, sitting in my wheelchair, I practiced my eyeliner and mascara in front of the mirror. Makeup was art for me, something I'd been playing around with since Junior High. It was a challenge to keep my arm up that long—it felt as if they weighed twenty pounds—but I pushed through. When I finished and looked in the mirror, I saw more of myself again.

More and more, little by little, I felt like me. I was so much stronger and healthier than when I moved to this ward four weeks ago. With no news of a transfer date to the rehab hospital, I started to wonder why I even had to go. It was almost the end of May, and I wanted to be home by mid-June for James' birthday.

"I'm really sorry," the nurse said to me and my mom when we asked about the wait. "There's still no beds. It's gonna be at least another few weeks."

Mom and I looked at each other and sighed. The longer it took to go to rehab, the longer it would take for me to get home. I'd already spent a month on this ward and didn't want to spend any more. I did my best to not let it get to me and continued to work on my therapy as hard as ever.

Every morning I rode the bike in the physio room. Every few days, I practiced standing beside my bed. When sitting in my wheelchair, I lifted my body and did tricep dips. I curled one-pound weights that felt like ten. I pulled myself up in bed with the monkey bar. Even though I was getting stronger by the day, late that week, when Samantha said it was time for me to try walking, I hesitated.

Walking? As in holding up my body and making it move with my legs? I wasn't sure I was ready. I couldn't stand for more than a few minutes; how could I possibly walk? With my feet still numb, I wasn't sure I'd even be able to place them properly.

It felt too soon.

"We can at least try." Samantha flashed her cheery smile, and I nodded my head. She grabbed the handles on the back of my chair and rolled me across the hall to the physio room, up to two metal beams called parallel bars. I sat in my wheelchair on one end, the two beams staring right at me. My mom sat across the room with Casey on her lap. Mom was ready to cheer me on as if I was a baby again.

Jerilee stood just outside the bars to my left, holding onto the back of the belt. Sam sat directly in front of my chair on a rolling stool. With their help, I stood from my chair.

"Step forward," Sam said. "The wheelchair's right behind you if you need to sit down." Another PT was right on my tail keeping the wheelchair close. I glanced down at my feet, then up towards my mom and daughter.

What if I'm not strong enough? What if I fall?

I pushed my left foot firmly onto the floor, then, as if in slow motion, I lifted my other foot in the air.

Mom teared up as I took my first shaky step. Then another. And another.

It was the strangest feeling. My brain commanded my legs to move, but I couldn't feel anything happening. My feet moved, but they were numb. I held on to the bars for dear life, my upper body doing most of the work. My arms vibrated. Sweat dripped down my face as I continued towards Mom and Casey. After a few more steps, I finally reached the end of the bars to carefully switch hands and pivot. Jerilee was in my peripheral, as was the other PT behind me with the chair. Slowly, with more confidence, I started back. By the end, my legs were so heavy my toes dragged along the floor. Out of breath, I carefully lowered my body down into the seat.

My legs were just barely strong enough to hold up my body and walk the length of the parallel bars—twice. I looked at my mom, beaming with joy. Casey had a big smile on her face, too, as if she knew. I never imagined my baby would watch me take my own wobbly first steps. But every step forward was a step closer to going home. I had faith that one day I would walk on my own again.

Samantha surprised me with a gift to celebrate: a small pedal machine I could use in my room whenever I wanted, as I otherwise only had access to the bike across the hall once a day. With this machine, I'd be able to sit in my wheelchair, and either use it with my feet on the floor or pedal it using my arms on the tray.

"Strengthening your muscles regularly is very important," Sam said. She was constantly pushing me. Looking back now, I'm incredibly grateful for that. Now I know that sometimes everything you've ever wanted is only one step outside your comfort zone.

I transferred from the wheelchair into my mom's van the next day. We used her vehicle as it was level with the curb, making it less work for me—my car would have been too low, and James' truck too high. Using the transfer belt, Sam and Jerilee helped me through the passenger door onto the seat. It was harder than transferring to the bed or my couch; I had to avoid hitting my head on the roof of the van and barely made it inside. But once I was in, I could shift my body into the middle of the seat. Then, after I caught my breath, we transferred back out to the chair. We practiced with James and my mom a few more times to make sure we could do it on our own, then headed back upstairs for more therapy.

"You have enough energy to keep going?" Samantha asked as we rolled back to my room. She wanted me to try walking again, this time with a walker, down the hall.

I was cautious once again but willing to try. "Yeah, I do want to try," I smiled. Sometimes my body knew it was time to stop; other times, I could push through.

Out in the hallway, I sat in my wheelchair, and Samantha moved a walker in front of me. It had brakes to keep it from rolling too quickly and a seat I could sit down on if I got tired. My PTs helped me stand, and I held on to the walker. Once I was ready, just like with the parallel bars, I stared down at the floor, lifted my foot, and stepped forward. I couldn't feel anything, and my legs felt like I had sandbags strapped to my thighs. My body poured sweat as I shuffled across the floor. It was shocking how much energy it took to take a few steps. I glanced down the hallway which looked a thousand feet long, wondering if I could go any farther.

"Take a break if you need it," Sam said, and I took the opportunity to sit. I could have stopped there but decided to get back up after a minute and take a few more steps.

I walked a few meters at a time that day—exhausting but exciting. I was physically using my legs again. I was walking years before doctors said I would.

That night I went home again, this time, with Mom dropping me off in her van. Deanne and another girlfriend, Jackie, came by and made us banana splits. We watched movies on my couch all night. At the end of the night, they decided I should sleep in my own bed. James grabbed my arms at the wrists, my girlfriends each took a leg, and they carried me up the stairs to my room. I was dead weight, so it was more challenging than we all anticipated. As they moved me down the hall, I glanced over at my daughter's bedroom on the way, trying not to let it choke me up that I hadn't seen it in months.

Our bed was tall, so the three of them tossed me upwards onto it. I crash-landed on the blankets. But they were my blankets, not the thin hospital ones I'd been using for months. To be in my own bed was amazing.

Expecting to have the most glorious sleep but I woke up in the middle of the night to pee. My bladder was unpredictable, and we hadn't thought this through. I woke up James, trying not to wake Casey in the bassinet beside us. He helped me slide off the bed onto the commode he brought from downstairs. Getting back on the bed was even harder; James had to pick me up and practically throw my body onto the high mattress. Three more times I had to pee, then stayed awake with aching pain in my feet from forgetting to take my meds.

We were exhausted the next morning. We once again hadn't thought ahead; with no one there to help, James had to pick me up in his arms and carry me back downstairs. He helped me dress and made breakfast and transferred me in and out of my chair whenever I had to pee. At least my legs were stronger for the transfers, but it was a major ordeal. I had James bring me a TV stand so I could get ready in my chair. I tried to straighten my hair, but every time the heat got close to my face, my body overheated, and I felt I might faint. My body still couldn't regulate temperature. I lifted my arms in an attempt to put my hair in a ponytail, but my left arm locked before I could reach far enough back. I still couldn't brush my own hair, either. Discouraged, I left it in a frizzy mess. Not giving up completely, I practiced doing my makeup—more therapy for my arms. They were shaky and heavy, and every movement felt harder than it should be. When I saw myself in the mirror, I looked nothing like the me I wanted to be.

"So, what do you want to do today?" James asked once I finished.

The thing about trauma is it can creep up on you, and any little thing can unexpectedly trigger you. I immediately started to cry at his question.

"What is there to do other than sit here and watch TV? I can't transfer to your truck, so we can't go anywhere. I can't just do what I want. I can't do anything." I couldn't walk across the house to grab a drink of water or help my husband with the dishes. I couldn't even put on my clothes or do my own hair.

Would I get out of this wheelchair? Would I ever be able to get up and go meet my friends? Would I walk up my own set of stairs again? Vacuum my house? Dance at a concert? Swim in a pool? Go on rides at an amusement park?

"I just want my life back," I started to cry. I thought I was over all of this.

James stood from the couch. "Let's go to the mall. We're going shopping." He said we needed to get out of the house and do something different. "I don't care if we haven't figured how to transfer into my truck yet. We're gonna figure it out."

So, that's what we did. Despite my hesitations, James lined the wheelchair beside the truck, helped me stand, and I pushed with my legs as hard as I could. I placed my feet on the running boards, reaching for the handle on the inside of the door. Using the belt around my waist, James lifted as I pushed with all my might—and I was in. Out of breath, James loaded up my wheelchair, then Casey, and we headed off to the mall.

James had to drive around for a while before finding a parking spot with a curb beside it. Without one, it was much farther down that I'd have to step, and in such a tall truck, it would be impossible to reach the ground. After fifteen minutes, we finally found a spot. James helped me slide out of the truck onto the curb, and I shuffled into the chair. With gravity on our side, it was much easier than getting in. My husband set the pink and green checkered pillow on the tray of my chair and laid Casey on top.

Rolling in the mall was like stepping into this world I hadn't been a part of for so long. Everyone rushed around at a much faster pace than I was used to. It felt like everyone turned their head to gawk at us once again, looking me up and down in my chair. Our four-month-old flashed a big smile at every person we passed, and their blank faces turned to huge grins.

James took me shopping for bras since none of mine fit. When I went to try them on, I wondered how I'd even do it as I could hardly get my arms above my head on my own. Thankfully, the woman working gestured us both towards the handicap room. James could come in to help.

"Can't say I've ever been allowed in a change room with my wife before," James chuckled under his breath.

My husband helped me try on bras, and I settled on three new ones, two whole cup sizes smaller than I wore before. Looking at myself in the mirror, it was shocking how much weight I'd lost and how much my body had changed.

The rest of the weekend at home went well. James carried me back up the stairs to sleep in my bed—this time, I slept through the night. The following day, two of my girlfriends, Jen and Jessica, visited. The three of us sat in the gorgeous sunny weather in the backyard, me in my wheelchair with Casey on my lap, and we chatted for hours. We talked about my time in the hospital and how I was so out of it whenever they came to visit. We laughed about how on my death bed, I had noticed Jen had a new iPhone (the first generation) and made a comment about it, then every time she came back, I said the same thing, "Oh my God, Jen! You got a new phone!"

Jess said she was at a loss for words as I lay paralyzed in the ICU and decided she should let me know the rap artist Nate Dogg had died. I didn't remember her telling me this, but I know I would have been interested to hear about anything other than how bad my condition was for once.

Being with friends was one of the few times things felt almost normal, like old times again, and sometimes I'd forget about having GBS. My girlfriends filled me in on the gossip I'd missed while I was away. It had been so long since I'd spent time with either of them.

Then Casey started to squirm, something she hadn't done much of yet, and I had to readjust her on my lap. My baby was getting to that age where she didn't want to sit still anymore. I tried to hold her up as she wiggled, but my arms were too weak. And Casey was getting heavier, too. Just as she began to fall, Jess reached out and grabbed her—stopping her from tumbling off my lap. My face felt like it went bright red with embarrassment. I couldn't hold up my daughter without someone's help. I shouldn't even be alone with her.

There was a lot I had to adjust to. One thing that really helped me was to focus on what I could do—things that gave me joy—and do them as often as possible. When I discovered my hands were finally strong enough to change Casey's diaper on the couch, I did it every single time. I wasn't very coordinated and looked awkward doing it, but with concentration, I could wipe her little bum and fasten on a fresh diaper. Something so simple yet tedious, that most parents complain about doing was a blessing for me.

Even though I was struggling, I could still find the good in every day.

*

Back to the hospital I went that Sunday night, as if I lived two separate lives. Different surroundings, bedding, TV shows, and very different meals. Everything tasted fantastic when I first started eating again. Now I was sick of hospital food.

In physio that week, instead of exercising, we walked using the walker. I focused on carefully stepping each foot in front of the other, Jerilee right behind with my chair. The first time I'd walked about a hundred and eighty feet around the hallway, on the second, I doubled that. I went from being overwhelmed and fearful of my future to confident, brave, and strong. I still desperately needed the support of the therapists behind me and the walker in front, but one day, I knew I'd do this on my own. And I'd never take my body for granted again.

My legs were stronger from using the pedal bike and walking, and eventually, I could stand up from the bed, take a few steps, then carefully lower down in my chair. This was so exciting, as I didn't have much independence—now I could get in and out of my wheelchair and commode without help from anyone.

My nurses barely did anything for me anymore. They didn't need to use the lift or help with transfers into my chair. I was showering on my own and could squeeze shampoo and conditioner from the bottles. My legs were strong enough that when I put pants around my ankles, I could stand, then bring them up to my waist. Other than my socks and shoes, I could dress myself. I ate with normal cutlery and used the washroom on my own. My left arm was even getting better, and I could finally brush my hair. The only thing the nurses did anymore was bring me pills. After a while, instead of gowning up to come into my room, they started to hand me my meds in my wheelchair right at the door.

I questioned why I needed to stay in the hospital anymore.

During the week, Mom, James, and I spent most of our time watching TV, taking turns with Casey in our arms. I was strong enough to completely hold the bottle in my hand to feed my daughter. My husband was at the hospital between eleven in the morning and eight every night, and we struggled to find things to do between my physio sessions at ten and two. There were only so many times we could stroll around the hospital. We were bored to tears. The days dragged on. When we counted the days on the calendar, we discovered I had been in the hospital for one hundred days. It was almost hard to believe.

One afternoon while relaxing in my hospital bed, I looked across at Casey playing on her daddy's lap as he sat in the chair. Our baby is a person now, I thought. She made faces and smiled, and she could grab and hold. I thought about how she had spent the past four months of her life in this hospital, here almost every day for eight hours— sometimes more. She was growing before our eyes in these four walls of my hospital room. And it broke my heart. I at least had twenty-six years living my life. She'd spent most of hers here. The guilt ate me up inside. I just wanted to go home for good and help raise my daughter.

The next time I had physio, it only made me question being at the hospital even more. For about ten minutes, Samantha and Jerilee took me for a walk with the walker around the unit, then brought me back to my room. That was it—no strengthening, no exercises, nothing else. I was frustrated; I sat around for hours and hours waiting to do my therapy, and it lasted only ten minutes. Now I'd have to sit around for three more hours until my next session. Why was I even here?

Sitting in my chair, I told my mom how I felt. I had no idea she was feeling the same.

"I don't see why you have to stay here anymore, why you can't just wait for the Glenrose at home." She began to cry as she said how much she hated watching Casey grow up in a hospital. The last we heard, it could still be another few weeks before I'd get admitted for rehab. And who knew if that was even accurate.

"Maybe it's time for you to leave the hospital," Mom suggested. I could obviously live at home; the last few weekends we did just fine. The only thing I'd miss out on was my physio. Mom reminded me we had money from the fundraiser to help. "You can pay a physiotherapist to come to your house with that kind of money." James was still on paternity leave and would be off work till October, so it's not like I'd be alone. "And I'll be around to help," she said.

The more we talked about it, the better it sounded. I hadn't done stairs yet—that was the next thing I was to learn in physio—but spending most of my time on the main level of my house until I was strong enough to do them sounded better than staying here. I was healthy; my blood pressure, heart rate, potassium, and magnesium were all normal again. The only medications I was still on were Gabapentin and the antidepressant, which I took by pill. Mom said I could easily get a prescription and take them home. There were no real medical reasons for me to be in a hospital anymore.

By the end of our conversation, I had made my decision. It was time for me to go home.

15

Nothing But Time

I could not wait to get out of this place. How amazing would it be to live in my house with my family again. I'd get to help take care of my baby the way I should be. I could help feed and bathe her and put her to bed in the crib she had yet to sleep in. Mom researched physiotherapists who could provide therapy for me at home while waiting to get into the rehab hospital. That same morning, when we told Dr. Yousef of my plan to go home, I was confident he'd support the idea.

I was wrong.

"I understand you feel like you're a lot better," Dr. Yousef said to me as I sat in my wheelchair. "But there's a lot more work you still need to do."

Mom and I glanced at each other out of the corners of our eyes.

"I can't force you to stay here, Holly, but I don't think you're ready to leave yet."

Disappointment grew.

"How does James feel about this?" he asked.

"Well, we haven't had a chance to talk to him yet. We just decided this morning," I said, my confidence hanging on by a thread.

"Okay. I'll come back to see you when your husband gets here, and we can talk more about it then. Remember, he has a say in this, too."

James arrived shortly after and was told what I wanted to do. "I think it's time for me to come home." I explained everything Mom and I discussed, how I could wait to get into the rehab hospital at home. Being at home with him and Casey would be such an uplifting joy.

"Are, are you sure?" James stuttered—and I immediately sensed hesitation in his voice. "I don't know . . . what does your neurologist think?"

Once we had Dr. Yousef back in the room, he sat down beside my bed.

"So, here's the thing. To get into inpatient therapy at the Glenrose, you have to be *in* a hospital. If you go home, you'll lose your spot and will only be considered for outpatient therapy." He assured me being at the Glenrose full time was better; I'd spend a large chunk of my day in physio compared to only a couple of hours a few times a week as an out-patient. "If you only spend a few days a week on your therapy, your recovery might take twice as long. I understand why you want to go home, and it's your decision, but I want you to really think about it before you decide."

I nodded my head, frustrated. I hadn't realized how much this choice could affect everything.

He went on to tell us that being home for the weekend is a lot different than everyday life. James put things like laundry and vacuuming aside so he could focus on me. With being around permanently, he'd have to take care of not only me and Casey but everyday errands and all the chores around the house. I didn't have the strength to cook or clean.

"I know you feel more independent, but you're not quite there yet."

I couldn't do stairs, so unless James carried me up them every day, I wouldn't be able to shower or sleep in my bed.

"I honestly believe that staying in the hospital is in your best interest," Dr. Yousef said.

Reluctantly, I agreed with everything. Out of all the doctors, even if he seemed condescending at times, Dr. Yousef was an intelligent man and understood a lot about GBS recovery. I respected his opinion.

Maybe I should just stick it out here...

I thought about being stuck on Unit 52 for even one more day. I couldn't lay in my bed or roll around the hospital anymore. Sick of this place, of the smell, of the routine, I was utterly bored. We could only watch so much television. "I want to be at home with my husband and my daughter. I don't want to wait here forever." One of the nurses had told us a patient once waited months to get into the Glenrose. "I can't sit here for months. Ten minutes of physio twice a day is not worth it."

The doctor nodded his head. "I get it. How about day passes?" he suggested.

My ears perked up a little.

Instead of just weekend passes, I could go home every day after my two o'clock physio. I'd spend the rest of my afternoon and evenings at my house, then come back to sleep and do my therapy the following day. "You'll still technically be a patient here, which will qualify you for your spot at the Glenrose."

I'd get to go home every day, but unfortunately not to live as I wanted. I glanced at James, who had a big smile across his face, much bigger than mine. I just assumed he'd want me home as soon as I could, but it must have been overwhelming for him. Having me at home was a lot of work, and as it was now, at least he got a break during the week.

This idea was the best of both worlds– he'd have me home in the evenings and still have his mornings to get things done around the house.

"And I'll talk to physio about doing longer sessions with you," Dr. Yousef said.

I reluctantly smiled in agreement. "If I can get day passes and more physio, then okay, I'll stay." But I wouldn't stay forever. If I hadn't been moved by June 19th, my original goal to be back with my family, I'd give up my spot at the Glenrose and go home. Almost three weeks away, that was as long as I was willing to wait.

Both James and my doctor were good with that. Mom and I took it upon ourselves to look into therapy as an out-patient—just in case I did end up going home. I knew it would only be a few days a week which meant my recovery might take longer, but at this point, being at home with Casey was more important than my recovery. In the long run, what did it matter if my recovery took a few months longer—at least I'd be at home with my daughter. She needed me, as much as I needed to be with her.

It was gratifying to make my own decisions and finally be in control.

After our conversation, Dr. Yousef must have immediately crossed the hall to tell Samantha everything because ten minutes later, she and Jerilee were in my room apologizing.

"We didn't want to push you too hard. That's the only reason why we've been keeping your sessions so short." GBS patients fatigue very easily during recovery, they reminded me, and if they pushed me too hard, I could regress. "If you feel you can handle more physio, we'll give it to you," she assured.

In addition to practicing walking, we agreed I'd also ride the bike more often, and do different leg-strengthening exercises with another PT. "Since you'll be spending more time at home, we'll look into getting you your own wheelchair, a walker, a commode, and a bath seat for you to keep there." Samantha also had us apply for an accessible parking permit so that when James and I went out, we could legally park in the handicapped stalls. Mom researched wheelchair lifts to get me up and down the stairs at home, just in case. Even with my improvements, there was a chance I might not recover more than this—I could be permanently disabled. I couldn't depend on James carrying me forever.

"Hope for the best, but plan for the worst," Mom said.

She'd drilled that into me since the first time I went to her for advice. If things didn't go as planned, at least we'd be ready with a lift. It was all coming together, and I felt good about my decision to stay for now.

Late that afternoon, a familiar face peeked his head in my hospital room: Mike, the respiratory therapist from the ICU, checking in to see how I was doing. I loved visits from the staff in Intensive care. It was nice to see someone we'd grown close to, someone who knew my history so well. Sitting in my wheelchair, I told him how great I was doing, how I was using a walker in physio, and that I'd hopefully be going to the Glenrose soon.

"That's amazing, Holly. It won't be long before you're ready to take that trip to our place in Phoenix." He smiled and winked.

I looked over at James. I remembered what Mike had said back in the ICU, how he offered up his vacation home after I did that awful NIF test for him. I didn't think he was serious. But as he explained the house like a sales pitch, how it had a pool, tons of bedrooms—how it would be the perfect place for our family to relax, I realized he was dead serious.

"When your friends and family threw you that fundraiser, my wife and I thought about donating our vacation home for people to bid on. But we decided just to let you use it instead. After all that you've been through, you deserve a holiday."

James and I were speechless.

"When do you think you'd want to go?" Mike asked.

James rolled with it. "Let's say Holly is home from rehab in six weeks. We could give it a few more months at home to adjust. So maybe September or October?"

It was hard for me to picture where I'd be in my recovery by then. I'd have to be well enough to travel. Would I still be using a wheelchair? I had no idea how long it would take for me to be strong enough to walk on my own.

"That sounds good to me," Mike said. "We'll stay in touch. Let me know when you get into the Glenrose."

James was excited and couldn't stop talking about it. I didn't say much. Fall seemed too optimistic. I didn't want to go too soon as I'd never been to Phoenix before and wanted to be able to fully enjoy doing things like getting in and out of the pool. Going on a vacation in a wheelchair didn't sound fun, and honestly, I didn't think the trip would end up happening. Either way, I was incredibly grateful for Mike's offer. The generosity of people during this time was truly amazing.

That same day, Dr. Yousef came back into my room which wasn't like him to come twice in one day. He said, "I've got promising news." Apparently, the rehabilitation hospital had called to request my file. "They usually do that when they're preparing to move the patient." He figured it could be soon.

My heart raced, excited at the thought of finally moving to the Glenrose. I wondered if Dr. Yousef had pulled some strings. He was a contractor who also worked out of that hospital. It seemed like too much of a coincidence that within hours of telling him I wanted to go home, they had called. I figure he must have phoned over to get the ball rolling.

In the end, it didn't matter if he made a call on my behalf or if they phoned on their own. I was ecstatic. As much as I simply wanted to go home with my family, I knew the rehab hospital was the best place to work on my recovery and learn to walk.

That week I went home at three every afternoon, returning around eight each night. It was so nice being at home with my family again. James made delicious home-cooked meals, and we ate dinner together in the living room, with me in my wheelchair. Now that I could transfer on my own, James didn't have to help me on and off anymore.

Over the weekend, we ventured out of the house to a friend's birthday party. It was a backyard BBQ with no steps anywhere, making it possible to attend. We were blessed with sunny weather, and the moment James rolled me into the yard with Casey on my lap, friends rushed over to say hi. Other than my closest friends who'd visited the hospital, I hadn't seen many of these people for months. And with Casey being so young when I was admitted, some of them hadn't even met her yet.

"How are you doing?" everyone asked.

I was pleased to tell them, much better, that I would hopefully be getting out of the hospital soon. There was a time I didn't believe I'd ever go home or even survive. Yet here I was, enjoying the sun and the company of friends, like real life once again.

It wasn't easy being at a BBQ in a wheelchair. I was improving at wheeling myself around my room, but it was more challenging in the grass, and I didn't want others to see me struggle. So I stayed in one spot, watching everyone mingle around with ease. Whenever I wanted to get a drink or food or talk to a friend, I had to ask someone nearby to move me in my chair. There was no reason to feel embarrassed or guilty, but I did. After doing everything on my own my whole life, it was frustrating to still depend on others all the time.

More friends visited the following day at our house. We spent the afternoon on the couch chatting and reminiscing; James told stories from the hospital, which helped remind me of how far I'd come. As much as I cherished my time at the BBQ, visiting with friends at home was when things felt most normal for me. Socializing took the focus off what I struggled doing or could no longer do.

In physio that week, I walked with the walker for about twenty minutes every day—either through the halls or outside around the hospital grounds. Even with taking breaks and Jerilee holding tight, it took a massive amount of energy and concentration. Every day I walked the halls, I passed a sign on the wall.

Somewhere, someone is doing something that seems impossible.

Wasn't that the truth. Even with all the help I had, walking was such a challenge, but worth it. The more I walked, the longer I could go the next time. Sometimes James would join with Casey, walking alongside me with her stroller. We were finally getting to go on our walks, even if I was still learning.

I began to understand what Sam meant about pushing too hard. Some days felt as if I'd hit a wall and was too tired to go on. I listened to my body and let my PTs know when I reached my limit, sometimes only halfway through the walk. Then we switched back to the wheelchair.

During my walking, Sam and Jerilee noticed my toes always dragged on the ground. The muscles in the front part of my foot were weak, causing drop foot from my feet naturally falling forward when I was bedridden. My physical therapists gave me several exercises to work on, including sitting in my wheelchair and lifting my feet and standing on my tippy toes. I couldn't do either, even a little, but I knew the importance of trying them anyway. Like breathing and walking, the more I worked at it, the stronger I'd get. Working hard was the only way.

Another thing to help strengthen my leg muscles was to take on stairs. Although I had only been walking for eleven days, Samantha wanted me to try them. When I wheeled up to the pre-built wooden stairs in the physio room, I was afraid I wouldn't be strong enough. The five steps looked like a mountain to me. I managed to push through the fear. I stood, and Samantha wrapped the fabric belt around my waist.

"I'll follow right behind you up the stairs. Step with the same foot up, then switch, and we'll come back down."

I lifted my right leg in the air, something I hadn't done before, and placed it on the first step. I was used to surprising myself, but I didn't expect my foot to go that high. Then I lifted my left leg to join the other. It was hard work. My legs were weak, my balance off, and felt at any second, I'd tumble off the steps.

"I have you, don't worry," Samantha reassured me as my eyes grew wide. "You're not gonna fall."

I slowly continued up the stairs, planting my foot one step at a time. Samantha helped lift me with the belt. Using every ounce of energy, I finally made it to the top, conquering the mountain I wasn't sure I could. It meant so much to me to reach that peak, because once I mastered stairs getting up to my bedroom meant James wouldn't have to carry me there anymore.

But the one-way trip up meant getting back down.

Samantha helped me pivot on the top step, and I lowered one leg to the one below. Instant sharp pains shot through the back of my calf as if it were ripping in half. Samantha said my calves were extremely tight. Once my foot landed on the step, the pain went away, then returned as I lowered the next leg. I continued, pushing through the suffering, eventually making my way to the bottom of the stairs, my brows and armpits dripping in sweat.

What a struggle.

"You want to go up again?" Samantha asked.

I shook my head—absolutely not. One mountain climb was quite enough.

"All right, just remember that you did say you have about twelve steps at your house," said Samantha. More than double what I just did.

I hadn't thought about that. But I was too tired and didn't want to push myself anymore.

"I'll try again tomorrow," I promised.

A couple of days later, I tried walking with a cane in the hall outside my room.

"We just want you to see how it feels," Samantha said. It wasn't a standard one; it was a quad cane with four small feet that extended from the base, to give me more support. Jerilee held on to the belt around my waist as I stood from my wheelchair. It was hard to keep my balance, and my body swayed as I tried to place the cane in front of me, then step forward with my wobbly legs. A definite challenge for my strength and coordination, and I had to lean my body on Samantha for assistance. Jerilee held the belt tight. When I passed the sign that read, *Somewhere, someone is doing something that seems impossible,* I smirked to myself. This felt impossible, but I was doing it. I hobbled the entire loop of the unit, about a hundred and fifty feet, mostly with my PTs support.

"It'll be a while before you're ready to use the cane, but now you know what it's like," Samantha said. I looked forward to getting back to practicing with the walker, which felt like a breeze compared to the stairs and cane.

"Did you hear about the new patient?" Dr. Yousef asked once I was back in my room. "A woman with GBS moved to Unit 52 a couple of days ago."

My heart skipped a beat at the thought of someone here with the same illness as me, knowing I was not so alone.

"Her name is Leanne. She didn't have it quite as severe as you did. She spent about a week in ICU and didn't have to be trached but will need to learn to walk again. She just got into a wheelchair, and I was hoping you might be able to motivate her by showing how far you've come already."

Dr. Yousef and I shared a smile. It was incredible to think I could help someone else going through what I did not that long ago.

Samantha later introduced us in the PT room. Leanne, the young woman around my age, was in her wheelchair waiting for her first assessment. I was on the stationary bike, feeling the strength in my legs as I pushed the pedals with little effort.

"You came from ICU," I said to Leanne.

"Yeah, I was lucky. I didn't have to be ventilated," she said. "I was pretty close, but once I got the IVIG, my breathing improved."

I told her all about my journey and the months I spent in the ICU.

"I saw you walking with a walker the other day," she smiled. "It gave me hope that maybe one day I'll walk again, too."

My heart felt like it was exploding from my chest. I understood completely. Every time Kit walked into my room, it gave me the strength and courage to keep fighting. I held my head high, knowing I had inspired someone else now, the way Kit did for me.

James picked up all the equipment for me to use at home, including a new wheelchair, a walker, and a bath seat through a provincial program that provided it for free. The gear wasn't cheap, and I was thankful our healthcare covered it. Every evening at home, I practiced with the walker from my living room to the kitchen, to the bathroom, and back. My husband was nervous about me doing it myself; at the hospital, Samantha and Jerilee were always at my hip for support. Even with James there to help, I wanted to prove to everyone I could do this on my own.

I felt like a boss walking around my house by myself.

My stepdad installed handrails on the wall going up my stairs, so I could practice here too. Even with practicing in physio a couple more times, where I'd gone up and down them twice, doing them at home was brutal. James held the belt around my waist and held onto me tight, but I was only able to take a few steps, one at a time before needing to stop for a break. It took ten minutes for me to get up my stairs, one leg at a time, but hey, at least I could do it. Then James brought up the wheelchair and walker so I could venture around, most importantly, into my daughter's bedroom.

Her room was perfect. The cherrywood crib was all made up, with the pastel pink bumper pads I'd bought and a soft white blanket with grey and pink polka dots. I hadn't liked any of the baby blankets I'd seen in the stores when I was pregnant, so I picked out fabric, and Mom made one for Casey just before she was born. It brought back warm memories to see it almost exactly as I left it, as Casey still slept in the bassinet beside James.

Getting upstairs meant I could enjoy the piece of equipment I was most excited about—the bath seat—a long plastic bench about the length of three regular chairs. Two of its legs rested in the tub, the other two outside of it on the bathroom floor. James helped me undress in my wheelchair. Then I transferred onto the part outside the tub and scooted my way to the other.

James handed me the showerhead and closed the curtain.

It was a piece of heaven. Nothing compared to finally showering in my own home.

When I finished, pieces of my hair were scattered on the chair and accumulating at the bottom of the tub. My hair was growing so long, and without brushing it often, I assumed it was normal shedding. But it was shocking to see how much more came when I combed it out after getting out of the shower. This wasn't normal, my hair seemed like it was falling out.

I also got to see my husband give Casey her baths. I sat on the seat of my walker beside the tub, then got to change her out of her hooded piggy towel into her jammies once we were downstairs on the couch. I'd smile at her, and she'd smile back, and life felt like it was heading in the right direction. I wondered if Casey realized I was at home with her again.

Back at the hospital, I worked on the exercises PT assigned me. Jay visited on his days off and helped Mom and me organize all the photos and videos in the hospital on mom's laptop. One morning, as the three of us clicked through the dark memories in the ICU, a nurse walked into the room, which was odd since I didn't see them often anymore.

"Good news," she said.

Jay and I turned to look at one another, both our eyes lighting up with anticipation.

"They're ready for you at the Glenrose," the nurse said with a smile. "You're moving there first thing tomorrow morning."

16

The Flock

Paramedics helped me transfer onto a stretcher, and I rode in an ambulance to the Glenrose under a perfect blue sky. My new home on the other side of the city was about half an hour away. With rush hour traffic, the drive was long and slow, but I didn't mind—I had a view of the city. It was strange being strapped down to the bed, nonetheless, I enjoyed the drive. We passed familiar buildings, like the Wendy's I used to go to as a child. Sunshine beamed through the windows.

Before we left the Grey Nuns Hospital that morning, mom and I had made our way around to say our goodbyes to the people we'd met. The woman in the cafeteria who sold my family their meals. The woman at the flower shop who asked how we were doing every day. Of course, Jerilee and Samantha, my PTs across the hall, and everyone down in the ICU. The massive grins on everyone's faces as we said goodbyes made me realize how lucky we were to have made so many connections and new friends. That was a huge positive I'd get to take from all this.

It was a long six weeks on Unit 52—a hundred-and-seven-days total in the hospital. I was excited to start this next chapter. One step closer to going home. But I was also afraid. The rehab hospital encouraged independence—

they wanted me to be able to do every task I could, by learning to do it all on my own. Mom would not be staying overnight with me. Visitors were discouraged from coming so I could focus on my therapy. It was scary to think I'd be there all alone. My transition from ICU to 52 was not easy, but at least I had James and my momma bear to protect me. What if I couldn't keep up in physio? What if they put me through more pain? I had no idea what to expect and it scared me.

My mind continued to wander as I watched the clouds roll by. I couldn't help but think back to the horrible times not so long ago, like when I woke up from surgery and intubation. When I couldn't hold my daughter. The unbearable nausea, vomiting, and pain. As traumatizing as the flashbacks of being paralyzed back in the ICU were, I welcomed them, as they helped remind me of how far I'd come. I'd since learned how to use my fingers, hands, and legs—all over again. I knew the road ahead was not going to be easy, but with a lightness in my chest, I felt confident that I'd accomplish it all.

At the Glenrose, I laid on the stretcher staring up at the ceiling for almost half an hour in silence, while my paperwork got completed by one of the admission clerks. Sitting in a hospital waiting room during admission is one thing; laying on a stretcher when you feel completely fine is weird.

A porter eventually rolled my stretcher upstairs to my new room, where Mom was unpacking my pink suitcase. We were on the spinal cord injury ward. Because GBS is rare, there isn't a specific area for us to go to, like stroke or cardiac patients. This ward made the most sense since everyone here was in a wheelchair, like me. People zipped past us as we made our way to my room. It was intimidating to watch as I lay weak in the stretcher. I was strong enough to wheel myself in my chair, but I usually had someone pushing. I wasn't sure how far I could go on my own.

My nurse, a cheery older woman, gave us the rundown. At the entrance of our ward, Unit 3B, she explained, was a massive whiteboard with a list of patient names and their scheduled classes. Unit 3B patients were a lot healthier than where I came from, so I'd be able to join the therapy classes even with my bladder infection but had to avoid touching the other patients.

"It's your responsibility to wheel yourself to your classes," she explained. "Unless you're having a bad day and really don't feel up to it. Then just ask for a porter to bring you down." When we didn't have class, we were free to roam as we pleased. There were a few cafeterias with rows of long tables and chairs, several lounges with a TV, and an area outside the lobby with big concrete ashtrays where the smokers hung out outside. The Glenrose reminded me a bit like high school. Like mine, it also had a salon. Before I could go out on my own, though, a physiotherapist would have to observe me transfer to make sure I was capable. The PT wouldn't be by until sometime that afternoon.

I tried to assure the nurse I'd been transferring in and out of my chair for weeks now and was comfortable getting out of bed on my own.

"We have to ensure your safety. It's protocol, hun." Until PT assessed me, I'd have to use the lift to get in and out of my chair. Mom and I thought it was overkill, and I felt ridiculous being strapped in and hoisted through the air when I could have literally just stood and stepped over to sit. Thankfully, the nerve pain during the move was minimal, nowhere near as bad as before.

Later, when PT watched me stand and transfer with ease, the young woman smiled and said I was good to go. "We aren't used to seeing people this far along," the therapist said. Most patients came shortly after an initial incident, like a car accident. They *started* their physio journey's here. I had already done six weeks with Samantha and Jerilee.

When James and Casey got to the Glenrose, we rolled over to check out my schedule on the board. It was already Thursday, and I didn't start classes until Monday. Surprisingly, I only had two, sometimes three, one-hour classes a day, with breaks between—which meant I'd have a lot of down time. Technically, my mom, James, and

Casey could have come when I was free, but it wouldn't have made sense. I'd be going to my classes alone, and it would be pointless for them to drive across the city to have to sit and wait until I finished.

"Hopefully, you can still get evening and weekend passes," James said. That way, he could pick me up to spend my evenings at home, then return me to sleep like before. I assumed it wouldn't be a problem.

"You're going to have to talk to your doctor about that one," my nurse chimed in. "They don't usually give evening and weekend passes to someone unless that person is very close to being released."

A tight knot formed in my stomach. Maybe my assumption was wrong.

Being at home with Casey and James, relaxing on my couch, hanging out with family and friends, and sleeping in my own bed was the highlight of my life. Being able to go home again was what was keeping me sane.

"You can ask the neurologist tomorrow when he comes to see you," she added. That meant I wouldn't be able to go home that evening and wouldn't find out about the weekend until the next day. Not much I could do but wait.

James and Casey stayed until eight, and I crawled into bed to read. My girlfriends had brought me magazines months ago, but I didn't bother trying to read them because my fingers were curled for so long. Besides, there was always someone around. For the first time in four months, I found myself alone.

You'd think I might have been lonely or afraid, but it was nice to finally have some me-time. I'd come a long way since the days of panic attacks when anyone left my room. Bundled up in bed, I embraced the quiet and looked around to check out my new home.

Because of the bladder infection, I got to have my own room. The room was big, with a walk-in bathroom and shower three times as large as my last. The shower floor had no entry edges, it was simply an extension of the room's floor. All I had to do was roll my chair under the showerhead and turn it on. This place was designed for those in wheelchairs. Grateful to be here, I looked forward to starting my classes.

The next day Mom, James, and Casey came back to the Glenrose, and I had my assessment with my new neurologist, Dr. Robinson. He was one of two neurologists on the ward. The other had evaluated me back on 52. Just as before, he tested the strength in my arms and legs, and read my file from the Grey Nuns.

"We're gonna get you fitted for AFO leg braces," he said. "I'll set you up for a fitting next week." The ankle foot orthosis (AFOs) would help me walk by supporting the weak muscles to reduce movement on my lower leg. My ankles were flimsy, and the braces would prevent my toes from dragging.

I pictured the metal leg braces Forrest Gump wore as a child.

"You've been through something pretty traumatic," he noted, reading more on my file. "I'm curious if you've noticed any hair loss lately."

"Now that you say that, yeah, I have," I said, thinking about the mounds of hair that came out of my head after every shower.

He explained that it's common for hair to fall out a few months after severe emotional or physical stress, and there was a name for it, something called telogen effluvium. "Don't worry. It's temporary."

At least there was a reason behind the shedding.

"Not sure if they told you," I said as he continued to skim the pages in my file, "but I've been going home every evening and weekend. I was hoping to get the same passes here."

The neurologist glanced up at me then over at mom and continued to read. He adjusted his glasses then put down the folder. I had improved drastically, he said, but I still had a long way to go. "Usually if someone is well enough to get a weekend pass, then they are well enough to be home all the time.

My heart sank as he said the words, "You're not ready to be at home yet."

I felt sick to my stomach. I couldn't be stuck here, sitting by myself for the next who knows how long. I couldn't imagine not getting to go home anymore for dinner with my family, not being able to be there with my daughter, and I felt panicked at the thought of losing that time with her again.

"But here's the thing," he added. "Even though I don't think you're ready for home passes, you've been going for over a month now. You've obviously figured out a way to function just fine. I'm not going to be the jerk that takes away your passes when you already got approval from someone else."

I flashed James and my mom a relieved and grateful smile. I'd continue going home to be with James and Casey every evening and weekend, which meant everything to me.

"So, how long do you think she'll be here?" my husband asked.

The doctor couldn't give us an answer. Every Wednesday, the entire team who worked with me would meet and discuss my progress. They would come up with a release date right away, and as I progressed, every Wednesday, they'd decide together if that date needed to change.

"You don't have classes until Monday, so we won't meet next week," Dr. Robinson said. Their first meeting would be the following Wednesday, thirteen days away. Past James' birthday, my original goal date of being home.

I was a little disappointed, but I knew it was best.

When we finished with the doctor, we packed up my things and headed home for the weekend.

James and I took Casey to her first birthday party that Saturday—one of my girlfriends' daughters was turning one. Another backyard BBQ on a beautiful sunny day was easy for me to attend. I'd gotten used to missing events and now wanted to make up for lost time and attend every possible one. It was always nice being with friends. I noticed Casey loved it, too. Sitting on my lap in my chair, she'd watch and stare at every person that walked past us on the grass, then smiled and giggled the second they looked at her. At almost five months old, her personality shone through. She lit up around everyone. I shouldn't have been surprised as she was always surrounded by people in the ICU.

My friend set up a blue plastic kiddie pool in the middle of the yard. My mom, who was at the party too, rolled my wheelchair up to the side and took Casey off my lap. She held her just above the water so Casey could get her toes wet. Casey's first time in a pool, she went crazy splashing and kicking her tiny feet. Her smiles were infectious, and she looked so happy. Mom continued to dip Casey in and out of the pool, and my little girl giggled the cutest little laugh whenever her toes hit the water.

A part of me was upset. I wanted to be the one holding my daughter while she experienced this. I couldn't bend down in my chair like that. I wondered what else I'd miss out on doing with my child if I stayed in a wheelchair. It would be hard for me to ever dip her in a pool, take her swimming, play tag, or hide-and-go-seek. Would I always just be watching from the sidelines? Wanting to be a part of every possible experience, I knew I had to do whatever it took to walk again. I had to do it for her.

On the other hand, I also felt grateful to get to watch her squeal with delight as her toes dipped into the cool water. At least we were making memories outside hospital walls. I was a part of my daughter's life again.

Monday, June 13th, was my first day of rehab, my first day at the hospital on my own. Unfamiliar with the Glenrose, I had a porter bring me down for physical therapy to a massive gymnasium filled with other patients and PTs. There were parallel bars, about three times as long as the ones at Grey Nuns. Someone was walking through them in a harness fastened to the ceiling, which I thought was genius. Most of the class was assessing my strength in my wheelchair, and figuring out my weak areas.

"You won't be here long," my PT said at the end of the class.

I smiled in return. Her encouragement was reassuring.

The porter wheeled me back to my room, and I opened Mom's laptop, which she had brought me to help pass the time. Outside my room, people rolled by every few minutes, some making eye contact with me as they passed. I scrolled through Facebook while sitting in my wheelchair, surprised at how hard it still was to use my hands to type.

My neighbor across the hall, an older man in a baseball cap, stopped his wheelchair at my door as he left his room. "You know you can use your laptop in the cafeteria," he shouted across. "Or if it's nice out, you can go outside. That's what I always do."

I appreciated the suggestion, but I was nervous about wheeling myself around. The most I'd done was in my room, and I was scared to get too tired if I went too far. "Thanks," I replied. "I just want to stay in my room for now."

My second class was occupational therapy, where I met with an OT in the small studio with a therapy bed off to the side. An OTs job was to help improve my motor functions, making everyday activities easier to do. They typically teach patients how to transfer, and when I hopped onto the bed on my own, the OT was pleasantly surprised by how far I was in my recovery. She helped me with a few things right off the bat—like how to put on my socks and shoes, which James and a nurse had been helping me do. While lying in bed, I could lean over to put them on, which was doable, unlike bending over in my chair. She also helped me transfer onto a toilet seat raiser instead of the commode I'd been using. The raiser fit right on top of the seat, unlike the commode that went over it. With two metal bars on either side, I could use them to push up.

"This will help strengthen your legs so that eventually you can push up without using the bars." Once I was comfortable using the seat in my room, she'd get me one to use at home. "I'm also going to put you in a hand class, which will help you with your fine motor skills." My upper body was much stronger than my lower but nowhere near normal.

After our session, I decided to roll back to my room. It was three floors up, but I knew I wouldn't get better by having a porter bring me everywhere. Using my arms wasn't as hard as I thought it would be, and I made it back—very slowly.

"Don't worry!" the man in the baseball cap shouted from his room when I passed by like a turtle. "It gets easier."

When James picked me up from the Glenrose, he helped me transfer into the truck, and we made the long drive across the city back home. I practiced going up and down the stairs and using the walker around the house. It was exhausting, and I was slow but was getting a little easier each time. We ate dinner on the couch, watched TV for a couple of hours, then James gave Casey her bath. At eight o'clock, my husband brought me back to the Glenrose, where I read for a bit in my room, then went to bed. This became my new routine for a while.

My sessions at the Glenrose were challenging but valuable; the therapists were friendly and supportive. In physio, we practiced walking using the walker around the halls outside the gym. I did the loop twice every session and rarely felt tired at the end. All my work at home helped. I walked the entire length of the parallel bars and back—without the harness because I was strong enough on my own. My PT helped me go up the ten steps that went nowhere, challenging but doable. I also did mini squats, which I did while holding on to the bars with both arms because my balance was horrendous.

In my hand class, I sat at a table in my wheelchair, inserting and removing pegs from a vertical board. I worked on fine motor skills by using a tiny screwdriver to fasten even tinier screws into the wood. It drove me crazy because my hands were so shaky, and I kept dropping the screws again and again.

"Keep going," the therapist encouraged. Sometimes I wanted to just stop and give up, but I appreciated that he pushed me. Like the cones on Unit 52, with practice, it did get easier. I also reached for things above my head and curled two-and-a-half-pound dumbbells in my chair.

My favorite session of all was the support class. We sat in our wheelchairs in a large circle, and everyone introduced themselves and what brought them to the Glenrose. They talked about how hard things were in a wheelchair, how difficult it was to watch everyone else live their lives with ease. Some were parents who missed their kids, which helped me feel less alone. But it was shocking to hear how many had severe spinal cord injuries and may never walk again. I felt fortunate for all my progress.

When we got to one man in the circle, a guy in his forties in a motorized wheelchair, he spoke about a disease that had paralyzed his body completely. He had no function in his legs and struggled with his upper body. He didn't have the strength to wheel himself—hence the power chair.

"What's the disease called," another patient asked.

I almost choked when he replied, "Guillain-Barré Syndrome."

Someone else here had GBS.

As he shared his journey, I learned he had been diagnosed in January, a month before me. His recovery was taking a long time. I felt guilty when I told him I, too, had GBS, as I was much further along than him.

In physiotherapy the next day, my PT introduced me to a man in his sixties who had recently been admitted to 3B—he was in a wheelchair and also had Guillain-Barre. I was meeting *another* survivor of GBS. My disease didn't seem to be as rare as I thought. His case wasn't as severe as mine, and he never went to ICU. He was on the stroke and neurology ward at the university hospital for his entire stay. But even though he was diagnosed around the same time as me, he had yet to even try walking. Dr. Yousef had told me that my young age was on my side, and I felt lucky that my recovery was speeding along as fast as it was—even though it didn't always feel that way.

Already after a week at the Glenrose, I was getting stronger and faster at everything—from my walking, standing, transferring, doing stairs, and wheeling around.

I noticed my hips aching, as if they were bruised, which I later found out was from walking so much in physio. My weak hip flexors were getting quite the workout every day.

"Hopefully soon you can get out of this chair," my therapist said in physio, one of the most exciting things I could hear. My sessions were so beneficial, and I knew I was in the best place for my recovery. But spending free time reading magazines in my room by myself, either in my chair or in bed, I grew lonely. I was used to having my mom, James, and Casey with me all the time. Every evening for a few hours, I saw my husband and daughter, but I missed them both nonetheless and wished I was home for good.

Mom came by to visit and 'take me out for lunch,' so we ate in one of the cafeterias at the Glenrose—my first time. I'd been eating breakfast and lunch alone in my room, as I thought most people did. As it turns out, the cafeteria was packed. My neighbor from across the hall waved as he rolled by to get himself a drink.

"It's nice to see you outside your room!" he said, grabbing a Pepsi from the fridge. "You should come downstairs for a smoke with everyone on your next break.

"Oh, I don't smoke," I told him.

"Well, you can still come downstairs for the company. Sitting in your room must be getting pretty lonely."

I smiled and nodded, as it really was.

The following day, I ventured outside on one of my breaks, rolling out the front doors to the right, where the smokers hung out. More than ten people congregated in their wheelchairs, including my neighbor. Not everyone was smoking.

"You came!" my neighbor in the baseball cap said. He turned to the rest of the group. "Guys, this is—wait, I don't even know your name."

"I'm Holly," I replied.

An older man with uncombed hair motioned me to roll up beside him. "What are you in here for?" he asked.

Everyone in the group laughed as if we'd all done something wrong to end up here.

"I have Guillain-Barre Syndrome," I said.

No one replied. They'd obviously never heard of it.

"It's a rare autoimmune disorder, kind of like multiple sclerosis. My immune system attacked itself and paralyzed me." It was hard to explain my whole experience in just a few sentences.

"I'm Craig," my neighbor said. "I'm here because I had this crazy thing happen to me where the blood vessels in my spine randomly tangled together." He intertwined his fingers then twisted his hands to imitate his body. "It paralyzed me from the waist down. It's pretty rare."

GBS wasn't the only rare disorder that devastated people's lives.

Craig lit his cigarette. "There's not much they can do for me," he said. "I probably won't walk again so I'm here to learn how to function on my own."

Though he was smiling, I looked down to the ground. Sadness bubbled in my stomach for Craig's permanent loss of independence.

"I'm Jen," said a dark-haired woman in the wheelchair across from me said. "I fell and broke my back on my thirtieth birthday." She had fallen off a ledge. Completely paralyzed from the waist down, Jen would likely not walk again. She said it so matter of fact as if it were no big deal.

The man with unruly hair beside me spoke next. "The name's John. They aren't sure what's wrong with me," he said. He had gone to the hospital with sudden weakness and paralysis like I did—but it wasn't GBS. His paralysis had only been on one side of the body (in Guillain-Barre, it's usually symmetrical.) "The ER sent me home at least three times up in Grande Prairie where I'm from. They thought I was a junkie trying to get pain pills. When I dragged myself in through the doors the last time, they finally admitted me." It was appalling they turned him away. Thank God the doctors I saw believed me.

"They're still trying to figure out what's wrong," he said, "but it might be MS. I'm not sure if I'll walk again or not."

Hearing person after person say they may never walk again broke my heart. But as we each talked more about our journeys, we quickly discovered we shared a common bond. We had all spent time in the hospital before coming here; we'd experienced fear in the ER, tremendous amounts of pain and suffering, the worry for our futures. Now we were here, doing therapy, fighting for our independence again. We were survivors, and I felt strongly connected to these people I had only just met. I was glad I chose to go outside. It was great to meet other people who'd gone through something as traumatic as I did. It's not that my family wasn't supportive—they were incredible—but to talk to others who understood what it was like to lose everything was comforting.

An hour later, it was time to head to my next class.

"It was so nice to meet you," Craig said as I rolled out of the circle. "We'll see you later tonight or over the weekend?

He wouldn't, as it was Friday. James would be coming by shortly to pick me up for another weekend pass. A friend from out of town was coming to visit, too. "I won't be back till Sunday. I'm going home for the weekend," I said.

"Lucky girl!" Craig said.

Everyone in the group seemed surprised. Not many patients got weekend passes. I assumed they were envious of me, but they didn't show it.

"Enjoy your weekend, Miss Holly!" John said with a huge smile. "See-ya Sunday!"

Back home to my double life, I went, but I was much stronger than just the weekend before. I climbed the stairs easily by hanging onto the railings as tight as I could and dragging myself up. I didn't bother bringing in my wheelchair from James' truck and forced myself to use only the walker inside. We also moved the commode upstairs and fastened the new seat raiser onto the toilet in our main floor bathroom.

Just as I was learning and growing, so was my daughter Casey. She'd discovered her voice and was babbling more than ever these days. She was also starting to giggle at everything, and I became obsessed with trying to make her laugh. Casey could sit up entirely on her own, no longer falling over like I also once did. I wasn't strong enough to pick her up yet, but James had the great idea of setting her rubber Bumbo chair onto the seat of my walker and putting her in. Now I could walk around the house with her, and my baby could accompany me all the time.

My girlfriend Carmen stayed for the weekend, and we celebrated James' twenty-sixth birthday. Friends came over for a party. I drank my usual vodka-water-Mio's and got tipsy. We laughed and played board games and had an absolute blast. I never thought I'd make it this far, that I'd get to enjoy life like this again. It wasn't so long ago I was vomiting in my ICU bed, unable to breathe on my own, or reach out to touch my daughter's hand. I was grateful to get to have drinks with my family and friends, grateful to be using my body again. But I also felt guilty, knowing many of the people I met were back at the hospital, alone in their beds.

After a few too many drinks, I had the crazy impulse to take a couple of steps from my walker to the table.

"What are you doing!" my girlfriend Jen shouted with a smile as I took my hands off the walker. I wobbled like a child learning to walk as I took my first steps on my own.

My friends cheered.

Being here felt like home.

On Sunday night, James dropped me off at the front doors of the Glenrose as if I were reporting back to jail. I noticed Craig, John, and a few others sitting in the smoking area, and I decided to roll over and say hi. I figured I'd chat for a few minutes, then head off to bed. It was already nine, and I liked to be sleeping by ten, so I'd be fully rested for Monday sessions.

"How was your weekend, Miss Holly?" John said.

"It was good, thank you." Three other patients lounged in their wheelchairs, two in chairs like mine, one in a motorized chair. I'd seen them rolling around the hospital from time to time and was curious what their stories were, especially since two of them looked younger than me.

One of the guys, a young Inuit kid, started talking first. He was twenty-one, from the Northwest Territories. "I was paralyzed in a sledding accident—it was pretty bad. I had to be airlifted off the hill."

"Sledding? Like, snowmobiling?" I asked.

"No, tobogganing. The way I crashed broke my back." He was completely paralyzed from the waist down instantly.

I couldn't believe something so fun, and innocent could cause so much damage. His life was changed forever in the blink of an eye.

Steve spoke next, a man in his late forties who'd recently had a stroke. He lit up a joint and took a hoot, then passed it over to me. "We'll see how therapy goes," he said. It was hard to say what his recovery would look like. "Hopefully, they can get my Alberta Health Care figured out soon. I moved here from BC just before my stroke, and hadn't switched my health care over yet. I'm getting a bill for fifteen hundred dollars a day to be here."

My eyes grew wide as I puffed on the joint and handed it to Craig. I'd never considered this all must cost something. I'd heard stories of US citizens paying out of pocket for hospital expenses but was naïve to just how much the costs could be. As Canadians, we were privileged that everything was covered. I would never see a bill for what I'd been through. I also noticed that as I got high from the weed, the tingly aches and pains in my limbs faded away.

Craig spoke for Dan, the young man in the motorized chair. "Dan is eighteen. He can't talk." He communicated by typing into the small laptop by his right hand that vocalized for him.

"Hi, Holly," the computerized voice said after he clumsily typed.

Craig told me Dan was jumped by a group of guys on his way out of a 7-11 store in a rough part of the city, not far from the Glenrose. They never found his attackers and they don't know what provoked it. He was beaten so badly that he had severe brain damage. He'd be in this wheelchair for the rest of his life.

My heart was devastated for this kid.

He typed again into the computer. "Don't worry about me," his computer voice said. "The ladies love me here. I can still get pussy, even in this chair."

I burst out laughing, not expecting crude humor. Craig held up the joint so Dan could take a puff. The six of us talked and smoked and shared stories from our time in the hospital. From the crazy hallucinations to the heavy narcotics we'd all been on, to some of the awful nurses we had, we laughed at some of the similar things we went through.

"I didn't shit for over eleven days!" John said.

Our experiences were horrific at the time but hilarious now. Before I knew it, it was almost midnight, and we were rushing to the front doors before they locked them for the night. I couldn't believe we talked for three hours.

Sleep didn't come as easily, as I couldn't stop thinking about the people I'd met tonight. Like me, sudden events and illnesses out of their control forever changed their lives. These people may never walk again and would have to learn how to function in wheelchairs, possibly for the rest of their lives. My journey was hell—the unbearable pain, the heartache for being away from my daughter, and I still had a long way to go. But I was already walking again. I took my first steps on my own the day before. It would take time and a lot more hard work, but one day I'd likely be free of my wheelchair. I understood how much worse things could have been, and I was thankful all I had was GBS, an illness I could recover from if I worked at it.

On Monday, I got my AFO leg braces, made of molded plastic—I'd picked leopard print—they weren't metal like Forest Gump's. The braces fit behind my calf, were strapped to my leg, and could be hidden under my pants. James bought me running shoes one size bigger so the bottom of the brace could fit inside.

"You need to wear them every time you walk," the orthopedist said. Over the weekend, I'd discovered wearing flip-flops was out of the question; the muscles in my feet were too weak to keep them on my feet. I'd be stuck in runners all summer.

The AFOs were stiff and awkward but made my legs feel sturdy and strong through physio. I stood without having to hold on to anything and conquered the entire flight of stairs on my own. My body responded amazingly to physio. The week prior, in hand class, I struggled to get my hands above my head. After only a week, they were finally flexible enough to be able to put my hair up into a ponytail. Another tiny accomplishment that meant so much more than anyone could possibly understand. I learned how to write using a pen (my writing was atrocious), and I could lift heavier weights than before.

Three or four times a day, between my physio sessions, I sat with the group outside. Quite a few people were always there, but I spent most of my time with Craig, the man with the rare disorder in his nerves, John, the guy who likely had MS, and Jen, the girl who'd fallen off the ledge. The three of them were the comedians of the group, and I spent most of my time laughing at the hilarious things they said.

"We're like a flock of seagulls," John said, looking around at the group of people close together in our wheelchairs. "From now on, we're called the 'flock.'"

Everyone burst out laughing.

I still went home every evening to hang out with James and Casey, but when I got back to the Glenrose, I'd have James drop me off to the 'flock,' and we'd spend hours sharing stories, laughs, and joint after joint. Not only did my new friends make me laugh more than I had in months, but they also inspired the hell out of me. They were paralyzed in wheelchairs and may never walk again, yet they were the most positive and outgoing people there—the same people I'm sure they were before coming here.

"When I get out of here, I'm gonna try sledge hockey," Jen told us. Before her accident, she was an avid hockey player, and she was determined to get back on the ice one way or another. Jen wouldn't let her circumstances get in the way of her passion. Years later, I saw on Facebook that she accomplished that goal.

I was attaining my own goals and was so close to walking on my own again. If they could be this happy and optimistic, I knew I had more than enough reasons to be. I had much to be thankful for.

Then came amazing news.

In physiotherapy, after walking the loop with my walker twice on my own with ease, my PT said I was ready to use it all the time going forward. "The AFO braces are helping a lot. It's time to say goodbye to the wheelchair," she said.

I had never used the walker outside of physio or inside my home—and the thought was nerve-wracking but exciting. The moment I'd been waiting for was finally here—no more wheelchair.

My first trip down the elevator and outside was a breeze; it felt the same whether I walked five minutes or twenty. When I walked up to the 'flock' with my walker, every person turned their head in surprise.

"Miss Holly!" John shouted with a smile. "What the hell! You're using a walker?"

Although we talked plenty about my time in the hospital with GBS, I hadn't explained that if I got strong enough, I'd get out of the chair. "Yeah, I can walk with a walker all the time now, for short periods at least. And if things keep going the way they are, I should recover well enough to walk on my own one day."

John's smile grew even wider. "No way. I'm so happy for you, girl."

Everyone in the group congratulated me on my success with smiles. It was powerful because even though they may not make it to a walker, they were happy I did; they shared in my joy.

This inspired me to keep fighting as hard as possible—because I physically could.

In physio, we switched to a cane to learn on—a standard one, not a quad like the one on Unit 52. The PT held the transfer belt tight around my waist, and we walked around the gym. I was wobbly and struggled not to fall while simultaneously placing the cane in front of me while I stepped. But I reminded myself just because it was hard did not mean it was impossible. Just because something was difficult to do didn't mean I couldn't do it. The more I practiced, like the walker— the easier it would get. I was much sturdier compared to the last time, especially with the braces strapped to my legs.

Because I couldn't squat very low without my ankles aching and giving out, I couldn't ever get down on the ground to be at my daughter's level. My PT taught me how to lower myself without having to squat. I leaned onto my walker for support, then bent down onto one knee. This took the pressure off my ankles and gave me just enough strength to lower the other. Once I was on all fours, I shifted my hips and legs to the side into a seated position on my bum. Going back up was the same, in reverse. I moved onto both knees, then using the walker, I pulled myself up onto one, pushed onto the other, then pulled to stand. It took a couple of tries and some coordination and work, but it was easier than I thought it'd be. Now I could play with my daughter on the ground again, the first time in months.

*

On Wednesday, June 22nd, I anxiously waited in my room with Mom for Dr. Robinson. His meeting with my therapists was to happen that day, and they were supposed to be coming up with my release date. Would it be another week or three? A month? Or two? I had no idea as the amount of time patients spent here varied greatly—some spending months.

When the doctor arrived, my heart pounded in anticipation.

"So, we had a chance to meet today," he began. "You've improved drastically, but you still have a long way to go before you're independent again."

Mom and I exchanged nervous looks; a lump grew in my throat. I was progressing, but nowhere near back to normal. Stronger but still weak.

"If it weren't for your husband being at home to take care of you, I wouldn't even be giving you weekend passes right now."

I held my breath, afraid of what he was going to say next.

"But the fact that your husband is home all the time and not going back to work until October, then I think you're almost ready."

The lump faded.

"If he weren't on paternity leave, I'd be keeping you here for at least another three weeks. But you can go home Tuesday."

Tuesday. Six days away.

That meant that in less than a week, I would be going home.

I rubbed my hands together in excitement, and Mom wrapped her arms around me. After over four months in a hospital, I'd go home to live an everyday life again—sleep in my own bed, spend everyday with my husband and daughter, and we'd make memories again. I'd be back to being me.

Tuesday could not come soon enough.

The last few days of the week went fast. In physio, we practiced walking with the cane, and the therapists assessed me one last time to note how much I'd improved. The most significant change was that I arrived at the Glenrose in a wheelchair, and I'd leave with a walker. In just a few short weeks, I'd improved so much. Two weeks ago, I struggled to wheel myself around the halls, but now I was speedy as ever. When I first got here, James had to help me transfer in and out of his truck; now, I could grab the handle and step outside myself. I could go up and down stairs (though still one leg at a time). I could put my hair up. In my hand class, I mastered twisting those tiny screws into the holes.

My body was so much stronger now, and I couldn't have been prouder of my hard work.

That weekend at home was my final weekend pass. We went to a friend's outdoor BBQ where I used the walker for the first time outside the hospital. It was a hot day, and I decided not to wear my braces because the plastic made me sweat. My body still could not regulate temperature properly. But my walking wasn't too bad without the AFOs. Hanging out with my friends outside, eating burgers, and having drinks made me eager to get back to living my life again. I was so close; I could taste it. I thought going back to the hospital Sunday night would be tough, but it wasn't. I looked forward to saying goodbye to all the amazing people I met.

Monday morning, I started packing up my things.

Dr. Robinson peaked his head in my room, I assumed to arrange my release for the following day. He said, "I know you're supposed to be leaving tomorrow . . ."

I swear my heart stopped.

"But another patient that's taking your spot is ready to be transferred. So, you can go home today. As soon as you're packed, you can leave."

I nearly cried; it was so unexpected.

"I get to come home today!" I shouted over the phone when I called James, then my mom. It was one day early but the best news for us all. Casey had just gone down for a nap, so I asked Mom to pick me up. I packed up the pink suitcase we'd been lugging back and forth and took one last look at the room I'd spent nineteen days in. No more sleeping in those beds. No more nurses. No more hospital food.

Downstairs I walked with my walker to join the 'flock' and let them know I was going home. To my surprise, John stood behind a shiny new walker like mine.

"You're walking!" I said, my mouth opened wide.

"Yeah, I'm getting a lot stronger in physio, too," John said. "They think I might be able to go home soon."

My eyes filled with tears, and I put my arms around him. "I'm going home today, like now," I said to the group. "I'm gonna really miss you guys."

"We'll miss you too, Miss Holly. Good luck with everything." John said.

I made my way around the 'flock' and hugged everyone goodbye.

I loved my time at the Glenrose, the friendships I made, and the hard work in therapy. But to be back home with my husband and daughter again was all I ever wanted. When Mom got there, she grabbed the pink suitcase from upstairs, snapped a few pictures of me in front of the hospital, then we hopped in her van. I'd made this trip to my house a million times, it seemed, but this was nothing like the others.

After one hundred and twenty-six days in the hospital, I was finally going home.

17

The Real Recovery

I couldn't wait to pick things up where I left them four months before. I could get back to being a mother and wife again. Now we had all the time in the world. I wasn't a hospital patient anymore. To celebrate, James took Casey and me out for dinner—my first time back at a restaurant. We parked in the handicapped stall at the front, which made me feel terrible that I needed to use it, but happy I actually could. At least I wasn't at the hospital anymore.

As we made our way to our table with the walker in tow, others stared, not used to seeing someone so young needing something to help them walk. It wasn't easy being in the real world, around regular people who couldn't possibly understand.

I was happy to head back home. Once James helped me out of the truck in our garage, I turned with my walker towards the door. Before I had the chance to lift the walker through the doorway, a chorus of screams, yelled "Surprise!" I turned to see my closest friends and family standing beside a huge Welcome Home banner spread across the fence in our yard. I might have cried if I wasn't so happy. They'd planned a party—with presents and cake. A friend gave me a sign that read *Home is the comfiest place to be,* and I hung it in our living room.

Being at home for good with Casey was the best part of everything. I loved sitting on my black leather couch, holding her in my arms and staring into her eyes. Having the dexterity and coordination to take care of her was a blessing, something I'd never take for granted again. I couldn't pick her up, so James did for me, but at night I'd change my daughter's bum then rock her back and forth till she fell asleep, like a normal mom did. In the mornings, I'd wake up to her cries, then feed her a bottle in bed. I never regained the ability to breastfeed again, but it wasn't the end of the world. At least we were spending quality time together, in the comfort of our home. After bath time, I lathered Casey's chunky legs with the Aveeno lotion we'd brought home from the hospital

For a few days a week, I returned for outpatient therapy at the Glenrose. I did the same things I'd always done but was surprised at how exhausted home life could be. My body was used to sitting in my wheelchair during most of the day, so being up in the walker all the time now was a lot more work.

"Fatigue is a common residual of GBS," Dr. Robinson had told me just before I left. "Make sure you pace yourself and rest when you need it. Your body is healing and will be for a while."

It was unbelievable at times how much energy it took to do things. Simple tasks like walking with my walker to grab a bottle from the fridge took my breath away, and after, I'd have to sit down for an hour. Going up the stairs was tiring, especially if I did it more than twice a day, which I learned not to do. I never realized how much I took for granted until every little task was so much harder. James did most things for me while I rested on the couch. If I overdid it and walked too much, I crashed and could hardly get off my couch for a day or two. The muscles in my legs ached in pain as if I walked barefoot for hours. Because of my wonky bladder, sometimes I couldn't make it to the bathroom on time; other times, I sat on the toilet and struggled to pee. Everything else down there worked fine. My husband and I started getting intimate again, though I didn't have much interest. I was too tired most of the time, and I think the antidepressant killed my sex drive.

I'd come a long way from the days when I could barely hold a cup or push a button on a remote control, but I certainly wasn't back to normal. My body had more healing to do. I napped constantly and still slept more than ten hours every night.

The walker limited most of my efforts to help with cooking, laundry, and other household chores. My grip was so weak I couldn't even open baby bottles. Lucky James had months of experience opening bottles. My legs weren't strong enough to bend down even a little, so I couldn't pick Casey up. Fortunately, James had that covered, too

I felt terrible because it was summer, and the weather was gorgeous outside. Normally we'd be spending time in the yard, or out visiting friends, but I just didn't have the energy. I'm sure James was bored, being stuck inside watching movies all day long. We spent most of my first two weeks home on the couch.

When I was still at the Glenrose, as much as I was independent, the nurses did a lot for me. I spent the majority of my time sitting in the chair. Taking care of myself proved much harder than expected.

Casey didn't cry very often, but when she did, I could not get her to stop. I'd sit on the couch and rock her back and forth, cuddling her close to calm her down. No matter how many times I whispered, "Shhhh," to my crying baby, her wails just continued.

James swept in, scooped Casey out of my arms, and the crying stopped.

Casey didn't know me the way she knew her father. She knew who I was, but she didn't know me as her parent. James fed her, changed her, burped her, and rocked her to sleep every night for the past several months, not me. I wasn't her source for comfort—that was James and that's who she wanted.

His ability to calm her was painful for me and made me feel like I was failing as a mother.

To be fair, I didn't know my daughter that well either. Casey would start crying, and James would say, "Oh, she's just hungry, that's all," or, "she needs a bum change," or "it's time for her nap." James was used to taking care of a baby, I was not. Months of not caring for her had taken its toll. I felt awful that I didn't know my own daughter the way I should. GBS had stolen so much from me.

I did my best to make Casey laugh but only managed to get a smile out of her most of the time. James would make one funny face, and she'd giggle hysterically for five minutes straight, her big round cheeks blushing. I became increasingly jealous of their relationship. I choked back tears every time she wanted her daddy instead of me. I worried I might not ever be the mother and wife my family deserved. While I laid in bed at the end of every night, I prayed to God that things would get better over time.

Even though Casey was too heavy for me to pick up, I could put the Bumbo chair on the seat of my walker so she could sit with me, and that's how we staggered around the house together.

As time went on, I gained more strength and balance. I eventually realized that Casey's stroller provided me as much support as my walker, if not more. So, when we left the house, I used that instead. I was still slow as a turtle as I dragged my weak legs around the neighborhood, but at least with a stroller instead of a walker, I looked a bit more like a normal person—a normal mom.

I practiced walking using Casey's stroller around the block every day.

*

After three weeks at home, James and I had a friend come over to babysit Casey. It was important, for our relationship, and the both of us, to get out and experience life outside our home. We headed to the theatre to see a movie with friends. Even if it was a lot of work, there was whole world out there I wanted to be a part of. Knowing Friday night would be busy at the theatre, I brought my wheelchair, so I wouldn't have to do the long walk from the car. This way, I could sit in the handicapped section in my chair.

Unfortunately, when we got to the theatre, there were no available seats next to the wheelchair section. The only free spots were in the first two rows. I had a choice of either sitting by myself, leaving (realistically, I could have asked someone to move to another seat) or trying to walk the few steps and sit on my own.

"Let's just put your wheelchair to the side, and I'll help you walk," James said.

It felt like all eyes in the packed theatre were on me as James helped me stand from my chair. Holding on to him as tight as possible, I shuffled my way through the aisle, plopping hard into the low seat beneath me. When the movie finished, James helped me up, and we walked together back to my chair. Much like a physio session, the walk was intense, and I was tired—but I did it. And I would have never known I was able to if I hadn't tried.

I was more capable than I gave myself credit, my legs stronger than I believed. I knew to reach my goal of walking on my own again, I had to push myself. It wouldn't be easy, and maybe I wouldn't be able to do it, but I had to at least try.

At home, I abandoned the walker and started using the cane instead. My balance was poor and with only one hand being used to balance instead of both, I was unstable and took sloth-like strides to get around. Every step felt strenuous and exaggerated. Using more energy than ever, I was even more fatigued. Daily practice with the cane resulted in hours exhausted on my couch. But it was worth it for me to utilize my energy for that. I was doing it.

Deanne finally booked her flight for the Caribbean and started her new job with Carnival Cruises at the end of July. There was a lot of red tape for her to cross back in February when she got the job, and I was selfishly pleased everything took so long. Otherwise, she would have left when I was still in the hospital. I don't know what I would have done without her smiling face beside my bed, lifting me up on the darkest days. Her contract was for six months, and it was hard to believe I wouldn't see my best friend for that long.

She invited James and me to her parent's cabin for a going-away party the week before she left. At first, I wasn't sure I'd go—being back in the real world was exhausting and demanding—but I didn't want my disability to hold me back from living my life. I'd missed out on so much and didn't want to miss anything anymore. My friends and family had always been important to me, and my experience with GBS intensified those feelings. I was blessed to have such supportive people in my life.

What if my GBS came back? What if I ended up in the ICU again? The chance of a second occurrence of GBS was rare, but I'd already experienced rare. What if a loved one was diagnosed with something awful or was in a car accident—or suddenly died. Life can change in the blink of an eye, as I knew too well myself. My fear of something terrible happening ignited a flame to spend as much time as possible with the ones I loved.

We dropped Casey off with her grandma and grandpa and headed out to the cabin. I wasn't just back to being a mom again, I was back to being me. In ICU, I promised myself I'd live life to the fullest if I survived. I'd let go, drink more red wine and spend more time dancing. I'd go to the beach, watch more sunsets, take more pictures. I was finally well enough to enjoy life again, and enjoy it, I did. I paid for it with increased muscle stiffness and body fatigue afterward but tanning on floaties on the lake with my girlfriends and sharing laughs around the campfire made it worth it.

A few days later, James packed up the truck, and we headed to British Columbia to visit my cousin Spencer. He'd been transferred to Golden, a small town in the mountains five hours away instead of the previous twenty, which allowed us to see him much sooner than if he'd stayed in Dease Lake. I desperately wanted to spend time with family now that I finally could.

The trip was long. When I got out of the car, it felt as if I'd sat crumpled up like a pretzel—my body so stiff and sore as if I were a hundred years old.

"The last time I saw you was in ICU, and you were completely paralyzed," Spencer said smiling from ear to ear.

I held on to a cane for support, but at least I could walk now.

"You look amazing." Spencer threw his arms around me into a bear hug.

That weekend, Spencer took the three of us to the hot springs, a naturally heated pool nestled within the picturesque Rocky Mountains in Radium, BC. It was Casey's first time in a swimming pool and my first time in public in a bathing suit since getting out of the hospital. I didn't get the chance to go shopping before we left, so I settled on bringing what I had—my favorite pink and white polka dot bikini. With one hand on the cane, the other out to the side for balance, there was no hiding the scar down my stomach.

"I wonder what people think when they see you," Spencer said as we slowly walked from the change room to the pool, and a sea of eyes scanned me up and down. You don't see a girl in her twenties walking with a cane too often, especially one with a massive scar down her torso.

"Meh, I don't care," I replied. I was here to spend the day with my family. I wasn't going to let stares get in the way of enjoying the day. Splashing around in the water with my daughter, seeing her face light up with joy over her first time in a pool was what mattered to me.

The next day Spencer took us to Takakkaw Falls, the second tallest waterfall in Canada, a half-hour outside of Golden. A parking lot lay at the base of the mountain, so we were able to see the waterfall right from the car. Water cascaded down the steeply sloping rock. Mist blanketed the foot of the mountain. It took my breath away. Like everything now.

"If we walk around the corner, we can get an even better view of the waterfall," Spencer said.

James gave me his 'are you sure look' and asked, "What do you think? Do you want to go check it out?"

A group of tourists were making their way through the trail. The path, though short, looked busy, and rugged. At times, I still struggled to stay upright on flat cement. I hated to pass on the opportunity but didn't think I was strong enough to walk it yet. "You guys go ahead," I said to my husband and cousin. "I'll stay in the car with Casey."

"We'll be back in less than five minutes," Spencer said.

I played with my daughter in the backseat, tickling her chin and making her laugh. I couldn't use my legs to go hiking, but I could use my hands to play with my daughter. It was good for me to focus on what I could do instead of what I couldn't. I understood how important it was for my mental health to focus on the glass being half full.

On the drive back to Golden from the waterfall, we suddenly smelled this raunchy sour egg smell wafting through the vehicle. The joys of babies. I discovered that Casey had an explosive poop that leaked through her diaper and ruined her outfit. Of course, this is the one time we'd forgotten her diaper bag, back at Spencer's. We stopped at a gas station on the side of the road for James to run in and grab diapers and wipes.

"What is he holding?" Spencer asked when James walked out of the store with something other than what he went in for.

We burst out laughing when we saw the roll of toilet paper and wet naps in his hands. There were no diapers or wipes. We cleaned Casey up as best we could with what we had, then wrapped her in a receiving blanket for the car ride home. It was an important parenting lesson for us, the first of many—to always make sure we had the diaper bag wherever we went. It was also hilarious. In the end, I was thankful to be experiencing real-life-mom moments, the way I'd always wanted.

*

By the end of my first month back at home, I was much stronger, and my balance was improving. Running my fingers along the walls and furniture when I walked worked well enough to steady myself—so I didn't have to use the cane. We always brought Casey's stroller when we went out so I could use it for support. The wheelchair and walker collected dust in the garage. My legs were strong enough to push myself up from a sitting position, so I no longer used the toilet seat raiser. And I could finally do the stairs like a regular person, one foot over another. I still depended on the shower chair since I didn't have the balance to stand for that long. Standing on one leg was even harder. When I put on my pants, I had to lean against a wall. I could also barely stand on my toes, but squatting was becoming a little easier, and I learned how to leverage my body against the furniture when bending down to pick things up.

I still didn't feel like me, though. It was hard to explain that to people because I looked healthy. I looked fine.

I wasn't.

My body still couldn't regulate temperature, so I was scorching hot all the time. I had to sleep with a thin sheet and fan pointed directly at me, even on cooler nights. My feet were hypersensitive; stepping on a tiny pebble felt as if I'd stepped on shards of glass. I slept with them dangling off the bed so the sheet wouldn't touch them—even though they were frozen to the touch.

I couldn't blow-dry or straighten my hair without feeling like I was going to faint. On top of my hair being a constant wavy mess, it fell out in chunks from the telogen effluvium.

I was tired a lot and spent most of my time on the couch. My writing was sloppy. It didn't even look like mine. My voice was still scratchy and hoarse, and I was tired of getting asked if I had a cold.

The neuropathy in my feet was the worst, the nerves were regenerating, which was a good thing, but it was horrifically painful. Sometimes my feet ached and throbbed as if someone had taken a hammer to them, then I'd walked a hundred miles. The Gabapentin didn't seem to do anything anymore. The only thing that helped was smoking cannabis and laying down with my legs in the air. Instant relief. Many times that summer, I'd sneak away to smoke a joint, then lay on the couch for hours with my feet up against the wall. Nights were the worst. I'd stand crying on tennis balls, pushing down as hard as I could to ease the throbbing.

I wondered if I'd ever be the person I was before GBS. Would I ever feel like her, look like her or sound like her again? When I looked in the mirror, I felt out of body—someone else stared back. I tried to cover up the red fleshy scar on my neck with makeup, so I looked more like Holly before GBS, but the scar was impossible to hide. I felt grateful I had a husband who already loved me because some days, I felt hideous.

Through it all, I was improving, even if it seemed to be taking a while. At least I was alive, out of the hospital, and with my family again. That was most important. James, Casey, and I went for walks around the block every day. By the end of July, I didn't have to hold the stroller anymore. I was slow and unsteady but could walk on my own.

The rest of our summer was amazing. We took Casey to the family reunion at the lake just as we planned and enjoyed more time with our loved ones. Walking back and forth between campsites was a challenge, and sometimes the ache in my ankles forced me to stop and take a break, but I never once used the cane.

I worked hard on my recovery at home, mostly walking around the block and doing resistance band exercises while watching TV. Most of my time was spent on the couch on my back, my daughter on my belly, and my feet up against the wall to ease the nerve pain. Despite my pain, I made her laugh and soothed her tears. It helped me bond with my baby girl. By the end of August, I could pick up Casey in my arms. I could use my straightener again to do my hair. I could also help with chores around the house, like sweeping and tidying up. This helped me feel more like the mother and wife I was working hard to be.

Another milestone in my recovery was when I didn't have to use the bath seat anymore and could put one hand on the wall for support in the shower. Along with the seat, James returned the toilet seat raiser, the walker, and the wheelchair. The company we got them from would lend them out to someone else to use. The cane was mine to keep, but it was usually tucked away in the front closet. I no longer needed mobility aids. I felt ready to take that vacation in Arizona.

Mike said the place was empty all of September and October, so we were welcome to stay as long as we liked. I'd never been gifted something so generous before. It felt strange taking him up on his offer. I don't know why. It's not like I didn't deserve it. I figured we could maybe go for a week, but James convinced me to go for three.

"Look at everything you've been through this year," my husband said to me when we were alone. "You need, and deserve a nice, long vacation."

Relaxing by the pool in the sun did sound wonderful. Phoenix would be the perfect place for my body to continue healing. We could spend time as a family in paradise. And it wouldn't cost us much more to stay longer. We weren't paying for accommodations and mostly only had groceries to buy, which we'd be purchasing at home anyhow. "And if we stay for three weeks, then when we get back, it'll be time for me to go back to work."

Once James returned to work, it would be just Casey and me at home—then we'd get to really bond. This trip would be the perfect end to our trauma and the perfect start to the next chapter in my life.

"You're more than welcome to bring other people. There's plenty of room," Mike wrote in one of his emails. We'd hoped that some family would join us, but the timing didn't work out for everyone. In the end, mom came for a week.

The flight to Arizona went better than expected. I thought all babies cried on planes so I assumed Casey would too. Instead, my daughter just smiled a big toothless grin at everyone and giggled. The flight attendants loved her. Other babies wailed and she looked across the aisles at them with eyes wide as if concerned for their wellbeing. I should have known she was going to be an angel; this is Casey we're talking about.

The Phoenix airport was massive, unlike any place I'd visited before. It had been six weeks since I'd last used my cane, so I never thought to bring it, but I immediately regretted that decision. It wasn't like strolling the block or the grocery store. Everyone was rushing through the airport with their suitcases—at least it felt that way for me. Mom and James walked ahead down the hall that seemed to never end. Like a child, I tried to keep up my pace, but my feet just wouldn't go that fast. Mom and James had to keep slowing down to wait. By the time we got our bags, crossed the airport to the shuttle, then made it over to the car rental, my ankles throbbed in pain. Outside, the air was scorching, and I instantly started sweating profusely.

But hey, we were in paradise.

The house was in a small community called Gold Canyon, nestled at the foot of the Superstition Mountains, a half-hour outside of Phoenix. I'd been to Vegas but just in the city, never out in the desert before. The red mountains, the rocky ground, and the cacti and palm trees everywhere were unlike any of the landscapes I'd seen prior—and it was stunning.

The house was just as breathtaking. A luxurious four-bedroom bungalow with granite counters and marble floors. Best of all, the massive pool, surrounded by palm trees. Most of the time Mom was there, I sunbathed by the pool or relaxed on a floatie, letting my body rest as much as possible. Casey at eight months old wasn't crawling yet and was content to sit in the shade with my mom or play in the pool with her dad. We swam in the pool, went out for dinner, did the trolley tour at the zoo, and James and I went golfing (with a cart). Activities with minimal walking. The most walking we did was a shopping trip in Scottsdale, which was nothing like in Canada—incredible deals and a selection unlike I'd ever seen before. I eyed up several pairs of gorgeous stilettos but instead settled on flats. No way my ankles could even stand, let alone walk, in heels anymore. I only lasted an hour and a half at the mall before my legs screamed at me to stop.

James and I left Casey with my mom and celebrated our second wedding anniversary by splurging and taking a helicopter tour over the Grand Canyon. I got to sit in the front with the pilot, and the floor underneath me was glass so I could see everything. We flew for ten minutes over a thick emerald-green forest, which I didn't know even existed in Arizona. Without warning, the trees ended, and my stomach dropped. The earth sprawled into a brown, red, and yellow-striped canyon, stretching as far as I could see. The stunning view made me forget all about my struggles with GBS. I was doing all the things I had always wanted to do. I think I found a lost piece of myself in that canyon that day.

Week Two was more time at the pool, and we rented a boat on a gorgeous lake—another of Arizona's mysteries. Casey hated the lifejacket, the first time I'd ever seen her grumpy until James let her sit on his lap and pretend to drive.

We spent a few days cuddled up on the couch when Casey got her first cold, and I loved how much she wanted to snuggle with her mama. Not long after, she army crawled for the first time on the carpet in front of the TV. We were so proud of her.

The third week in Phoenix was cooler, so we mostly stayed indoors. I made James binge-watch *Keeping up with the Kardashians* (my guilty pleasure), and he took us to an NFL football game to watch the Cardinals. Casey went wild in the stadium. She loved the excitement and noise—and she laughed and made faces with every person within five rows. In the second half of the game, she slept soundly across my chest.

Near the end of our trip, I ran out of Gabapentin, my nerve pain medication. I hadn't realized my prescription would run out while we were away. I decided to go without, not wanting to bother figuring out how to get more medication as a Canadian in the States. The neuropathy wasn't any worse during the day than before, but at night I suffered severe pain. I massaged my feet and cried for hours the last few days of our trip. I was not ready to come off those pills.

After three incredible weeks filled with memories we'd take with us forever, we boarded our plane back to Canada. It blew my mind how quickly I zipped through the terminal to our gate this time. When we first got to

Arizona, three weeks before, walking was still a challenge. We didn't do too much walking on the trip, but any bit I did was great physio for my legs.

On our first weekend back home, our friends got married. I spent the night on the dance floor with my girlfriends. It was weird to be wearing flats at a wedding as heels were now a thing of the past, but at least I got to dance for the first time in over a year. The next morning, every part of my body ached and throbbed like I'd rolled down a mountain, but the pain was worth it to be dancing again.

James headed back to work in mid-October. My husband had plenty of time with our daughter over the last eight months. Now it was my turn to be with Casey. It was as if we were finally starting maternity leave. On our first day at home together, I took her to the front yard, and we played in the cherry blossom leaves that had fallen all over the font lawn. Watching Casey in her cute little pink toque, throwing the leaves into the air, was precious. She thought it was the funniest thing in the world. It was amazing to watch her grow. Everything she did made me smile and laugh.

Casey and I finally got to truly bond. I was taking care of her again, on my own. I made all her bottles that I could now open and settled her into a routine for naps. I rocked her to sleep. I could make her smile and laugh on command. She knew I was strong enough to pick her up from the floor now, and whenever I walked by, she reached her hands up high. My baby girl wanted to be in her mama's arms every minute, which I adored.

One evening while going through Casey's closet, I came across a purple and green knit sweater that looked oddly familiar. Flashbacks of thinking how adorable it was rushed to my mind, though I couldn't place where I was.

"Where did this come from?" I asked my husband.

"You picked that out for Casey at the hospital." On one of the many trips to the lobby in my chair. It had been for sale at one of the kiosks. I'd asked to stop so James could buy it for my daughter—a gift from her mom.

I thought I dreamed that.

It would be a year or so before the sweater would fit her, but I felt unbelievably blessed that I'd be around to see it on her. At the time we bought it, I wasn't so sure.

I passed my road test to get my driver's license back at the end of October. One of the last steps toward my independence. Now I could leave the house whenever I pleased. Finally, I could take Casey to visit friends like I wanted to do when she was born. I loved finally getting to show off my daughter to the world. I also took time for myself. On the weekends, I left Casey with James and went to the mall to work on my endurance—and to shop.

"I'll be back in about an hour," I said to James and kissed Casey goodbye with my keys in hand. It was great to have a husband so comfortable with our baby. Unlike many moms who deal with fearful new dads, I didn't have to worry about leaving my husband for some me-time. James had raised our daughter since birth. As much as it hurt me for a while, the bond they got out of it made it worth it.

As I started the ignition and moved my foot to the gas, I paused for a second to think about how lucky I was to physically be able to hop in my car and drive again. To be able to stroll through the mall on my own and go shopping, like I used to do. James had taken me to the same mall when I was still in a wheelchair. That was only four months ago. Now I could walk like I was me again.

My legs were almost back to normal.

18

Run, Rest, Repeat

By January 2012 I was in a wonderful routine with my daughter. I had nap time and a feeding schedule down. I was already writing on my book, which I worked on whenever Casey slept. Writing allowed me to express and process everything I went through, and I was eager to get it out on paper. Sometimes it felt surreal that I went through all the trauma I did. As much as I wanted to forget, I needed to remember. I felt compelled to teach others more about Guillain-Barre Syndrome.

Life was wonderful. My relationship with James was fantastic. He was protective of me and continued to hold my hand tight whenever we left the house to help me balance. Sometimes I struggled on uneven or slippery ground, especially on the ice and snow in the winter. He worried about my walking.

James was a hands-on dad—changing diapers, feeding, and dressing our daughter. On the weekends, he got up with her in the mornings so I could sleep in. He adored being her dad, as much as I adored being her mom. We took our baby everywhere we went, to run errands, for lunch, to games nights with friends. Casey was so chill and slept anywhere. I was living life to the fullest, getting out as often as I could. Why sit at home when you can have fun? I celebrated my twenty-seventh birthday by inviting everyone I could think of; more than thirty people showed up to the bar—even though it was -36 degrees that night.

At times, fatigue was an issue, but my balance was much better after ten weeks of gentle yoga, a class for senior citizens. Dr. Yousef recommended it to me during my assessment in November. He noted my left side was much weaker than my right, and I could not stand on one leg. I still struggled to get out of the bath and up from the floor. I got down on all fours, then up on one knee, the way the Glenrose therapists taught me. I wanted to be able to stand up with ease. I wanted to get stronger and registered Mom and I for the yoga classes.

In a room full of women over fifty, I stuck out like a sore thumb. It was embarrassing how I wasn't able to do so many of the yoga poses, while they could, but I stuck with it, attending every session. For the movements I couldn't do, I modified or did something else. By the end of the program, I could do almost all the poses—I could even get up on my toes to do a Downward Dog. Hard work paid off.

I felt more like me, not completely—but close.

I wasn't covering up the scar on my neck with makeup as much, except when I went out and would be around a lot of strangers. It annoyed me to make eye contact with someone and their eyes immediately going to my neck.

My body's inability to regulate temperature wasn't as obvious in the cool months but being cold hurt my nerves to the core. The muscle aches and electric shocks through my legs were awful, and I struggled to fall asleep at night. Later, I had my Gabapentin medication increased. My medicinal marijuana card allowed me access to various types of cannabis to use for the bad nights, which instantly calmed my tingling nerves.

At least my hair was growing back. I started getting my nails done again like I did before I was a mom, making me feel even more like me.

Casey turned one on January 26th, and we threw her a big party at the house. I decorated the main floor with pink balloons and streamers and dressed Casey in a pink onesie with tights and a tutu. The onesie said Birthday Girl across the front. Surrounded by all our close friends,

Casey smiled and laughed, loving the attention and fuss. When we sang her Happy Birthday in her highchair, Casey had the hugest grin across her face, then unexpectedly turned shy and reached her arms for me to pick her up so she could bury her face in my chest. A spoonful of chocolate cake made her happy again, and she spent the rest of the day as happy as can be surrounded by everyone who loved her.

My heart was full of gratitude and love to be there on her first birthday, celebrating her special day. We made it, baby girl.

Stronger and with more endurance, it looked like I might be able to return to work soon. My insurance company set up a physiotherapy assessment with an independent consultant to determine when that might be. After the assessment, they'd advise my company of any problems or limitations I might have, recommend exercises to work on, and suggest a possible date to return to my job.

It was an interesting meeting. They assessed the strength in my legs and arms, only this time they weren't comparing me to my past assessments; they were comparing me strictly to where I should be as any average person.

My strength was okay but not great, and my ankles were excessively weak. Squatting was still a challenge. I also walked flat-footed—which I had no idea—I barely lifted my toes, instead subconsciously lifting my leg slightly to slap my foot on the ground. I should have been placing my heels down first as I stepped. My ankles weren't strong enough to lift the front of my foot, and they weren't strong enough because I wasn't raising my toes. It was a vicious circle. Because of this, there was no way I could run.

The therapist recommended eight more weeks of physiotherapy, all covered by my insurance. I wasn't a hundred percent yet, and they wanted to help me finetune my weaknesses before I went back to work. Plus, they were concerned with how being at a desk for eight hours would affect my muscles. Sitting for long periods is not good for anyone, let alone someone recovering from GBS.

At first, I was surprised they recommended an entire program. I was back to doing pretty much everything I did before GBS. Most importantly, I was walking again and felt grateful just for that.

"But don't you want to be better than fine?" the young therapist asked. "Don't you want to be stronger than you are now? To be able to run after your daughter? To play tag with her? To chase her around the park?"

He was right. I didn't want to just be good—I wanted to be great. An opportunity was right in front of me. Going back to therapy wouldn't be a setback, merely a way to continue working on my recovery. I wasn't a runner before GBS, but I wanted to be able to run with my daughter one day. I couldn't wear heels and hoped I'd get to wear them again. I couldn't just hope, I had to work for it.

Three days a week, I went to physiotherapy for two hours a day. The facility was just like a standard gym with squat racks and cable machines, treadmills bikes—and therapy beds along the wall. I walked flat-footed on the treadmill for ten minutes at first, then we increased it by five until I was up to thirty. After that, we worked on lifting my toes and improving my pace. The rest of my sessions were strength exercises such as squats, lunges, and bicep curls. Every few classes, I increased the weight or the number of repetitions to push myself.

The first time my therapist had me run was strange. My legs felt like rubber and the impact from my feet hitting the treadmill was painful. I only ran for a minute before slowing down.

"Then just run for one minute and walk for two," my therapist said. There were always ways to make the exercises work for me, something I took with me in the future when I got into fitness.

My friend, Deanne, got home at the beginning of February. Time sure does fly when you're busy. I couldn't believe she left more than six months ago to work on the cruise. We picked things back up right where we left them. I told her that I still couldn't wear high heels, but in PT, I was learning to run. She reminded me I was barely walking with a cane the last time she saw me.

"In my eyes, you're doing amazing," she said.

After eight weeks of hard work, I finished the physio program feeling much stronger everywhere than ever before. I could run one minute on and off for over thirty minutes straight. It wasn't long ago I was paralyzed, and my neurologist had told me I might not walk for two years. I was running again in less than one.

After therapy ended, I knew my recovery was entirely my responsibility. I no longer had my scheduled classes or the physiotherapist to push me. If I wanted to get stronger—If I wanted to get better, and faster at running, I had to put in the work. I wasn't going to improve my strength by going for walks and sitting on my couch. From breathing on my own and learning to walk again, I knew that everything takes time and a lot of hard work.

As soon as the snow melted in the spring, I laced up my hot pink runners, put on my headphones, and went for a run. I stuck with one minute on and off and ran for ten minutes around my neighborhood. It was different than the treadmill, harder on my feet and legs, and I'm sure I looked awkward doing it, but I felt blessed to run. How many people did I meet back at the Glenrose, how many GBS warriors did I know that would love to have the ability to run? I know they would want me to use my abilities. It was an excellent reminder for me to exercise—because I could.

The next day I went out again.

Only this time, I found out what happens when I didn't give my body a chance to rest. Halfway through my run, pain shot through my shins like knives. My ankles ached and throbbed as if they were broken. I tried to push through, but the pain was too severe, so I eventually had to stop and walk.

"Maybe I can't run outside," I said to myself as the pain radiated through my legs. The cement made it so painful. I thought about calling James to come and pick me up, but feeling crushed, I wanted to be alone.

For the first time in months, my strength faltered, and I broke down. "Maybe I should just accept that this is the best I can get. I don't know what I was thinking. I can't do this." Thank God I was wearing sunglasses because I limped the last ten minutes in tears.

Then I remembered the poster in the ICU.

Courage does not always roar... It's also the soft voice at day's end, "I'll try again tomorrow.

I felt defeated that day but knew I could always just try again tomorrow.

I didn't go back out the next day, deciding to take a break but went again a few days later. I laced up my runners, put on my favorite song, and headed out for another try. Giving up was not who I was anymore, not after all I'd been through. Those trying moments off the ventilator, the first time I stood, the walks using the walker through the hospital halls—I'd done it all. How many times had I overcome impossible tasks?

This time, I walked for five minutes to really warm up my legs before I took off running. After another five minutes, my ankles didn't hurt. Like all muscles, they just needed time to adjust.

Maybe I could do this.

I kept a slow pace and then walked after every sixty seconds to give my legs a break. Then I pushed myself back into a run. With the warm wind against my face, I planted my feet into the pavement then back off as fast as I could. For a moment, I lost sense of all time and ran and ran, with all my heart. The beat of the music echoed in my ears, the sunshine beamed down on my face, and a rush of euphoria flooded over me.

I was doing it without any pain.

That day I ran my first five kilometers.

Usually, it isn't our bodies that give up first—it's our minds. My body needed time to recover, so I never ran two days in a row again. But every time I went, I pushed myself to run a little faster. Before GBS, I didn't even like running, but now here I was, looking forward to my evening runs every few days.

Listening to my body was key; I figured out how not to overdo it, when to take breaks and when to push hard. I learned about progressive overload, meaning that to get stronger and faster, you have to make your muscles work harder continuously, or they will plateau. I continued pushing, making it a daily habit to strengthen my muscles with resistance bands at home. I treated my recovery like a job.

After months of hard work, I was in amazing shape. With improved endurance, I stopped using the disability parking pass and walked the long way into stores, which was cheap and easy physio for my legs. Casey wasn't walking yet, but one day I'd be able to run after her. I could do everything I was afraid I wouldn't be able to. I was able to walk, I could run, and I could dance.

*

Years later, when Casey was eight years old, I took her as my date to my stepsister's wedding. We went all out for the event, wearing beautiful dresses, had our hair curled, and wore fake nails. With her bright blue eyes and long brown hair a little lighter than mine, everyone said my daughter looked just like me—my mini-me, not just in looks, but in personality too. Like me as a child, she was a bubbly, happy-go-lucky, and affectionate little girl—introverted and quiet at first but doesn't stop talking once she knows you.

When the party kicked off and the DJ cranked up the tunes, the bride and her bridesmaids rushed to the dance floor, guests following suit.

"Do you want to dance?" I asked my daughter as we sat at our table.

Casey had never been on a dance floor before. When she was five, I put her in a dance class, which she hated, but at home, she loved making up routines and following along to Just Dance on TV.

"Mmmm, not yet," Casey said, peering out at the guests dancing with her hand on her chin. She didn't know many people at the wedding, so I wasn't surprised.

Casey came with me to grab another glass of wine, and we stood together alongside the wall near the DJ. My daughter watched a growing group of people dancing and laughing. After a song or two, she got the courage to bob her head and shake her hips to the music. She wanted to dance; I could tell. And when her favorite song at the time, "Old Town Road" came on by Nas X, she screamed, grabbed my hand, and yanked me to the dance floor.

For the next three hours, we danced and twirled, and I dipped my daughter in my arms. We'd take short breaks to indulge at the candy bar, then run back to the dance floor, singing at the top of our lungs to the songs we knew.

On one quick trip to the bathroom, Casey instantly kneeled in front of the toilet and said, "I don't feel good." Then she threw up. She probably ate way too much candy, and dancing didn't help.

"Are you okay, Case?" I handed her a paper towel to wipe her mouth. "Do you want to go home?"

"No," she said, standing. "I'm good. I want to go back and dance." She grabbed my hand and dragged me back to the dance floor. She was certainly my daughter.

We sang along to Backstreet Boys and Spice Girls and did the Macarena and the Cha Cha Slide. I was tipsy from too much wine, but we were also high on life. Like two best friends, we made up routines to Bruno Mars and danced the night away. It was pure joy and happiness. Watching my beautiful daughter get lost in the music, it was impossible not to think about being paralyzed in the ICU when I couldn't reach my hand to touch my baby girl. At one point, I feared I'd never walk again—that I'd be in a wheelchair for the rest of my life. Here I was with full use of my legs, dancing my heart out with my little girl.

"Mommy!" Casey shouted over the music, then leaned to my ear. "This is one of the best nights of my life!"

My heart felt as if it was going to explode, and my eyes filled with tears. Everyone around us dissolved, and it was Casey and I, alone.

"Mine too, Sweetie," I said, wrapping my arms around my daughter to kiss her on her cheek. My little girl was now my best friend, just as I always dreamed.

Epilogue

The Accidental Activist

"Who here has heard of Guillain-Barre Syndrome?" I asked. Seated before me was an audience of over a hundred and fifty 3rd year University of Alberta medical students. I stood at the front of the lecture hall in high heels, nervous and shaking in fear. The year was 2014, three years after my nightmare with GBS.

A handful of the students in the auditorium raised their hands.

"I had never heard of GBS," I continued. "But in 2011, it forever changed my life. This is my story."

After the videos of my recovery went viral, my life went on a different path. I wasn't simply Holly anymore, I was *Holly After GBS*, and I connected with people all over the world via social media. I was a survivor, not a victim, and I was doing something with my pain. It was wild to think how much I hated it when others filmed me in the ICU, yet if it wasn't for those videos, I would have never connected with others the way I have. I created content on my YouTube channel aimed at those suffering through GBS, answering questions like, what causes Guillain-Barre Syndrome and providing recovery tips. I educated medical students about the disorder and how physically and mentally heartbreaking it is to experience. I was interviewed on news programs and went on podcasts, aiming to inspire others to never, ever give up—no matter how bleak the situation. My mom wanted to help me with my mission, of course, and together we spoke at physiotherapist and pharmacist conferences, sharing insight should they ever work with a case of GBS in their careers.

I took the most terrifying experience of my life and used it for good.

After years of volunteering with the GBS/CIDP Foundation in Canada, I moved up to the Board of Directors a few years after my mom. Visiting patients in the hospital is always rewarding, but it's incredible to be part of projects that improve the quality of life for GBS patients at a federal and provincial level.

We've helped organize fundraising events, national conferences, and awareness campaigns. Every year we connect with more and more people affected by Guillain-Barre. I'm honored and proud to be a part of an organization full of inspiring individuals making a difference in the GBS and CIDP community.

Over the years, I've learned that no two cases of GBS are alike. The rare disorder is full of surprises, and some are severe, some very mild. Some patients recover quickly; some take years. I've talked to many people still making strides five and ten years on. But not everyone recovers. The majority of them have residuals, the most common being fatigue, and nerve pain. Other residuals include weakness, balance issues, muscle spasms, body pain, bladder and bowel issues, brain fog, PTSD, depression, anxiety, and fears of relapse.

Behind every survivor is a story that has given them no choice but to forge ahead.

Not all patients get a quick diagnosis of GBS, and some are turned away at the ER; many are told that the symptoms they are feeling are all in their head. That they're just having anxiety—or worse, looking for drugs. I'm grateful Dr. Clark immediately recognized my symptoms as GBS and that they progressed as quickly as they did. That worked in my favor. Sometimes weakness and paralysis in GBS spreads slowly over days or weeks, but that doesn't mean it's not an emergency.

It's not the doctor's fault they don't recognize GBS. As students, they are overwhelmed with information in university, and Guillain-Barre Syndrome along with other rare disorders usually only gets a small blurb in their textbooks. Doctors may never see a case of GBS in their careers. It can be tough to diagnose as not all patients' spinal tap will show high protein levels. But nerve conduction tests can also help diagnose GBS by showing a slowed/blocked nerve conduction. The GBS/CIDP Foundation of Canada has recently come out with symptom pamphlets for those who work in emergency rooms to help with diagnosis.

Five percent of patients die from complications, such as heart attacks, and not getting on a ventilator fast enough. Knowing this only makes me want to work harder to share what I've learned over the years. To educate doctors and nurses. To help patients get access to treatment and care. To maybe one day find a cure. In the meantime, to save lives.

I've had my fair share of survivor's guilt, knowing I recovered so well and don't struggle as much as some do. I consider myself lucky as thousands of people deal with severe fatigue and physical and emotional pain years after GBS. While many survivors see this disease as the best thing to ever happen to them (whether it put them on a different path, changed their perspective, or highlighted the important things in life), there are others, especially those left with disabilities, who struggle with accepting why this happened. Some are traumatized, devasted that their lives didn't go back the way they hoped. Not everyone is okay with the way things turn out after having Guillain-Barre Syndrome.

*

At one of the seminars that Mom and I helped organize in our city, Neurologists and specialists educated those in attendance, including Kyu's daughter Esther and other

GBS survivors I'd met over the years. During one of the breaks, an older couple I didn't know walked over as I helped myself to some coffee.

"We had to let you know that we saw your video," the woman said. "I'm Lorraine, and this is my husband Dean. He was diagnosed with GBS earlier this year."

Mom turned towards our conversation.

The man stood strong on his own, without any walking aids. "I thought I had no reason to live," Dean said. Your video gave me hope—hope that I've grabbed onto and haven't let go of since."

"We wanted to thank you," Lorraine said as she pulled me into her arms for an embrace. "For sharing your story. If it weren't for you, Dean would not be here."

Mom and I looked at each other, our eyes filling with tears.

Like many GBS survivors, I was sure Dean was dealing with an assortment of residuals and struggles, but he stood confidently in front of me.

Dean later filled me in on his experience in Intensive care. He told me when he was diagnosed with GBS, it came on suddenly, and he was fighting for his life on a respirator after just a few days. Doctors told Lorraine he might never recover, that he could be a quadriplegic for the rest of his life. She asked if he would be able to play ball with his sons or walk on the beach, and the doctor told her, "No."

Neither Lorraine nor Dean believed he was ever going to get better. Suffering through the most horrific pain of his life, kept alive by a breathing tube like I did, he wanted to let go. He was devastated every morning he woke up to find himself still alive.

Lorraine saw the suffering and pain in his eyes, and when she told her husband she'd pull the plug if that's what he wanted, Dean blinked yes. So, she spoke to the doctors about arranging medical assistance in dying—to take him off life support and let him die.

But before that happened, the GBS/CIDP Foundation of Canada sent her my YouTube video.

"When I saw you," Dean told me, "I thought, this person is just like me. She was on life support for months.

If this young girl can get through this with a newborn baby, so can I. I can toughen up. I can keep going. It might be a long haul, but I can do this. For me to see where you were and where you ended up, to watch you walk with a walker and go home again. I don't know where I would be without your video. It gave me peace and hope that I was going to be okay."

It's moments like those that motivate me to do what I do. I never want anyone to think they can't get through Guillain-Barre Syndrome. People do it all the time, all over the world, some with very little support. One survivor I met, a man from Nepal, had no medical support and recovered on his own at home. Most of the patients I connect with recover enough to walk again—on no specific timeline. Many return to their lives and move on from GBS. Dean, Kyu in the ICU at Grey Nuns, Davey, and Puschel in the US—they're walking again. Kit runs several times a week. There is hope for the future, and there is life after GBS.

*

Because of the strength that I gained from overcoming Guillain-Barre Syndrome, I survived my eventual divorce. And I survive my struggles now by knowing I can do anything I put my mind to. Things may not be easy, and I may have to take teeny-tiny steps, but I just keep moving forward. I can't ever give up. I've seen what I'm capable of—I won't doubt myself again.

We may not believe it at the time, but through perseverance, we can drag ourselves out of dark places. We are all stronger than we know.

Everything that happened brought me exactly where I was supposed to be. There used to be times when I'd get upset about my past, like how I lost out on so much time with my daughter, how I missed her first smile, or that we never got to make the memories I wanted in Mommy and Me classes. I don't have a single photo of just Casey and me at home before I was diagnosed. I thought I had all the time in the world to take pictures with my baby.

Sometimes I think if I pushed harder during labor, there would have been no c-section. Maybe I would have never gotten GBS if I didn't have surgery. But who knows.

It's okay to ponder the what-ifs and feel sad that plans went awry, but I see the blessings that came out of my time in the hospital. Every kiss, every embrace, and every walk I take with my daughter is a miracle. I'm grateful to be her mother, to watch her grow into the eleven-year-old girl she is today. We share an incredible bond. I can appreciate the struggling moments we had to endure to get here.

Casey is my heart and my soul, my whole world. She inspires me every day. When she started to walk at fifteen months, she made it look easy. I watched her place one foot in front of the other, trying to keep her balance, getting up every time she fell. I had twenty-six years of practice when I learned again. Casey did it from scratch. I can't count how many times I wanted to give up, she got back up again and again, wearing a huge smile. Every step forward strengthened her little legs and ankles—now Casey plays soccer and tag. And because of all my hard work, I'm able to be right there with her.

As I hoped. I walked my daughter to her first day of school. I had to smile when she brought drawings home of me with a little red dot on my neck. To this day, Casey loves me to rock her, especially when she's upset or sad. Even at eleven years old, I cherish being able to snuggle her in my arms and comfort her. I hope she always treasures that, the way I do when my mom massages my fingers. Casey still has her pink zebra print blankie, Cici from Kit and Tanya, and the pink and green checkered pillowcase I slept on in ICU—two things cherished just as much by her now as they are by me.

I still deal with nerve pain in my arms and legs from time to time, ranging from weird shock-like sensations to bugs crawling on my skin to tingling aches up my limbs. The pain is usually relatively mild, but the residuals worsen when I'm stressed or overtired. I'm no longer on Gabapentin (I came off after two years) and only use Advil or cannabis when the pain gets bad. I encourage GBS survivors to try various remedies and seek out other opinions—don't give up if you're suffering. Hot baths and massages are also quite helpful for me. My feet are still tingly from nerve damage, hypersensitive to touch, and are almost always freezing. They can't feel temperature, so I have to be careful when getting in the tub.

I also deal with fatigue, where I'll hit a wall and be too exhausted to do anything, even have conversations. Outwardly, I can look fine yet feel absolutely drained. I try to remind others that invisible suffering is real even though you can't see it on someone. When I push myself too hard (either at the gym or in life), I crash with debilitating fatigue. When this happens, I need extra sleep and rest for days. This sort of fatigue is not just being tired, it's a feeling of utter exhaustion in every fiber of my body, making it difficult to think and move. Just because we don't have GBS anymore and we don't look sick doesn't mean we aren't suffering. (*See end of book for a more comprehensive list of residuals from GBS.) I've learned to really listen to my body, to go slow, and to stop as soon as it tells me to. I don't feel guilty anymore for taking days to rest because it's key to bouncing back and reducing fatigue.

Over a decade after being in the ICU, I still can't regulate my body temperature. I can go from freezing to a hot flash in a second. Layers, heating pads, fans, and fuzzy slippers are my best friends. I struggle with my bladder to this day—I often feel like I have to pee because I can't completely drain my bladder. My voice never returned to normal. It's scratchy and low, though not as hoarse as it once was. I've only met two other people who lost their voice after intubation; most hoarseness improves a week after the tube is removed. I presume the breathing tube in my mouth damaged my vocal cords, though no doctor will confirm that. My throat now gets sore when I talk too long and projecting my voice in loud areas is a challenge. Sometimes I feel out of breath. Though not nearly as thick, most of my hair came back in, and a few strategic hair extensions have been a great way to fill in the thin spots.

Though it's written that GBS doesn't affect the brain, I struggle with brain fog and finding words during conversations—common to many survivors. I don't let that get in the way of living. Because no matter what I deal with, I'm grateful. We all take our health for granted and don't know what it's like to lose it until we do. I'm thankful I can breathe, talk, walk again, and be the mother I always wanted to be. And I'm forever filled with gratitude for the people who helped get me there. Overcoming GBS is a team effort. My family and friends, the doctors and nurses, my therapists in physio and occupational therapy—they all played a vital role during my recovery.

After I got into running, I stopped setting limitations. Despite my weaknesses, I completed Beachbody's Insanity program after seeing it on an infomercial. I got a gym membership, started strength training, and got into the best shape of my life. Exercising four to five days a week drastically helps with muscle stiffness, pain, and fatigue. I may struggle to open water bottles due to my grip strength and need to lean up against a wall to put on my pants from lack of balance, but I can squat more than my body weight and run five kilometers in half an hour. Maintaining a high level of fitness has been key to getting to where I am—though it's important to note some survivors will be intolerant to exercise.

After years of hours in the gym, I became certified to answer questions from others looking to regain strength. Now I educate other GBS survivors, and it feels as if my journey has come full circle. It's incredibly rewarding to show others how to improve flexibility and strength in a safe and effective way. I've gained a level of self-confidence I would have never gotten had I not pushed myself past what I believed I could do. My biggest struggles paved the way to my biggest accomplishments and passions in life. The person I was before GBS overflows with pride at how far I've come. And I've made some incredible friendships along the way with so many inspiring people.

At one point, I hated the scars I'd been left with, but now I embrace them. I see my body for the strength and abilities it has. I've grown a baby in my belly and overcome paralysis and pain. I'm physically stronger than I ever thought possible. These wounds tell a story, and I can't even imagine them not being there anymore. They are a part of who I am now, no different than the dimple on the left side of my face or the unique yellow specs in my blue eyes. My scars are a constant reminder that Guillain-Barre Syndrome tried to break me. That I found the strength to fight back. And that I survived.

Being on life support and enduring a near-death experience hasn't made me afraid of dying, only of not living, so I go after everything I want. I've learned the best way to plan for my future is to create it, so I travel and spend more time making memories with those I love.

*

In 2015 I started dating a man who cherished life as much as I did. He encouraged me to take risks and live more adventurously because life can change so suddenly. Jordan brings out the best in me and always has me striving for more. Before my illness, I was claustrophobic and afraid of heights. Over the years together, we've climbed to the top mountains in the Rockies, swam in caves, and even zip-lined through the Mayan jungle, and across Fremont Street in Vegas. The most thrilling thing we did together was rappelling eighty-five feet into a teal blue cenote in Mexico. I'm in awe of my body's resilience and strength, and I would have never tried these things without Jordan's push.

As someone who just wanted to get back to being a mom, I became so much more. My journey taught me that life doesn't always go as planned; sometimes, it can turn out better. I'm not the same person I was before GBS, I'm more driven and brave. I've accomplished things I've always wanted to, including writing this book. My next project is to write about life after GBS; how the residuals have impacted me over the years. How my health has changed my relationship with the world, with others, and mostly with myself. To this day, I still struggle, especially when dealing with flare-ups of fatigue and pain—but I don't ever quit. I might need a good cry or a day in bed, but I'm a woman determined to soar. I want to share how I discovered my love for fitness and how I left the corporate world to pursue my goals. I want to write about my love with Jordan and how he helped get me where I am today.

Instead of dreading the anniversary day of my diagnosis, I celebrate February 22nd each year by doing something I've always wanted to do. I've painted art and star-gazed through a telescope. One year Jordan and I tore through a snow-covered forest on a sled pulled by huskies. I've gone indoor rock climbing and scaled an ice wall, making it to the top both times. I took Casey and my mom to Disney World in Florida.

Because life is short, it can change in the blink of an eye. My advice to anyone that hears me speak is that we all have to go after our dreams while we can. Live life to the fullest. Spend more time with the ones we love. Travel and make memories. Create the life we want and deserve —and live our version of happily ever after.

Thank you for taking the time to read my story. If you enjoyed this book, please take a few moments to write a review on Amazon. Reviews are crucial for authors, and I appreciate all the feedback I receive.

Information about GBS

If you have been affected by Guillain-Barre Syndrome (or CIDP, the long-term, chronic counterpart of GBS) and would like more information and/or support, please register with the GBS/CIDP Foundation of Canada at www.gbscidp.ca. *Note that you do not have to be a Canadian to join.

To donate to our cause, please visit
www.canadahelps.org/en/charities/gbscidp-foundation-of-canada/

Did you know . . .
Guillain-Barre Syndrome affects on average 2 per 100,000 people per year.

The exact cause of GBS is unknown. The most common trigger is the campylobacter bacteria that causes food poisoning, usually found in undercooked chicken. GBS is also commonly triggered by the flu and respiratory illnesses.

GBS may target the myelin or insulation around the nerves, the axon nerve wiring, or both. In severe GBS, axon damage requires a longer period of recovery.
There are treatments for GBS (IVIG and plasmapheresis) that may help in recovery, but there is no cure.

While about 80% of GBS patients recover well enough to walk independently, 20% remain in wheelchairs or use walking aids. Many suffer from lingering effects.

These lingering residuals can come and go, meaning some days are better than others. Don't be surprised if you see someone in a wheelchair suddenly get up to walk (GBS or not). It's estimated 85% of wheelchair users can stand or walk—a wheelchair simply makes things easier.

For my GBS Warriors

I've compiled all the advice and suggestions I could from other survivors to write an open letter to those currently fighting Guillain-Barre Syndrome.

It may feel like you are never going to wake up from this nightmare, but one day you will. There is a light at the end of the tunnel, even if you can't see it right now. Things will not pass as quickly as you want them to, and you will believe this will never end. But take things one day at a time—sometimes one hour at a time. Don't worry about your future. Focus on the obstacle right in front of you.

GBS is the hardest thing you will face in your life, and sometimes it will feel so awful you won't be able to breathe. You may not think you are strong enough to handle this, but I assure you, you are stronger than you realize. Just because you are suffering doesn't mean you aren't resilient and strong. Try to maintain a positive outlook as much as possible. Celebrate every tiny success, no matter how small. Find inspiration and motivation to keep you going. Find your reason for fighting. You don't have to give it your all every day—most of the time, you won't be able to, but just keep trying.

Learn everything you can about GBS (when you feel ready) because the more you know, the better you will understand this is an acute disorder, meaning that once you hit your absolute worst, you will start to recover. Things will get better.

Don't forget that even if you are paralyzed, trached, suffering in pain, anxiety, or depression, you have a voice (your own, or through an advocate). When we are in a crisis, we tend to look for guidance from those we believe know better, but sometimes we need to speak up. Sometimes we know our bodies best.

Recovery is a marathon, not a sprint. It's a long, hard, and often frustrating climb. It's not something that happens overnight. It's not a drastic before, and after, it's a slow process of a million small accomplishments along the way. If you want to get better, you must work at it. If you get tired, learn to rest. Don't ever quit. Allow for bad days, trust me, I've had plenty. Measure your progress over months and years. No matter how long it takes, promise yourself you'll get back up again. That you'll never give up. You haven't failed until you've quit trying.

During recovery, don't focus on the things you can't do, work towards them while enjoying the things you can. Find any hobby you can do that you love and do it as often as possible. Don't let what you aren't able to do get in the way of the things you can. These are the moments that will help you through the hard days. Look forward to better days coming.

Exercise and stretch often—every day if you can, whatever little you can do. It's not only good for pain, aches, and your strength, but it's also great for confidence and mood. Don't ever assume something is unattainable. You have to at least try! Then celebrate every tiny victory as only you truly understand what it takes to accomplish them.

You will most likely be left with residuals, but that doesn't mean you can't have a successful, happy life. An entire community of survivors thrive post-GBS, despite what we've been left with. Don't ever be ashamed or embarrassed by what happened to you. Having GBS is not your fault. You are a warrior for overcoming it.

Pain changes you, for the better, if you allow it. Let this experience guide you into building the life that you truly want. Don't settle for fine, good enough is not great, and you deserve great. Go after the things you want for yourself.

One of the biggest blessings we have in life is the ability to rebuild ourselves again and again. One day, I promise, you will look back on all this and see just how far you've come. One day, the pain of yesterday will be behind you, and you'll see that you were always strong enough to overcome this.

For medical Professionals

and Family Members

My recovery was due in large part to neurologists, doctors, nurses, the respiratory, speech pathologists and physiotherapists, and other medical professionals who work with Guillain-Barre Syndrome patients in the acute phase. For the most part, I know you are doing your very best when providing us care. But until you've experienced GBS firsthand, you will never understand how devasting this disorder is. I've compiled a list of things us survivors wish medical professionals understood to help if you have a patient fighting Guillain-Barre.

Learn as much as you can about Guillain-Barre Syndrome. *GBS: An Acute Care Guide For Medical Professionals* is a fantastic resource from the GBS/CIDP Foundation International to help with diagnosis, treatment options (like IVIG and plasmapheresis—NOT steroids), and care. *Guillain-Barre Syndrome: From Diagnosis to Recovery by Gareth J. Parry (MB, ChB, FRACP) and Joel S. Steinberg (MD, PhD, FICA)* is another excellent book.

Understand that most patients will not follow the 'textbook case.' Every case of GBS is unique, often having different symptoms, length of recovery, and leftover residuals. Even if you've seen a case before, the next one can be completely different.

Excruciating, unbearable muscle and nerve pain is common in GBS, especially in the acute phase (though not all patients will experience it.) I assure you that the high levels of pain medication they plead for is warranted. Inflammation in the nerves causes the type of suffering that makes you question your will to go on each day, and

I would never wish that pain upon anyone. Do not make your patient feel like they are drug-seeking if they keep asking for more. A pain specialist should be consulted. The emotional suffering of GBS is just as awful. Suddenly being diagnosed with a rare illness most people have never heard of with no idea if there is a future is terrifying for patients and their families. Severe anxiety and depression is common and a natural reaction in those newly diagnosed—whether they have a mild or severe case. Speaking with a psychiatrist is recommended when possible, and medication may be needed.

Severe anxiety is a typical response to being paralyzed/intubated. On top of the pain, it is terrifying not being able to move or breathe. Do not ask us if we have a psych history. The strongest individuals with no history of mental health concerns can easily experience severe panic attacks and dark thoughts when fighting through GBS.

Constant attention is needed by a patient's care team, especially for those ventilated in intensive care. Allow family to assist wherever possible. It will help everyone involved and will ease the patient's anxiety.

Don't be afraid to try different treatments, therapies, medications, etc. Every patient is unique and may respond differently.

It's likely your patient can hear everything being said, even if they appear to be sleeping or disorientated. Be careful with your words. Communicate with your patient. Talk about what is happening to their bodies. Explain GBS and the procedures you are doing. Even if we can't respond. We deserve to be treated like a human and informed.

Wherever possible, assign nurses who understand the complexities of GBS and/or have cared for the patient already. It does not help anyone to have a nurse that

causes emotional or physical pain. Even light touches can feel excruciating.
It is very important for ventilated patients to change positions often, to help improve lung volume and oxygenation, clear secretions and break up routine. Aim for sitting up at least 1 hour a day.

Muscle atrophy and foot drop are major concerns in GBS patients. Physiotherapists need to be brought in early to ensure the muscles are kept moving through range of motion exercises and that the feet are stabilized at a 90-degree angle with some sort of splint/boot. Atrophy and foot drop prevention are necessary steps as tendons can permanently shorten. Doing this will help with recovery down the road.

This may be the most severe case you've ever seen but that doesn't mean a patient can't recover. I've seen many severe cases recover completely—one man I met spent almost a year on a ventilator and is walking again. Do not give your patients recovery endpoints or tell them it's time to manage their expectations about their future. GBS is depressing enough. Recovery looks different for everyone, and it's impossible to predict how things will go. Too many doctors tell patients where they are after two years is where they will remain, yet all the time I hear patients making progress years later. Even if you truly don't believe this patient will recover, there is always room for hope. Miracles happen every day. We need our doctor's hope, to motivate us to get up and work hard in our recovery. Do not be the person that makes them give up on themselves. Allow and challenge them to prove you wrong.

Below is a list of common residuals after Guillain-Barre Syndrome that can range from mild to severe and are often intensified by illness, stress, lack of sleep, hormones, and even changes in weather. It's important to note residuals do not correlate to how severe a case was.

- Fatigue is the most common residual of GBS, affecting over eighty percent of survivors. When severe, it can cause weakness and pain and even mimic another occurrence of GBS. Some days we can be full of life and feel fantastic, others it will be so crippling we barely have the energy to think straight or move—even if we look fine. We often feel as though we have a limited amount of energy to be used in a day and must be very careful with overexerting ourselves. Sometimes, another illness or infection may bring back some of the symptoms of GBS, but only temporarily.

- Neuropathy is the second most common residual, which can manifest itself as tingling, numbness, pins, needles, aches and pains, and sensory issues like severe sensitivity and random lightning bolt sensations. It can appear anywhere in the body but is usually found in the feet. Many survivors either insist on wearing socks and shoes at all times or can't stand anything touching their feet and prefer to go barefoot.

Other residuals include:

- Muscle spasms, uncontrollable twitching of the nerves, tremors, and shaking hands.
- Muscle cramps, usually in the feet and calves, that often happen at night.
- A 'banding' feeling around various parts of the body as if it were in a vice.
- Bowel issues, irritable bowel syndrome, bladder incontinence, and urine retention—which often lead to urinary tract infections.
- Muscle loss and muscle weakness, usually in the hips, legs, and ankles.
- Hyper-extension in joints, locking of knees.
- Feelings of extreme stiffness, limited range of motion.
- Inability to differentiate between hot and cold temperatures.
- Severe heat and cold intolerance.

- Balance issues, poor coordination, and proprioception—especially with eyes closed— which can cause unstable walking, particularly on uneven surfaces.
- Facial paralysis and struggles with facial expressions.
- Brain fog, loss of memory, difficulty finding words.
- Dexterity and fine motor skill issues, weak grip strength, hand cramping.
- Circulation issues, usually in the hands and legs.
- Drop foot requiring orthotics.
- Throat/esophagus weakness/tightening, issues with swallowing food.
- A feeling of breathlessness, especially with activity.
- Voice weakness.
- Hair loss.
- PTSD, depression, and anxiety, a lack of confidence due to being betrayed by our bodies.
- And fear of relapse, especially when having a flare-up of residuals.

Remember, every GBS survivor is unique. Our bodies are all different. Some may have most of these residuals, some may have only a few, or something else entirely.

Medical Acronym Glossary

- ICU: Intensive care Unit
- GBS: Guillain-Barre Syndrome
- CIDP: Chronic Inflammatory Demyelinating Polyradiculoneuropathy
- PT: Physiotherapist
- OT: Occupational Therapist
- RT: Respiratory Therapist

Further Reading

Many survivors have written harrowing journeys of their experience with GBS. I have not personally read each book listed but am sharing, in no particular order, for those interested,

- *A First Step: Understanding Guillain-Barré Syndrome, and Guillain-Barre Syndrome: 5 Years Later, by Brian S. Langton*
- *No Laughing Matter, by Joseph Heller*
- *Unknown: A memoir - Guillain-Barré Syndrome, by Meg Lumsden*
- *Paralyzed Without Warning: A Couple's Journey Back from Guillain-Barre Syndrome, by Suzan and John Jennings*
- *Healing Wings: A personal journey of miracles and healing through Guillain-Barre syndrome, by Natalie Sherwood*
- *Nothing but Time: A Woman's Struggle with Guillain-Barré Syndrome, by Judy Light Ayyildiz*
- *Chronic Pain Hacker: Because Healing is Hard, by Shannon Green*
- *Guillain-Barre' Syndrome: My Worst Nightmare, by Byron Comp*
- *Bed Number Ten, by Sue Baier and Mary Zimmeth Schomaker*

- *Solomon's Porch: The Story of Ben and Rose by Jane Riley*
- *No Time for Tears: Transforming Tragedy into Triumph, by Dorris R. Wilcox*
- *Learning to Walk Again: How Guillain-Barré Taught Me to Walk a Different Path, by Ann K. Brandt*
- *Guillain-Barre Syndrome: My Journey Back, by Shari Ka*
- *Geeyahn What? My Guillain-Barre Syndrome Survival Story, by Mrs. Wenesday*
- *Ketron*
- *Bouncing Forward: My Journey with Guillain-Barré Syndrome, by Carrie Campbell Grimes*
- *The Wave of Guillain Barre Syndrome, by Scott Earle*
- *In our Darkest Hour: Our Journey with Guillain-Barre Syndrome, by Brian L Beeks*

Acknowledgments

I would have never completed this book if it weren't for the many people that helped me along the way. No one, other than writers, (and their spouses, I suppose) truly understands the amount of work and effort that goes into writing and publishing a book. I can't count how many times I wanted to give up from being emotionally, physically, and financially exhausted. This book pulled me away from time with my family and friends, cost me a large chunk of my life savings, and at times turned me into an anxious mess of a person who I did not recognize. I felt the fear, worked through the emotions, and went ahead anyway.

Thank you to my daughter Casey for being my inspiration, my guardian angel, my reason to keep going, and for never giving up. I am so happy to have you not only as my daughter but as my best friend. I love you so much and don't know where I would be without you. I hope our story always reminds you how strong you are.

Thank you to my love Jordan, for constantly supporting and pushing me to go after my dreams. Thank you for talking me off ledges, for being my biggest cheerleader, for doing laundry and vacuuming, cooking and cleaning, keeping the kids busy, and not only allowing but insisting and encouraging me to just work on my book. How many nights did I cry in our bathtub, struggling to go on. You wrapped me in your arms and told me to keep going. You are the kindest, most patient person I know, and I love you forever. This book would not exist without you!

To my mom Marilyn, for being at my side every step of the way—while going through GBS and to this day now. I am the person I am today because of you. You gave me my strength.

Thank you to Eva, Chedan, and Casey for being patient and understanding why I have worked so much over the last five years. I know it hasn't been easy, especially when my stress levels were at their highest, but I hope to make it up to you now.

To James, for being my rock while I fought for my life and for being such a great father to our daughter, then and now. I know that in sharing my story, I sometimes had to tell yours.

Thank you to the rest of my family and friends for giving me grace. I've needed to make many sacrifices over the years and haven't always been able to be the best daughter, the best sister, or partner, mother, and friend that I've often wanted to be. Thank you for your patience.

Thank you to Deanne for everything, for being my best friend, my confidant, my manager, and for helping me grow my business into what it is today.

Thank you to my pup Benji for being my emotional support dog; for licking away my tears and always putting a smile on my face. Our daily walks got me through the tough days.

Thank you to my book coaches/mentors, Donna, and Jill, for giving me the tools to tell my story, improve my writing, and turn my words into a book.

Thank you, Allison, and Ashleigh from the Writers Bridge, for providing all sorts of knowledge that gave me the confidence to do this.

Thank you Sue for all the publishing advice, and of course, for the name.

Thank you to Ed, Martina, Kim, Dan Joan, Marie, and Don, members of my writing group, who helped turn this book into something beautiful.

Thank you to the GBS/CDIP Foundation of Canada for understanding and supporting my need to get my story out there.

Thank you, Dr. Zochodne and my other beta readers, for providing your input.

Thank you, Craig, for being such a thorough proof-reader and making this book into the best it could possibly be.

Thank you to the Alberta Foundation for the Arts for the generous literary grant, which made it possible for me to finish this book years sooner than I could have done on my own.

Thank you to the SPF Community and all the Binder groups for answering so many questions I've had and for being such an inspiration.

To my therapist Brian for helping me through this challenge so I could reach my goal of finishing this book.

To the nurses, doctors, therapists, and many others, who helped get me to where I am today, you are all angels. I wouldn't be where I am without you.

To my followers around the world, especially those who have patiently waited for this book for years and have continued supporting me along the way.

To all the complete strangers who've kept me in their prayers over the years.

It takes a village, and I am grateful for each and every one of you.

Xoxo, Holly

About the Author

Holly Frances is a Canadian writer, speaker, and certified personal trainer. She is also a mom in a blended family of six (including pup Benji) and the face behind Holly After GBS on social media, where her recovery videos have inspired millions of people around the world. Holly's background is in Human Resources, but her passion is in GBS advocacy and fitness, and she is currently the Vice President on the Board of Directors with the GBS/CIDP Foundation of Canada. When she isn't writing, and connecting with others on social media, she can be found hanging with family and friends, binge-watching documentaries, at the gym, or walking her dog. She's also well known for her love of dancefloors.

You can find Holly on Facebook, Instagram, YouTube, and TikTok under *Holly After GBS*.

To watch her recovery video on YouTube, check out: "Holly's Journey: From Guillain-Barre Syndrome to Happily Ever After"—and please share!

Holly's YouTube channel is a wealth of knowledge with many popular videos, including *Tips for those Newly Diagnosed, Ankle Exercises, Residuals after GBS*, etc.
For more information on her exercise programs aimed at GBS survivors, visit www.warriortrainingwithholly.com.

For media and speaking inquiries, send an email to hollyaftergbs@gmail.com

Printed in Great Britain
by Amazon

27645783R00189